HOW WE ADAPT OURSELVES

D0649397

All creatures must, if on survival bent,
Adapt themselves to their environment.

Pope

ADVENTURES IN SCIENCE

OUR ENVIRONMENT
How We Adapt Ourselves to It

BY

HARRY A. CARPENTER

GEORGE C. WOOD

PAUL E. SMITH

1953

ALLYN AND BACON
BOSTON   NEW YORK   CHICAGO
ATLANTA   SAN FRANCISCO   DALLAS

FOREWORD

This new edition of *Our Environment: How We Adapt Ourselves to It* places increased emphasis on the practical, everyday aspects of science. At the same time it expands its pictorial treatment by including more than thirty new illustrations, twenty-two of which are full-page pictures.

The new pictures feature outstanding developments like the newly-opened Friant-Kern Canal in California's Central Valley, the radio telescope for measuring solar "noise," a radiosonde balloon for atmospheric observations, an airplane attacking the 1949 horde of grasshoppers with DDT, an ultra-violet light to reveal the age of eggs, drilling for oil under water in the Gulf of Mexico, and a picture showing Uranus with its newly-discovered fifth moon. There is also a full-page cut showing the latest symbols used by the United States Weather Bureau, and a typical local weather map.

New text matter includes brief but illuminating discussions of topics like the possible use of sea water to supplement our dwindling water supply, the increasing use of fluoride to offset dental decay, the wide-spread use of DDT and similar compounds in agriculture, new methods of controlling insect pests and of combatting fungus and bacterial diseases in plants, and a presentation of the new theory concerning soil cultivation, particularly with respect to the new ideas concerning capillarity.

Considerable revision and expansion of certain fundamental topics have been made. For example, new data have been included in the section on the methods and codes used by the U. S. Weather Bureau. Comparable changes have been made in the sections on the phases of the moon, methods of stain removal, and conservation of our mineral resources.

The new edition continues the basic organization and content of earlier editions. There is also the same cumulative development of basic scientific facts which made this book and its companion volumes so successful in advancing the twelve-year science program in our schools.

The text is divided into *Units*, each unit presenting a unified picture of some phase of the student's environment. Each unit is composed of a series of *Topics*, developed in logical order, an understanding of which comprises a complete grasp of the larger unit division.

Problem-solving abilities are cultivated by the *General Problems* which comprise each topic. Each general problem may include a number of *Experiments* (laboratory work) or *Field Research* problems for independent choice and individual or group solving.

The problem method involves, first, a realization of the problem on the part of the student; and second, a background or foundation upon which he can base his attack. To these ends the student's everyday experiences must be reinforced by carefully directed observational training. Not only must the work of the classroom comprehend these purposes, but that work should be supplemented by out-of-school contacts to crystallize the habits of careful, accurate observation and judgment. For this reason, an *Observers' Club Calendar* is included. The observational work necessary in connection with the reports in this calendar is extremely valuable in putting into practice the *scientific method* without specific guidance or authority from the textbook.

Characterizing the presentation of each unit are the following special features:

1. Each *Unit* of study is introduced by a brief preview. This gives the pupil a glimpse of his environment in a new light, inviting him to prepare for interesting adventures.

2. The material of each unit is developed as a number of related topics, the general problems of which are minor generalizations that provide a framework for the building up and fitting in of the facts that are discovered, observed, and learned for the unit as a whole.

3. Each *Topic* is introduced by a preview picture of the subject matter. This feature, together with the *Do You Know* questions, relates present experiences and knowledge to the new problems.

4. The extra-class activities of the *Observers' Club Calendar* are supplemented in several ways. Within each topic will be found *Field Research* problems and Science Discovery Book *Projects*. The latter offer an opportunity for taking care of individual differences.

5. *Key Words* are found at the end of each topic. They offer an excellent basis for review work. As an oral exercise, their exact meaning may be brought out in short sentences or paragraphs, thus supplying drill in the formation of general concepts.

6. A group of *Key Statements* follows the key words in each topic. These sentences are summarizing statements, and may be used for topical, oral, and written exercises, thus providing for development of careful, exact expression.

7. A series of *Thought Questions* at the end of each topic tests the ability of the pupil to apply his science to new situations.

8. The *Bibliography* has been selected with special regard for the interests of the pupils using this book.

The *Glossary* provides simple understandable definitions of the key words and other science terms.

9. *Experiments* are numerous. The fundamental experiments are labeled *Key Experiments*, because they are especially important units in the organization of the subject matter. They focus discussion and develop the

scientific attitude of mind. They should be used as individual student experiments or at least should be demonstrated to the class by pupils. Since some classes may find it impossible to perform all of the experimental problems, the text has been made completely coherent without dependence upon the experiments in any way.

10. *Illustrations* have been selected in the belief that every picture should increase interest in science, amplify and interpret the text, present a problem for study, and be easy to understand. Every picture carries an explanation and often questions requiring close study of the picture and direct association of it with its context.

The vocabulary and the phraseology of the Adventures in Science Series have been kept as simple as possible. To that end scientific terms beyond the comprehension of the student have been omitted. The development of the series is logical and coherent, with transitions carefully worked out so that progress may be natural and smooth. The student is certain to carry from his science work a sound grasp of the *relations* of the natural phenomena of his environment, a realization of his need for *adaptation* to them, and a knowledge of how best to *control* them.

H. A. C.
G. C. W.
P. E. S.

ACKNOWLEDGMENTS

Many science teachers of Rochester, New York, contributed valuable suggestions and constructive criticism in the course of the preparation of this book.

The authors wish especially to thank Miss M. Elizabeth Tuttle, Mr. William McK. Hutchinson, Mr. Harold H. Miller, and Mr. Fred A. Newhall for helpful advice in the development of the text.

CONTENTS

vii

UNIT III. WATER

EXPERIMENTS

COLOR PLATES

FOG

A ground-clinging fog such as this makes an unusual picture from above. How would it seem to a person walking along the street? How does a fog like this affect nearby airport operations? What is science doing about making landings and take-offs possible even in such a fog as this?

Introduction

Science moves ahead so fast that even the best reporters cannot keep up with its discoveries. Atomic power plants, penicillin, television, jet aircraft, radar, Diesel engines, omni-range radio signals — our modern world progresses almost overnight.

And yet in spite of its advances, science always finds more problems to attack. The following story describes some of the difficulties that still face airline pilots and crews. Soon, however, airlines will no longer be fogbound or kept from their courses by treacherous weather. The general use of radar and of Ground-Control-Approach will take care of that, but the scientist will go on, searching for new devices to solve our problems and help us better adapt ourselves to our environment.

FOGBOUND

"Hello, Bill and George," said Captain Melrose of All-Service Airways. "You boys chose a good day to visit the airport. Some of our ships can't take off because the coastal airports are fogbound, and so I have plenty of time to show you around. What would you like to see first?"

"Some of the planes, please," answered Bill promptly.

Captain Melrose laughed. "Certainly," he said, "but first let's go into the chartroom. That's interesting, too."

In the pilots' chartroom Bill and George saw large weather maps on the wall, and voices could be heard coming from loud speakers calling out the weather conditions, "Ceiling 400 feet, temperature 25°, wind 35 miles per hour, visibility poor." Men were studying the weather map. One was adding new weather data that came in by radio from many places.

Next the Captain led the boys from the terminal to a small private plane. Bill and George climbed into the pilot's seat and examined the neat, simply-designed instrument panel. Finally they entered a huge four-engine passenger plane which could carry many passengers besides the pilot, co-pilot, and stewardess.

Inside the ship the boys had boarded they saw ever so many instruments on the instrument board. It looked like the instrument boards of a dozen or more automobiles all put together. Captain Melrose pointed out this dial and that and told the boys what they were for. "This one tells the height

Courtesy Lear, Incorporated

AN AIRPLANE INSTRUMENT PANEL

Every dial has a special meaning to the pilot. Can you see why knowing how to fly an airplane involves science?

above sea level. This one shows the ship's direction. That one tells the air temperature outside the plane, while that one shows the wind speed. All these instruments measure something."

George was bewildered by what Captain Melrose was saying, but to Bill, who had studied science, these words had meaning. Bill was thrilled to see the things he had studied about in actual use, and it interested him especially to be shown why their use was so important in safeguarding the ship and passengers when in flight over the ocean.

One thing Bill couldn't understand was how the navigators of the ship could measure the number of miles they were from any land. "How do you know where you are," he asked Captain Melrose, "and how do you tell in what direction you are flying?" The captain tried to explain, but Bill's knowledge of the stars and latitude and longitude was not quite equal to it. But he said to himself, "I'm glad I'm going to study a little astronomy this year in science. I'd like to learn more about the weather too."

"Funny," he thought, "how closely related weather and astronomy are to the flying of an airplane."

When the captain talked about the radio, radio beams, and direction finders, Bill was a little more at home because he was a radio "bug," as the boys called him. He knew, too, that in some manner weather and the sun's spots affected radio. He noticed the ship's clocks, and suddenly realized that the pilot of the plane must have the exact time in order to fly and land his ship safely.

How about you? Have you realized, as Bill did, how one thing in science is related to almost everything else in science? Do you and Bill and Charles and all your classmates know how important science is in your lives? You know that science not only has contributed the airplane, made weather prediction practical, discovered many interesting facts about the solar system and the stars of the heavens, but that science protects your health, your home, your food.

Science also contributes to the practical conservation of our natural resources. Scientific conservation is no mere guess based upon wishful thinking. It is based upon careful scientific observation and experiment.

The study of science is useful in many ways. But do you know how scientists work to make their discoveries? That is most important, because you will do your work better, no matter what it is, if you can work and think like a scientist.

WORKING SCIENTIFICALLY. — Scientists do not work in haphazard ways. They are systematic. They study their problem carefully, they learn what others have found out about it, and then they plan their attack.

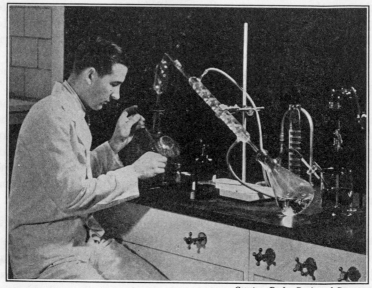

Courtesy Parke, Davis and Company

A SCIENTIST AT WORK

This chemist is working scientifically. He is shown here separating and concentrating some of the B vitamins. These vitamins are necessary for happy normal lives.

The scientific attack starts with a problem or question the scientist wants to solve or answer. After learning what he can about it from the reports of others, he puts down what he has discovered and then tries to learn some new facts.

New facts are usually learned by trying experiments. Sometimes experiments are tried over and over again to see if the same results are always obtained. A place where experiments are tried is often called a *laboratory*

In the laboratory are kept books for reference and apparatus and materials to use in the experiments.

Experimenting requires good judgment and straight thinking. First, one must try to avoid any dangerous schemes or experiments that may cause damage or accidents. Next the experimenter must watch very carefully to see just what happens, and he must think hard to figure exactly why it happens.

Of course a good scientist keeps a notebook record of what he does, how he does it, and what he discovers. Most records are helped by drawings. His next step is to look over all he now knows about the problem, organize his data, and try to get an answer. This he writes down as a temporary conclusion or theory. A scientist tries to learn the truth whether it agrees with what he would like to know or not. He must write down what he really concludes.

The temporary conclusion or theory must be checked and double-checked by other scientists as well as by himself before it is finally accepted as the best conclusion. Even then the experimenter must be ready to change his opinion, if and when new facts are discovered that challenge his statement.

SUCCESSFUL SCIENTISTS. — A scientist is a thinker. Thinkers must be doers. The most successful thinkers of history and of today are men and women who have closely, patiently, accurately, and thoughtfully observed the working of nature, both out-of-doors and indoors. And with their thinking have come problems they wanted to solve. To solve these problems they started at once on voyages of discovery into the unknown. Such voyages always include hard work and sometimes disappointment, but, on the other hand, nearly always reward one with the joy of success.

One early scientist, Galileo, died while a prisoner in his own house, but he gloried in the knowledge that he had discovered certain great truths. The world owes much to his discoveries.

GALILEO MAKING OBSERVATIONS WITH HIS NEW TELESCOPE
From a painting by Gatti

Aristotle, one of the greatest thinkers of all times, is sometimes called the father of science. He was probably the first to give us a systematic plan for studying science according to the subjects we now call biology, physics, chemistry, and astronomy.

Wilhelm Röntgen, a man who liked to blow glass and take pictures, because of his interest in experimenting with electrical discharges through a vacuum, discovered the X-ray. What an aid his discovery is today in medicine and surgery and in all science!

Kelvin, Pupin, Steinmetz — scholars, engineers, inventors — through their research and study have done much to give us our control over the giant power, electricity.

Louis Pasteur, one of the great men of all time, spent his life in scientific study of invisible organisms called *bacteria*. Because of him the world is a better and safer place in which to live.

Luther Burbank, one of our own countrymen, devoted his life to improving old and creating new fruits, flowers, and vegetables. It is due to his experimentation with *crossing* and *selection* of plants that we enjoy many new fruits and flowers.

Francis Bacon said, "Man can govern nature only by obeying her laws, and therefore he must find out what her laws are." It was Bacon who taught the world the *scientific method of experiment*.

The Bettmann Archive

LOUIS PASTEUR IN HIS LABORATORY
From a painting by Adelfeldt

The scientists mentioned here have all contributed to our welfare. Perhaps in your own town or state there is a scientist who is contributing right now to your welfare and the welfare of all the world. Perhaps his name will find its place in the Hall of Scientific Fame.

YOUR CHANCE. — You are fortunate to be studying science, for you, too, can discover things for yourself and perhaps for future generations.

Like Galileo, Newton, Darwin, Pasteur, and all discoverers, you must *record your discoveries*. Your Science

Discovery Book is to be the story of what you do, how you do it, what you think, and what you discover. Who can tell — you may be another Galileo!

Your Science Discovery Book

A scientist is a person who *wants to know the truth.* To learn what he wants to know he listens, looks, reads, experiments, and thinks. With his problem (what he wants to know) clearly in mind, he collects all manner of facts in all manner of ways. He then arranges his facts as they relate to his problem, discarding those that are not of use. With his facts laid out before him he searches for the answer to his problem.

The answer comes. Is it true? The scientist with infinite care and patience tests his answer by applying it to new conditions, to new but similar problems, until he is satisfied that his facts are accurate, his judgment good, and his answer true.

Perhaps you will put down in your book a secret ambition to know more and more about something that has appealed to your imagination. Has that imagination to do with a shooting star, a hurricane at sea, the changing form of an insect, an epidemic of disease? What is it you want to know? To help you make discoveries use the *Observers' Club Calendar* at the back of the book. Each week plan to make some of the observations called for in this calendar and record them carefully in your *Science Discovery Book.*

Your *Science Discovery Book* is the place for your records of facts and their relationships, your own conclusions or answers to your problems. It is the place for you to put down what you do and what you find to be true.

When it is evening, ye say, it will be
fair weather: for the sky is red.

Matthew

UNIT I

⟩‖WEATHER‖⟨

Ceiling zero! Serious words to the aviator flying toward his landing field with gasoline nearly exhausted!

Less dramatic but even more important to agriculture, shipping, and to aviation generally are the daily weather reports. They enable farmers, fruit growers, and transporters to protect the nation's food from damage and perhaps total loss.

The government has established a weather bureau which foretells changes in weather conditions. Thus the farmer is warned of frost and freezing; the aviator is warned of fog and storm; forest-fire wardens are warned of threatening droughts; fishermen are warned of storms at sea. Successful shipping, transportation by land, water, or air, bridge building, and irrigation planning in this country depend greatly upon the United States Weather Bureau reports.

Weather is important to you personally. When you have learned about weather factors and the principles of science that help to explain the weather, you will better appreciate the work of Uncle Sam's weather men.

9

A. Devaney

OVER THE RAINBOW

One of the most popular weather signs for amateur forecasters is the rainbow. Are weather predictions based on the appearance of a rainbow truly scientific?

TOPIC I

Weather Signs and Superstitions

*Some are weather-wise, some
are otherwise.*
— Franklin

Do you know:

1. A sure weather sign?
2. Whether or not the moon controls the weather?
3. Whether or not animals are good weather prophets?
4. How to make a rainbow?
5. The cloud family?

General Problem 1. Are Superstitions Based on Evidence?

Foretelling Weather by Animals. — Do animals with heavy fur or birds with heavy feathers in the fall indicate a cold winter to come? Do geese flying south foretell oncoming winter? Do crickets tell the temperature? Does the groundhog's shadow on February 2 have anything to do with the weather? These and many other questions are not new to you. However, unless you understand the science of weather and weather forecasting, you cannot answer them correctly.

Science through careful observation and experiment has shown that the coat of fur on animals and feathers on birds depend upon the supply of food available during

11

the spring and summer, and not at all upon the animals' sense of coming weather changes.

New York Zoological Society

WEATHER PROPHET?

According to superstition, there will be six weeks more of cold weather if the groundhog can see his shadow on February 2. Do you think this animal's shadow has anything to do with the weather?

It is true that animals of all kinds make preparations for changes of seasons, such as laying up food and preparing a den, but they do not know any more than you do whether the season is to be normal or otherwise. Fur-bearing animals have heavier coats of fur during the winter, and shed most of the fur in the summer. Preparation for a change in season does not involve "knowledge" of an unusual season.

FIELD RESEARCH:

Make observations of your own on the preparations birds and animals make for the winter. Compare your report with others.

Naturally, geese and other migrating birds stay in the nesting regions in the north until their young are strong and able to fly long distances. By the time this period is ended, the food supply has usually begun to dwindle, due to the freezing over of ponds and lakes.

Some birds, like geese, cruise leisurely southward, flying now in one direction and now another, searching for food on their journey. Some fly by night and feed by day. Others fly great distances without stopping until they reach their destination. No one really knows exactly why birds migrate, except that they follow the food supply.

Gendreau

GEESE FLYING IN FORMATION

One sure sign of the changing seasons is the migration of birds. The migrations of geese are well-known because of their V-formation while in flight.

LIBRARY RESEARCH:

Investigate the migration of birds to discover reasons for their movements other than that, as some people say, "they know cold weather is coming."

The robin's rain song, the dry fog, and low-curling smoke are but a few of the many weather signs which come to us out of the nature-lore which generations of farmers, hunters, and other outdoor folk have built up. Our job is to learn to distinguish between those signs which are based on scientific sense and those that are not. Careful, long-range observations of nature and weather changes, joined with what we learn in the laboratory, will disprove many weather superstitions. You will get the scientific knack of searching out the facts, and you will find fun in some of the foolish but still quite commonly accepted superstitions and misbeliefs.

The Moon and the Weather. — There are many weather signs and superstitions relating to the moon. The weather does not depend upon the moon and, therefore, the moon cannot indicate the weather. Such sayings as "When the crescent moon can hold water it will be dry," "Fish bite best as the moon grows full," and many similar statements are just not true.

Statements relating to the moon and weather probably result from observations of the moon during certain kinds of weather. However, if the observations are continued long enough, the study shows that the moon has no influence upon the weather. The motions and changes in shape of the moon occur and recur with clocklike precision. Do weather changes occur with that same regularity?

FIELD RESEARCH:

Talk with your friends to learn as many sayings as possible about the moon and weather. Give your reasons for thinking the sayings have or have not any facts behind them.

General Problem 2. Are There Scientific Weather Signs?

Rings, Rainbows, and Rain. — A ring around the moon or the sun may indicate the approach of a storm. The ring is produced by the action of light on ice crystals or water particles in the air. As the ice or moisture-laden air moves toward us, the ring often grows larger, and hence there is some truth in the old saying: "The bigger the ring, the nearer the storm." However, the moon is about 240,000 miles distant from the earth, while the icy or watery clouds are only a few miles

Ewing Galloway

"RAINBOW AT MORNING, SAILORS TAKE WARNING"

This picture shows the skyline of Tampa, Florida, framed in the ring of a rainbow. If it were seen in the afternoon, it might mean fair weather ahead. Why?

above the earth.   Light from the moon illuminates the ice particles causing the ring appearance.

Sometimes a large ring of color is observed about the sun.   It is caused by the light shining through a layer-like cloud of ice particles, high above this earth.   Such rings probably have little, if any, influence on the weather.

A colored ring close about the moon or sun is called a *corona*, while the larger rings are called *halos*.   The first is usually caused by water particles and the latter by ice particles.

> Rainbow at morning, sailors take warning;
> Rainbow at night, sailors delight.

There is some scientific reason in this "sailor's warning."   A rainbow is caused by the sun shining on particles of moisture in the air.

A rainbow in the morning is caused by the sun shining on rainclouds or moisture-laden air in the west.   As the air moves from west to east (the usual course of a storm due to the earth's rotation) the weather condition moves with it.   The rainbow at "night" indicates clear sky in the west — a sign that the storm clouds have almost all passed through the area where the rainbow is visible. With their passing, of course, comes clear weather, and so the old saying has some basis of fact.

"Rain before seven, stop before eleven" is often true, not because "seven" rhymes with "eleven," but because the heat from the sun during the middle of the day acts to warm the clouds and causes their moisture to evaporate. Warm air, you know, can hold more moisture than cold air.

Clouds. — You know that there are fair-weather clouds and storm clouds.   While observation and study of clouds alone will not give reliable weather forecasts, still a close observer of clouds is able to tell in advance some things about approaching changes in weather. This is because different kinds of clouds are due to changing air currents, temperature, and amount of moisture in the air.

Courtesy Canadian National Railway

CUMULUS CLOUDS

This is how large, cottony, cumulus clouds look from an airplane flying above them. They are sometimes called "storm-building" clouds. Explain.

Some clouds are well-known as fair-weather clouds. You have seen them, the white billowy clouds looking like great piles of fluffy cotton with flat bases moving slowly along in the sky. These *cumulus* (hillshaped) clouds (⌂), as they are called, float at a height of about a mile above the earth, where the air is cool. They are fair-weather clouds when the air is dry. But when warm air, filled with moisture, rushes upward, it cools rapidly. This causes condensation of the moisture.

The front edge of the cloud will assume a dark, threatening appearance. The peaceful cumulus cloud thus becomes the threatening thunderhead.

Contrasted with the cumulus clouds are the fleecy, feathery clouds that are often observed high in the sky.

Courtesy National Youth Administration

CIRRUS CLOUDS

These are sometimes called "mare's tails." Clouds of this type often foretell an advancing storm.

They are the highest of all clouds, sometimes floating five or six miles above the earth and usually not nearer than three or four miles. They are near the top of the *troposphere*, the cloud-bearing part of our atmosphere, above which is the *stratosphere*, a region without clouds. The upper troposphere is a region of very cold air and the clouds there consist of ice crystals. These *cirrus* (curl) clouds (¬) are usually the advance guard of a storm. They travel with rapidly moving air currents, sometimes nearly 100 miles an hour.

As the storm nears, the shape of the cirrus clouds may change to low-lying *stratus* (layer) clouds (——). Stratus clouds can change into *stratocumulus* (‿), and are called *nimbostratus* if rain falls from them. They hang low in the sky and are wide in extent. Strato-

Courtesy U. S. Weather Bureau

COMBINATION CLOUDS

Large billowing cumulus clouds have spread out to form these strato-cumulus clouds. At top right you can still see part of a cumulus cloud.

cumulus clouds are often seen at sunset, just above the horizon.

Each of the common kinds of clouds mentioned often combines with others or changes into one of the other three forms. Frequently more than one kind of cloud can be observed in the sky at a time.

All told, there are over twenty-seven kinds of clouds which are combinations of the simple cloud forms. Nine of these cloud forms, based on the cumulus cloud, are low (L) clouds. Another nine, also having cumulus characteristics, occur at higher altitudes in the air and are referred to as middle (M) clouds.

A third group occurring at high altitudes are grouped as high (H) clouds. They are the various kinds of cirrus clouds. Cloud forms are given symbols, three of which you have seen. You will be interested to learn more of these symbols shown on page 103 and to use them in your reports of the weather.

FIELD RESEARCH:

Take pictures of clouds and label them with the proper symbol. Not only will you get some beautiful cloud pictures, but you will have pictures to mount in your Science Discovery Book to illustrate your discussions.

Facts versus Fancies. — Superstitions and misbeliefs are always indications of ignorance on the part of people who believe them. Such beliefs prove that the persons who accept them are not careful, accurate thinkers. In time, people of this sort may become very narrow-minded and find it difficult to sympathize with the scientist's thorough search after facts.

The results of the study of nature by the scientific method have led to the disproving of many superstitions. Yet progress of this kind has always been opposed by people who are superstitious. Perhaps you know some such folk whom you can interest in your study of science and thus save them from the folly of superstition and misbeliefs.

You who are studying science should always have an open mind, ready to accept knowledge that is based upon facts. The true scientist is a seeker after truth.

Thinking Things Over. — The scientific forecasting of the weather requires a knowledge of the weather factors, their causes and effects. Weather signs are often based upon observations that are not fully explained by the principles of science. Usually the observer does not take the trouble to check his prediction of the weather with what actually follows, nor with the weather that precedes his observation. The weather of tomorrow grows out of the weather of many yesterdays and of today.

As we continue our study of the weather, we shall learn how careful weather scientists take into account a vast amount of accurate information. They record wind, air moisture, temperature, air pressure, and the movements of great air masses across the country from inland toward the sea and from the sea inland. These are the weather factors.

Key Words

Amongst men who confound their ideas with words there must be endless dispute. — LOCKE

Words are useful to convey our ideas to others. Proper choice of words will lead to the clearness and understanding which are so necessary to successful work in science. It was the custom of certain ancient philosophers to use words to express ideas without the foundation of proof by experiment. Hence they "confounded their ideas with words." In science, words are used to express ideas based upon facts and their relationships.

Your science study provides you with an opportunity to discover facts and their relationships. You will need the right words to indicate these facts. The *Key Words* at the end of each topic deserve your special study in this respect. Be certain that each *Key Word* has a real meaning for you so that you can use it without "confounding your ideas." Always complete the *Key Word* exercise in your Science Discovery Book to the best of your ability.

cirrus	evaporate	rainbow
cloud	facts	reason
corona	foretell	ring
crescent	halo	stratus
cumulus	migrate	superstition

Key Statements

Key Statements, which appear at the ends of topics through-out this book, express key thoughts based on facts learned in each topic. The *Key Statements* will help you to express your understanding of these facts and the relationships between them.

Mere memory of these statements, however, will be of little value unless they have real meaning for you. Test your understanding by discussing each *Key Statement* in some detail. When *Key Statement* exercises are provided in your Science Discovery Book, complete them in simple, concise sentences to show that you have fully grasped the meaning of each.

1. The sun, the earth, and the earth's motions are closely re-lated to weather.
2. Superstitions are not founded on fact.
3. Only people who are ignorant of the facts are superstitious, and their superstitions tend to keep them ignorant.
4. One cannot foretell the weather by observing animals.
5. The moon does not influence the weather.
6. Certain natural phenomena, such as rings and rainbows, do have some significance with regard to the weather.
7. Cloud formations indicate coming weather, to some extent.
8. Scientific weather forecasting depends upon exact knowledge of many weather factors.

Thought Questions

1. How can you distinguish between a superstition and a fact?
2. Why is it that a ring around the moon may indicate certain weather conditions?
3. Explain why "sailors take warning" when they see a "rain-bow in the morning."
4. Why is the rainbow method less satisfactory than information from a weather bureau?
5. How can one overcome a superstition?

Projects for Your Science Discovery Book

These projects are for your own scientific investigation and report and should be completed as directed by your teacher.

This is your opportunity to do some original and independent work, and to prove your ability as a scientist. Be sure to enter your findings on each project in your Science Discovery Book. If space has not been provided, the project may be worked out on notebook paper and inserted at the proper place. Use drawings wherever you can for illustration.

1. Keep a record of the changes of the moon and changes of the weather for a few months to discover whether or not there is any relation between them. How many sayings do you know about moon and weather?

2. Try to discover how some superstition about the weather started.

3. Experiment with a glass prism and sunlight to discover how rainbows are formed.

4. At what time of day would a rainbow show the largest curve? The smallest curve? Why does one never see a complete circular natural rainbow in the United States?

5. Report on what you can discover about the reasons for the migration of birds.

6. Make a rainbow by spraying water into the air when the sun shines. Remember the spray must be viewed from a particular angle.

7. Collect as many weather statements as possible relating to rings, rainbows, and other atmospheric conditions and examine each statement to determine whether or not it has any foundation in facts.

© *Morris Rosenfeld*

SAILORS' DELIGHT

More perfect sailing weather would be hard to find. What weather conditions are suggested by the picture?

TOPIC II

Weather Factors

The sun was warm, but the wind was chill —
You know how it is with an April day.
When the sun is out and the wind is still,
You're one month on in the month of May.
But if you so much as dare to speak,
A cloud comes over the sunlit arch,
A wind comes off the frozen peak,
And you're two months back in the middle of March.

— From "New Hampshire," by Robert Frost

<u>Do you know:</u>

1. How to read a thermometer?
2. The temperature at which water freezes and boils?
3. What air pressure is?
4. What a barometer is?
5. What causes winds?
6. How moisture gets into the air?

General Problem 1. What Is Temperature?

Nature's Weather-Makers. — Nature's principal weather-makers are *air temperature, air pressure, air motion,* and *air moisture.* Temperature is important because a change in temperature affects the pressure, the motion, and the moisture of the air. Varying pressures are the cause of the winds, which are simply air in motion.

25

Finally, the moisture in the air is seen in clouds, fog, rain, mist, and snow. The shapes of clouds depend on air pressure and temperature, and their speed and direction follow the motion of the air. Thus each of these weather-makers affects the others. Together they are the weather.

RAISING THE TEMPERATURE

In orange groves, when the temperature drops near freezing, oil pots are lighted to protect the fruit from the frost.

What Is Temperature? —It is easy to say "it is hot" or "it is cold." But what do these expressions "hot" and "cold" really mean? Changes in heat and cold in our bodies, in the liquids we use, in the air about us, and in the fires which we build make us very familiar with this weather factor, temperature. Every one of us knows what it is to feel hot or cold, but to be real scientists we need also to know exactly what temperature is.

Temperature is the intensity of heat energy in a body. Or we may say more simply that temperature is the degree of heat of a body. Note carefully that temperature is not the amount of heat in a body, neither are heat and temperature the same thing. Heat (energy) is a cause of temperature. Energy, which causes a feeling of warmth in a body, tends to move from a body of higher temperature to one of lower temperature. One body is hotter than another, if it can give heat to the other. It is colder if it takes heat from the other. It is clear that if a glass of water and a boiler of water are heated to the same temperature, the boiler of water has more heat energy because there is more water, but it would not give off heat to the glass if they were side by side.

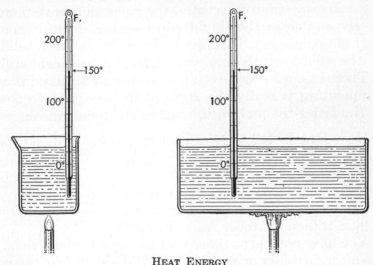

HEAT ENERGY

What is the temperature of the water in each container? Which contains more heat energy?

All of these statements merely tell us some effects of temperature or some facts about it. They do not tell us what temperature is. Some of you will remember that all substances are made of molecules in rapid motion. We cannot see molecules with the naked eye but some of them have been seen and photographed by means of high-powered microscopes and special cameras. Thus earlier beliefs about molecules have been proved true.

It has been shown that if two substances are alike in all respects except temperature, the molecules in the one with the higher temperature are moving faster than the molecules in the one with the lower temperature.

You know that when water is heated hot enough the liquid changes to steam. Probably this happens because the molecules move so fast they fly out of the liquid in the form of a gas. Of course they continue to move faster than they did in the liquid state. When heat is taken away from the steam, the molecules move more slowly and form the liquid state again. If still more heat is taken away, the liquid freezes, or becomes solid. In the solid form the molecules move more slowly still.

These examples are given to help you understand that temperature is really the state of motion of molecules — the faster the motion the higher the temperature.

How Hot Is It? — Now that we have considered the meaning of temperature, we are ready to think about its measurement. Not only can the temperature of objects on the earth be measured, but scientists even have ways of measuring the temperature of stars that are many trillion trillions of miles from the earth.

You have noticed at times that when you enter a room, the air feels colder or warmer than it does at other times. This is often true even though there has been no actual change in the temperature. Can you explain the apparent difference? It may have to do with the amount of moisture in the air, or the motion of the air, or both — or perhaps you are not a good temperature measurer.

FIELD RESEARCH:

Place one hand in hot water and the other in cold water for two or three minutes, and then place both hands in lukewarm water. Explain your sensations.

Such experiences with air temperatures and hot and cold water prove that our sense of feeling is not a good measure of temperature. Therefore, scientists have invented certain instruments, called thermometers, which will measure temperature accurately.

General Problem 2. How Are Temperatures Measured?

Metallic Thermometers. — Many common household thermometers contain no liquid. They are usually circular in shape. The temperature is indicated by a pointer which moves across a scale.

Inside the thermometer, and attached to the pointer, is a *bi-metal* strip, made of two different metals fastened together. When the metals are heated, one expands faster than the other. This causes the bi-metal strip to curve or bend. Thus the pointer attached to it moves.

When the bi-metal strip is cooled, one metal contracts at a faster rate than the other. This causes the strip to straighten. The pointer then moves in the opposite direction than it did when the bi-metal strip was warmed.

A metallic thermometer is better than a liquid thermometer for many purposes. Frequently a metallic thermometer is easier to read. It is not so delicate as a liquid thermometer. Thus metallic thermometers are being used more and more at home, while the mercury-containing liquid thermometer, which gives a higher degree of accuracy, is usually employed in scientific work.

FIELD RESEARCH:

Go to a watch repair man and find out how the balance wheel helps to regulate a watch.

There are many devices which you can find out about, all using double strips of metal as a metallic thermometer. One of them is the thermostat used to control the temperature of houses and boilers.

EXPERIMENT 1

How can metals be used to show changes in temperature?

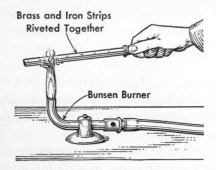

Brass and Iron Strips
Riveted Together

Bunsen Burner

Before you start this experiment and other experiments, be sure you know exactly what you want to find out, and have everything ready to use.

Have a reason for what you do, and watch everything that happens, so that you can explain it. For instance, why must the brass and iron strips be riveted together? Why does not the wood handle get hot?

WHAT TO USE: — Two strips of metal, one brass and one iron, riveted together; a Bunsen burner or some other means of heating the metals.

WHAT TO DO: — Heat the strip hot, and then cool it.

WHAT HAPPENS: — 1. Does the strip curve when you heat it?
2. If it bends, which metal is on the outside of the curve?
3. Does it straighten out when it gets cold again?

CONCLUSION: — Can you think of an explanation of the bending?
When metals are heated, they expand. Suppose one of the metals expanded faster than the other. Does that help explain your observation?

APPLICATION: — Secure a discarded oven thermometer. Take it apart and find the two metal strips.
If you can get a thermostat taken from the cooling system of a car, you can investigate how its action depends on a two-metal (bi-metal) strip.

Thermometers Containing Liquids. — Many common *house thermometers* consist of a glass *bulb* and *stem* nearly filled with a liquid, called *mercury*, or with red-colored alcohol or a similar liquid. The stem of the thermometer has a very fine *bore* (lengthwise hole) which is sealed at the top and broadens into the bulb at the bottom.

In order to understand how this kind of thermometer works you must remember that when a liquid like mercury, alcohol, or water is heated it expands, that is, it increases in volume. Mercury and alcohol expand uniformly. They expand equal amounts with equal changes in temperatures, at least for ordinary changes. Their freezing and boiling points occur at convenient temperatures, and so they make splendid indicators for use in thermometers. For example, if a liquid freezes at 20° F., it would be unsuitable for temperatures below 20° F. On the other hand, a liquid to be used in a thermometer must have a boiling point higher than the temperature it is to measure. Mercury (quicksilver) has a freezing point of $-37°$ F. and a boiling point of 675° F.; hence it can be used between those temperatures. Alcohol freezes at $-179°$ F. and boils at 172° F. Therefore, alcohol cannot be used for temperatures above its boiling point, namely, 172° F.

You have seen examples showing that liquids expand when heated and contract when cooled. You will see that this is to be expected if what we think about the motion of molecules is true. As the molecules move faster they take up more room.

Experiments 2 and 3 will help you to prove what happens when liquids are heated and cooled.

When the bulb of a thermometer containing mercury or alcohol or any other liquid is heated, the liquid in the bulb expands (takes up more room). This causes

EXPERIMENT 2

Do liquids expand when heated?

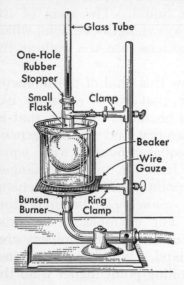

You could do this experiment without putting the flask of water in a beaker of water, by applying heat directly to the flask itself. Why do you think it is better to do it as shown in the diagram?

If the hole (bore) in the glass tube were smaller, would the water level in it move up and down more than in this size tube? Why?

What is the need for the wire gauze?

WHAT TO USE: — A small (50 cc.) flask; a one-hole rubber stopper to fit the flask; a glass tube 12 inches long to fit the hole in the stopper; a large glass beaker or basin of water; a Bunsen burner; a clamp support for the flask; and a ring support, wire gauze and ring stand to support the beaker.

For home experimenting a pickle bottle partly filled with water can be heated in a double boiler on the stove.

WHAT TO DO: — 1. Fill the flask brimful with water and insert the stopper with the glass tube just sticking through it. The water will probably fill the flask and a little of the glass tube. The top of the water in the tube should be marked by tying a string around it at that point or by some other means.

Support the flask with the bulb immersed in cold water in the beaker. The beaker should be placed on a wire gauze on the ring.

2. Heat the water in the beaker for a few minutes, and mark the new level of the water in the tube as before.

WHAT HAPPENS: — 1. When the stopper was inserted in the flask, did some water go up into the glass tube?   Why?

2. When you heated the water in the beaker, did the water in the flask get hot?   How?

Did the level of the water in the glass tube go up or down as you heated the water in the beaker?   How much did it change?

CONCLUSION: — Why did the level of the water in the tube change?   Did the water in the flask take up more room when it became hot than when it was cold?   Why?

APPLICATION: — How does the liquid in a thermometer indicate higher temperatures?

If the radiator of your car is filled to the brim with cold water, will some water overflow when the radiator gets hot? Why?

the liquid in the stem to rise higher.   If the liquid in the bulb of the thermometer is cooled, it contracts and the liquid in the stem goes down.

Perhaps you are wondering why thermometers have bulbs.   The bulb is to hold the liquid.   The bore in the stem is small so that when the large amount of liquid in the bulb expands even a little, the top of the liquid in the stem moves a good deal.   The bore is sometimes so small that the thread of liquid in it is difficult to see unless it is magnified in some way.

Let us try Experiment 3 to prove that liquids contract when cooled.

FIELD RESEARCH:

If you have an ice-cube freezer in your refrigerator at home or at school, try the following: Fill a tray as nearly level full of water as you can.   Then put it in the refrigerator and let the water freeze. When it is frozen solid, note if the ice takes up more room than the water?   Does water expand when it freezes?

EXPERIMENT 3

Do liquids contract when cooled?

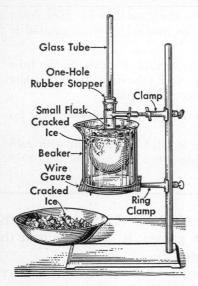

Glass Tube →
One-Hole Rubber Stopper →
Clamp
Small Flask
Cracked Ice
Beaker →
Wire Gauze
Cracked Ice
Ring Clamp

When you look over the apparatus for this experiment, do you see a good reason for putting the flask in a beaker of water? What is used in this experiment to cause the water in the flask to change in temperature? What was used in Experiment 2 to cause a change in temperature? Is the wire gauze needed here for the same reason it was used in Experiment 2?

WHAT TO USE: — Use the same equipment as in Experiment 2 except the Bunsen burner.

WHAT TO DO: — Fill the flask so full that, when you put the stopper in, some water rises in the tube. Place the bulb of the flask in cold water in the beaker, and add cracked ice. At home the pickle bottle can be placed in the refrigerator.

WHAT HAPPENS: — Describe just what changes you observe.

CONCLUSION: — Do liquids contract when they are cooled?

APPLICATION: — Why does the water in an automobile radiator take up less room when it is cold than when it is hot?
How does the liquid in a thermometer indicate lower temperatures?

The Fahrenheit Scale. — One of the first thermometer scales was devised by a scientist named *Fahrenheit* who was born in Danzig in 1686.

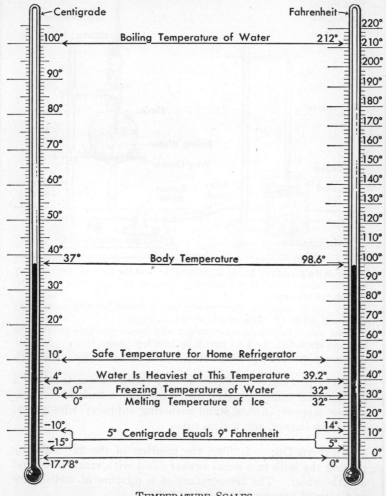

TEMPERATURE SCALES

Compare the fixed points on each scale. Which is larger — one degree Fahrenheit or one degree Centigrade? The Fahrenheit reading equals the Centigrade reading multiplied by 1.8 plus 32. Try it.

KEY EXPERIMENT 4

*How may a thermometer be tested by its "fixed points," 32°
and 212°, to determine its accuracy?*

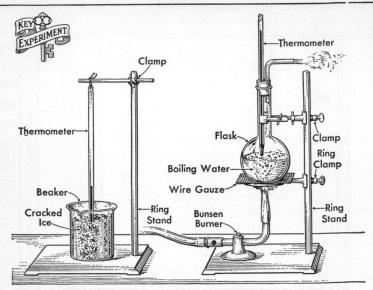

Why is it a good thing in this experiment to heat the flask of water directly with the flame instead of in a beaker of water as in Experiment 2? What use has the wire gauze?

Why do you suppose the thermometer bulb is placed just above the boiling water and not in it? Suppose you try it both ways.

In the part of the experiment with ice, why would you have to leave the thermometer bulb in the ice longer if the bulb were larger?

This is called a "Key" Experiment. This means it is especially important.

WHAT TO USE: — A glass mercury thermometer that has a 32° and 212° mark; cracked ice; a beaker; a flask with 2-hole rubber stopper; a ring stand with ring support; wire gauze, a Bunsen burner, and a glass tube.

WHAT TO DO: — 1. Test the position of the 32° mark by placing the bulb in a small beaker filled with cracked ice and a little water. The temperature of a mixture of melting ice and a small amount of water is 32° F.

Leave the bulb in the melting ice until you are certain the mercury in the stem has come to a stationary position showing that all the mercury in the bulb is at the same temperature as the melting ice.

2. Now carefully observe the 32° mark on the stem to determine whether it is exactly on a level with the mercury in the stem. If it is, the thermometer is accurate as to this fixed point. If it is not, make a note of the amount of variation, above or below.

3. To test the 212° mark on the thermometer, place the bulb in the steam of boiling water. Insert the thermometer through one hole of the 2-hole rubber stopper and place the stopper in the flask about ¼ full of water. The bulb of the thermometer should be just above the surface of the water. In the extra hole in the rubber stopper place a tube to allow steam to escape from the flask; otherwise it will burst. Support the flask and heat the water to boiling.

The temperature of the boiling water increases with increased air pressure and lowers with reduced air pressure; so results may not be as accurate as for the other test but will be accurate enough for your purpose. The steam from boiling water for a given pressure stays at a constant (same) temperature as long as the water boils.

Check the position of the 212° mark with the top of the mercury. What does it show?

HOUSE THERMOMETER

This thermometer does not read beyond 130°. Is that satisfactory for its purpose?

Can you test this thermometer by the boiling-point test?

WHAT HAPPENS: — 1. In the first part of the experiment, did some of the ice melt?

Can you check its accuracy by the freezing-point test?

2. Was the 32° mark exactly opposite the top of the mercury? If not, how much was it in error? + or −?

3. In the second part, was the 212° mark exactly opposite

the top of the mercury in the stem of the thermometer?   If not, how much was it in error?   + or −?

CONCLUSION: — State how accurate you found the thermometer as indicated by the 32° and 212° marks.

APPLICATION: — Commercial thermometers are calibrated (marked for reading) by placing them in constant temperature baths and marking the mercury (or liquid) level for certain temperatures.   Then with a dividing machine the stem is marked off into equal spaces with these marks as starting places.   Or the spacing of the marks is transferred to the metal back.

Use a tested thermometer to check one that may be inaccurate.

NOTES:

1. A thermometer with a wooden back should not be placed in boiling water, for the hot water may injure the finish on the wood.

2. A thermometer that does not register as high as the 212° mark should not be used, since placing it in boiling water might cause it to break.

LIBRARY RESEARCH:

Consult your librarian for information about Fahrenheit. Find out how his first thermometer was marked and how the changes to the present markings happened to be made.

The common house thermometer has a Fahrenheit scale.   When the bulb of a mercury thermometer with a Fahrenheit scale is placed in melting snow or ice, the top of the mercury will drop to a certain level in the stem and remain stationary.   This place on the stem is marked 32°.   If the bulb of a mercury thermometer is placed in boiling water or steam at standard air pressure, the liquid will rise to a level which is marked 212°.

The stem between the 32° mark and the 212° mark is divided into 180 equal divisions, and each one of these divisions is called a *degree*. The 32° mark is the temperature at which ice melts or water freezes. The 212° mark is the temperature at which water boils under standard air pressure. These two marks are sometimes called the "fixed points" of a thermometer, and they can be used for testing the accuracy of a thermometer.

You can test the accuracy of a mercury thermometer by following the plan in Experiment 4.

The Centigrade Scale. — The *Centigrade* thermometer scale differs from the Fahrenheit scale in divisions and the numbers for the "fixed points." On the Centigrade thermometer, the point at which the liquid in the stem should stand when the bulb is in melting ice is marked 0° C. The level for boiling water is marked 100° C. The space between 0° C. and 100° C. is divided into 100 divisions, hence the name *centi* (hundred) *grade* (marks). A thermometer with a Centigrade scale may be tested in the same manner as the Fahrenheit.

The Centigrade scale is the most commonly used scale in science, since most measurements are made so they can be divided into tenths, hundredths, and thousandths by changing the position of the decimal point. The meter is also divided into tenths, hundredths, and thousandths. The meter belongs to the metric system which is used by scientists the world over. Contrast this with our yard which is divided into 3 feet and 36 inches.

LIBRARY RESEARCH:

With the help of your librarian and your science teacher look up about the metric system and its advantages over the English system for use in science.

Thermometers for Special Needs. — The doctor uses a small thermometer of special make to "take" (measure) the temperature of a sick person. The normal temperature of a healthy body is 98.6° F. A slight

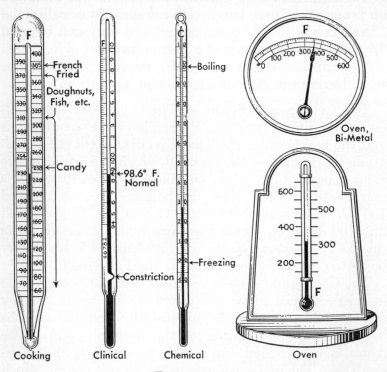

THERMOMETERS

How many of these thermometers do you recognize? Which one has the greatest range? Which one reads the highest? Why? Which do you think is most accurate?

Why wouldn't an oven thermometer make a good cooking thermometer?

variation above or below normal is an indication of trouble. It is necessary therefore for the doctor's thermometer to be very accurate.

The doctor's thermometer, called a *clinical* thermometer, has a short stem with a much smaller bore than ordinary thermometers, so that a slight change in temperature will cause a considerable change in the level of the mercury in the stem.

The front part of the glass stem is shaped in such a way as to act like a lens and hence magnifies the small thread of mercury in the bore so that it may be seen more readily. The face of the stem is marked off in units of one fifth of a degree. Between the long slender bulb and the stem, the bore is made even smaller than the bore above or below (see the picture on page 40). Because of this, once the mercury gets above the squeezed-in part it is not drawn back into the bulb when the thermometer cools, as happens in an ordinary thermometer. Such a device allows the doctor time to read the temperature accurately. Perhaps you have seen him "shake" the mercury back into the bulb after he has read the temperature.

Some other special thermometers are for use in making candy, deep fat cooking, making maple sirup and sugar, cooking meats, and for a great many industrial processes. The special thermometers may contain liquid or they may consist of two metal strips called metallic thermometers.

As you have learned, mercury is not the only liquid used in thermometers. Some contain colored alcohol or similar liquids. One point to remember is that different liquids have different boiling temperatures. Alcohol, for example, boils at about 172° F. Therefore an alcohol thermometer may not be used safely for temperatures as high as that. On the other hand, alcohol must be cooled to a much lower temperature than mercury to freeze; therefore, alcohol thermometers can be used to measure much lower temperatures than can mercury thermometers.

General Problem 3.   What Causes Differences in Air Temperatures?

Variations in Air Temperatures. — Latitude, wind direction, altitude, and large bodies of water are the

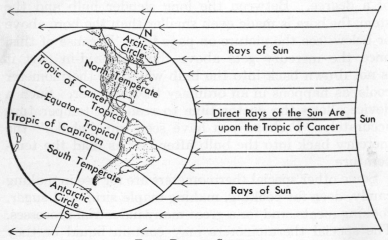

FIRST DAY OF SUMMER

On the first day of summer in the northern hemisphere the sun is directly overhead at the Tropic of Cancer.

What is the northern limit of the sun's rays at this time? the southern limit? What changes would have to be made in this diagram to make it represent the first day of winter?

What are the limits of the sun's most direct rays from season to season?

principal regulators of air temperatures over the earth. The sun has very little direct heating effect on the air for reasons which we shall consider later.

Latitude influences air temperatures because the farther a place is from the equator, the more the earth slopes away from the sun's rays. Or to put the fact another way, the more slanting the rays of the sun, the less heat the rays supply. Thus the Frigid Zones are much colder than the Temperate or Tropic Zones.

But we must be careful not to think that a place will have a uniform temperature because of the Zone or latitude in which it lies. The other regulators of tem-

Courtesy Pan American Union

ALTITUDE AFFECTS CLIMATE

The peak of Cotopaxi Mountain is snow-covered, though this part of Ecuador is very near the equator. Explain why the temperature drops with increased altitude.

perature may and do cause wide variations. For example, air temperatures in the Temperate Zones range from 60° below zero to 110° above.

Consequently, the so-called temperature zones shown in the diagram on page 42 represent only general conditions of temperature. Their real purpose is to show the changes in the direction of the sun's rays caused by seasonal changes in the relative positions of the sun and the earth. We shall consider the heating effects of these changes in more detail when we study the seasons.

The temperature of the air of a place is affected by the direction of *winds*. Wind coming from the north is usually a current of cold air, and consequently the temperature of a place in its path will drop. Also, air moving over a body of cold water is cooled and will cool the localities over which it passes.

Fairchild Aerial Surveys

WATER AND TEMPERATURE

What effect does this large body of water have on near-by land?

Altitude above sea level has a marked influence on air temperature. Even though the top of a mountain is nearer the sun, it is cooler there than at its base.

Many boys and girls, and adults as well, are curious to know why the air is colder with increase in altitude. All your experiences show that the nearer you are to a hot stove the warmer you feel. How can it be, then, that it is colder above the earth, which is nearer to the hot sun, than at the lower levels of the earth's surface?

Air near the earth gets more heat from the earth than air above it. Also the upper air does not absorb (take in) as much heat from the sun as the lower air. This helps to make the air near the earth warmer than the air above.

As we have seen, the sun has little effect in warming the air. It warms the earth, which in turn warms the air near it. As the warm air rises, the pressure on it becomes less and less, and the molecules spread farther and farther apart. The air gets lighter, going higher and higher, farther and farther away from the warm earth. As it rises, it gets "thinner" and colder.

If you apply heat to air, you make it expand; if, on the contrary, air is allowed to expand by lessening the pressure on it, it cools off.

Thus the warm air rises, expands, and becomes colder. It rises gradually to about 6 or 7 miles, getting colder all the time by expansion. At that height it is so cold it does not rise any higher, but begins to settle back toward the surface. For this reason air gets colder up to about 6 or 7 miles.

Above the height of 6 or 7 miles its temperature remains about the same, 60° to 70° F. below zero, for several miles more in what is called the *stratosphere*. Above the stratosphere the temperature of the air is thought by some scientists to increase as the natural result of being closer to the sun.

Since rising currents of air contain moisture which condenses and forms clouds, the highest clouds are not higher than 6 or 7 miles. As noted on page 18, the layer of air containing moisture and clouds is called the *troposphere*. It reaches about 6 or 7 miles above the earth. Above the troposphere is the cloudless stratosphere.

The temperature of the air of a locality is affected by the nearness of large bodies of water. A large lake or ocean makes the summer temperature of near-by land cooler and the winter temperature warmer than they would be otherwise.

The temperature of the air of certain places near the ocean is also affected by the great ocean currents. These currents are like huge rivers flowing in the ocean itself. If the current comes from the Tropical Zone, as the Gulf Stream does, its waters are warm and will heat the air of places near it. On the other hand, if the current comes from the north, its waters are cold and will make the air of near-by places colder.

LIBRARY RESEARCH:

Ocean currents owe their motion partly to the fact that cold water is heavier than warm water and partly to winds. The direction of ocean currents is influenced by the rotation of the earth as well as by wind direction. Follow up these hints by further reading to determine why a particular ocean current takes the course it does.

General Problem 4. How Can Air Pressure Be Measured?

What Is Air Pressure? — The earth is covered with an ocean of air called its *atmosphere*. There is really no "top" or upper surface of the atmosphere, as there is to the water ocean. The atmosphere merely thins off into space.

In your science study last year, perhaps you experimented and found that air is composed of oxygen, carbon dioxide, and moisture. Can you recall how you tested for these three substances? From your reading you learned that air also contains nitrogen and several rare gases.

The air has about the same composition up to an altitude of sixty to eighty miles, except for ozone. However, without special aids to breathing most men cannot live long above three and one-half to four and one-half miles from the earth on account of low air pressure. It is possible that above 100 miles the atmosphere contains slowly decreasing amounts of oxygen, but no hydrogen as was formerly thought. Nitrogen is the principal gas at all heights.

We know that air is matter and that all matter has weight. *The weight of the air is called air pressure.* A column of air one square inch in area, and as high as the air extends upward, weighs 14.7 pounds at sea level under normal conditions. Since there is a similar column of air over every square inch of ground and every square inch of water, we may say that the atmospheric pressure on the earth is 14.7 pounds to the square inch at the level of the sea.

The pressure of the air against this one square inch of white surface is 14.7 lbs.

To help you understand about air pressure, think of a large pile of loose straw. It would be more pressed together or compact at the bottom than at the top, for the straw at the bottom would bear the weight of all the straw above it. The same is true of air. The lower portion of the atmosphere is the most compact or *dense.* The molecules are more closely packed together. As one goes up from the earth, the air becomes thinner (less dense). Therefore, the air pressure decreases very rapidly as one leaves the earth. At a height of about three and a half miles, approximately half of the weight of the air is below one. That is, at that altitude the pressure is approximately 7.3 pounds per square inch.

Measuring Air Pressure. — Air pressure is measured by instruments called *barometers.* There are two types of barometers in general use, *mercurial* (or *liquid*) and *aneroid* (*without liquid*) barometers. Here is the story of the invention of the mercurial barometer.

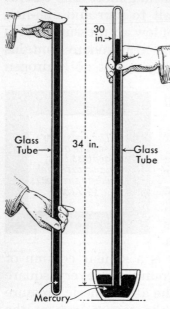

Galileo, knowing that water would not rise in a pump higher than about 33 feet, reasoned that the fact had something to do with the pressure of the atmosphere. He asked one of his pupils to solve the problem. The pupil, Torricelli (tôr′rĕ-chĕl′lē), by his now famous experiment proved that Galileo's idea was correct.

Torricelli filled a tube about a yard long, and closed at one end, with mercury. Placing a finger over the open end, he inverted it, putting the open end in a dish of mercury. On removing his finger, he noticed that not all the mercury came

MERCURIAL BAROMETER

Note the length of the tube.

The height of the mercury in the tube is measured from the surface of the mercury in the dish.

What holds the mercury up in the tube?

out of the tube. It settled down and came to rest with the top of the mercury in the tube about 30 inches above the surface of the mercury in the dish.

Torricelli reasoned that since there was no air in the tube above the mercury (the tube had been filled with mercury and no air was allowed to enter), the column of mercury must be held up or balanced by the pressure of the air on the surface of the mercury in the dish.

The aneroid barometer is decidedly more convenient for general use than the mercurial barometer. The former can be manufactured as a small and light instrument. Moreover, containing no liquid to spill, the aneroid is readily portable.

The part affected by changes in air pressure is a flat metal box with flexible top and bottom. It contains practically no air. Increasing pressures squeeze the top and bottom together and decreasing pressures let them spring apart again. Their movements are transmitted to a pointer on the face of the aneroid by little levers and chains. Another important advantage of the aneroid is that its readings can be recorded automatically.

While it is convenient to express air pressures in

Courtesy U. S. Weather Bureau

ANEROID BAROMETER

The cover has been removed from this barometer to show the parts inside. Notice the round metal box. What does it do?

terms of inches of mercury because the greater the pressure the higher the column of mercury stands, nevertheless, this is not the best way. Scientists prefer to use another unit of pressure in recording air pressures. This unit is called the *millibar*.

A column of mercury 30 inches high is equivalent to 1015.9 millibars. One tenth of an inch of mercury equals 3.4 millibars. Because most barometers are marked off in inches, a table showing both inches of mercury and millibars has been placed in the Appendix of this book. Weather maps now use the millibar; so this unit of pressure will be discussed again under weather maps.

KEY EXPERIMENT 5

How does atmospheric pressure affect a barometer?

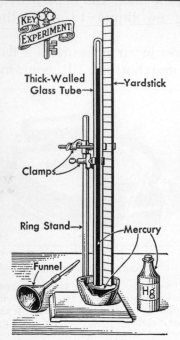

KEY EXPERIMENT

Thick-Walled Glass Tube→

←Yardstick

Clamps

Ring Stand→

Mercury

Funnel

Hg

What new materials are used in this experiment? Why must the glass tube be more than 30 inches long? Why must it be closed at one end?

Mercury is very heavy and easily spilled. Be careful because it is expensive. If mercury gets on a gold ring, the gold will turn white but will be all right again if it is kept warm a while. Try not to get mercury into a cut on your finger. It might make it sore.

This is another "Key" Experiment.

WHAT TO USE: — A thick-walled glass tube 34 inches long, with a bore of ¼ inch and sealed at one end; mercury; a ring stand and two clamps; a yardstick; a small, flat-bottomed dish; and a small funnel with small glass tube attached to transfer mercury to the tube.

WHAT TO DO: — 1. Set up the barometer as Torricelli did and fasten it in an upright position on the ring stand.

2. At a certain time each day for one week measure the distance from the surface of the mercury in the dish to the top of the mercury in the tube. Record your readings in a table.

WHAT HAPPENS: — 1. Did the mercury stay in the tube with a level of about 30 inches in height? What kept it from flowing entirely out of the tube into the dish?

2. Did the height of the column of mercury vary from day to day? How much?

CONCLUSIONS: — What is the effect of atmospheric pressure on the mercury column of a barometer?

APPLICATION: — Keep a record of the air pressure and air temperatures for a few days. Note differences or similarities in their readings.

General Problem 5. What Is Wind?

Air Motions. — On a hot summer day you may be enjoying a gentle breeze. In other sections of the country a wind may be blowing with such terrific velocity that it tears down buildings, pulls up trees, and destroys everything in its path. A wind like the latter is called a *tornado*. The velocity of a tornado may reach 200 or 300 miles per hour. Wind of ordinary velocity moves from 3 to 15 miles per hour. *Wind is air in motion*.

In order to understand the cause of this moving air, called *wind*, let us consider some common observations. Almost everybody knows that hot air rises. Do you know why? Perhaps you can get an answer by experimenting at home.

Warm air rises because cool air which is heavier settles and pushes the warm air up. If air over the earth is heated more in some places than in others, the air will

move, because cold air is heavier than warm air and therefore settles, pushing the warm air out of its way.   For this
reason air will move from
a colder region to a warmer
region.

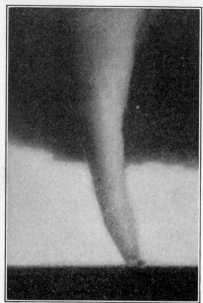

Moving Air Masses.
— The summer breeze,
the sailing breeze on the
lake, or the heavy wind
that sometimes precedes
a thunderstorm may be
local disturbances of the
air set up by local unequal
heating of the air. Or they
may be part of a great
mass of air which moves
because of unequal tem-
peratures over large por-
tions of the earth's surface.

Courtesy U. S. Weather Bureau

A RARE PICTURE

It is seldom that anyone as near
as this to a tornado cloud has the time
or the courage to photograph it.

Great masses or blocks of
air, many miles wide at the
front and thousands of feet
thick may move from the
cold polar regions southward.   When these come from
over the continent, they are called *continental polar* air
masses, abbreviated cP.

Other great masses of cold air which begin over polar
seas are called *maritime* (sea) *polar* air masses.   This
name is abbreviated MP.   If the air mass comes from the
continent where the temperature is warm or tropical, it is
called a *continental tropical* (cT) air mass; if from a
warm sea, like the Gulf of Mexico or South Atlantic
or Pacific, it is called a *maritime tropical* (MT) air
mass.

FIELD RESEARCH:

If you have a hot-air furnace in operation, place a tuft of cotton or a feather over the hot-air register. Does the cotton move up or down? Which way does it show that the air is moving? If you have no furnace but have a stove, make a little smoke near the stove pipe. Does the smoke go up along the hot stove pipe? Which way is the air moving, up or down?

Or open a window a bit at top and bottom, when it is rather cold outdoors and there is no wind blowing. Test the air movement. Does the air come in through the open window at top or bottom? Does it go up or down after it gets in?

These large masses or blocks of air move over the land without being mixed very much, unless a cold mass meets a warm mass. Then the *front* of the warm mass may ride up over the *front* of the cold mass because warm air is lighter than cold air. Where two fronts meet in this way, storms are likely to occur. Sometimes the two

Courtesy U. S. Weather Bureau

RESULTS OF A TORNADO

The tornado that did this damage traveled only a short distance and spent its force after thirty minutes. This destruction, however, was done in only a few seconds.

masses rub shoulders, so to speak. This results in the sides of the air masses being mixed up so that storms occur.

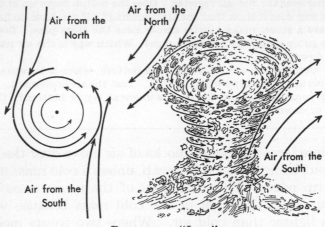

Air from the North

Air from the North

Air from the South

Air from the South

BIRTH OF A "LOW"

Have you ever seen leaves being swirled around and around by the wind? Imagine this same thing happening much more slowly and on a larger scale. That is how low pressure areas (cyclones) begin. It is now believed that low pressure areas are born along the boundary between a mass of cold air and a warm air mass.

If a warm mass moving northeasterly meets a cold mass moving southward and to one side, a counter-clockwise whirl of air is produced which is called a *low*. The *low* is usually a storm center and is many miles across. The whirling air formation called a *low* moves more or less rapidly in paths across the United States often passing into the Atlantic Ocean over the Gulf of St. Lawrence. When we study weather forecasting we shall learn more about the movements of the *lows* and corresponding *highs*. Highs are whirling air masses in which the air moves clockwise.

The *low* is often called a *cyclone*. A cyclone has a slower speed of air (wind) and should not be confused with a tornado.

The rotation of the earth has an interesting effect on the direction of moving currents of air or water on the earth's surface. In the northern hemisphere the rotation of the earth causes such moving bodies of air to shift their direction to the right. This helps to explain why the air movement in a *low* is counter-clockwise. Study of the diagram will help you to understand this effect of the rotation of the earth.

FIELD RESEARCH:

One result of this whirling movement of air currents can be illustrated by whirling water in a glass. The water will whirl with the glass but will pile up at the sides of the glass and will be shallow in the center. Try it.

The whirling mass of air (*low*) acts in a similar way to whirling water. The center portion of the whirling mass is shallow and has a low air pressure. That is why it is called a *low*. Some lows begin in the southwest and move in a curved northeasterly path over the United States toward the St. Lawrence River. At the same time, other lows are being formed far out in the Pacific Ocean. These pass over the United States in a curved path from the state of Washington and out the St. Lawrence River region. See the map on page 107.

Wind Velocities. — The speed with which air moves is an important factor in forecasting the weather. You can learn to estimate wind velocity rather accurately by using the table on page 57. In making wind observations it is important also to notice the direction.

Winds are named from the point of the compass from which they come. Hence a weather vane, a flag on a pole, or smoke from a chimney will indicate wind direction.

EXPERIMENT 6

How can the direction and velocity of the wind be determined?

This experiment calls for you to use your eyes out-of-doors. If you can observe a weather vane, why do you not need the compass? Could you tell the directions without either a weather vane or compass? How?

WHAT TO USE: — A weather vane (or a magnetic compass); a flag on a pole; and smoke from a chimney.

WHAT TO DO: — Determine the points of the compass — North, East, South, West, and equidistant points between — eight in all. Observe and record the direction of the wind as indicated by the weather vane, flag, or smoke.

In your notes you can use the words "North," "North-East," "North-West," etc., to record the directions from which the wind comes, or you can use symbols like those found on the weather maps — a circle with a short line pointing in the direction from which the wind is blowing.

By reference to the table of velocities on the next page, estimate the velocity of the wind at each observation.

WHAT HAPPENS: — Record your observations.

CONCLUSION: — Tell how you determined the direction and velocity of the wind.

APPLICATION: — Keep a record of the wind direction and velocity for a few days to discover if there is any relation between a high wind and a particular direction.

WIND VELOCITIES

(From Civil Aeronautics Bulletin No. 25, September, 1940, United States Department of Commerce, Civil Aeronautics Administration, Washington, D. C., "Meteorology for Pilots," by B. C. Haynes.)

BEAUFORT NUMBER	MAP SYMBOL	DESCRIPTIVE WORD [1]	VELOCITY (MILES PER HOUR)	SPECIFICATIONS FOR ESTIMATING VELOCITIES
0		Calm	Less than 1	Smoke rises vertically.
1			1 to 3	Direction of wind shown by smoke drift but not by wind vanes.
2		Light	4 to 7	Wind felt on face; leaves rustle; ordinary vane moved by wind.
3		Gentle	8 to 12	Leaves and small twigs in constant motion; wind extends light flag.
4		Moderate	13 to 18	Raises dust and loose paper; small branches are moved.
5		Fresh	19 to 24	Small trees in leaf begin to sway; crested wavelets form on inland water.
6			25 to 31	Large branches in motion, whistling heard in telegraph wires; umbrellas used with difficulty.
7		Strong	32 to 38	Whole trees in motion; inconvenience felt in walking against the wind.
8			39 to 46	Breaks twigs off trees; generally impedes progress.
9		Gale	47 to 54	Slight structural damage occurs (chimney pots and slate removed).
10			55 to 63	Trees uprooted; considerable structural damage occurs.
11		Whole gale	64 to 75	Rarely experienced; accompanied by widespread damage.
12		Hurricane	Above 75	

[1] Except "calm," these terms are not to be used in reports of velocity.

An interesting way to represent wind directions and velocities is found on modern weather maps. The location of a weather station is indicated by a circle. A short line is drawn to the circle from the direction in which the wind is coming to indicate wind direction. Velocity is indicated by "feathers" on the end of the line, as shown in the table. A short "feather" equals 1 and a long "feather" equals 2 on the standard wind scale. Two long and one short "feather" would equal 5 and so on. There are twelve standard wind velocities on the Beaufort wind scale.

Wind Pressure. — You know that it is difficult to walk against a strong wind. This characteristic of the wind is called *wind pressure*. Wind pressure varies or increases in proportion to the square of its velocity. For example, if a wind of 5 miles per hour increases to 10 miles per hour, the wind pressure becomes four times as great. That is, the pressure at 10 miles per hour is as much greater than that at 5 miles per hour as 100 (10 × 10) is greater than 25 (5 × 5).

FIELD RESEARCH:

A wind blowing 10 miles per hour exerts pressure of about 0.27 pound per square foot. What would be the total pressure on a window of your school or house? (Height and width × 0.27 pound.)

General Problem 6. What Is the Humidity of the Air?

Moisture in the Air. — You have learned that the moisture in the air is really water. Usually it is in the form of an *invisible* gas and is referred to as the *humidity* of the air. The invisible moisture is the gaseous state of water. You have, however, *seen* fogs, clouds, and rains, and so have had first-hand evidence of the presence of those forms of moisture in air. The amount of gaseous moisture in the air varies from time to time. The air very rarely, if ever, is *saturated* with moisture; that is, it rarely contains all the moisture it can hold. The actual amount of invisible moisture required to saturate the air depends upon the temperature of the air.

Warm air can absorb more moisture than cold air. The amount of moisture in the air at any one time is always *relative* to the amount which the air would hold if completely saturated at the same temperature. For example, if the air contains three fourths as much moisture as it could possibly hold at a given temperature, the *relative humidity* is 75 per cent.

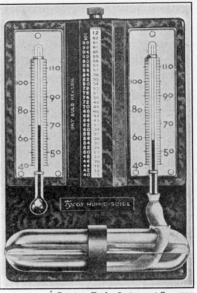

Courtesy Taylor Instrument Company

HYGROMETER

Why is a wick attached to only one bulb? What is the per cent relative humidity indicated by the readings on this hygrometer? (Use the Table of Relative Humidity in the appendix.)

Hygrometer is the name of the instrument used to measure the relative amount of moisture in the air. It usually consists of two thermometers with the bulb of one thermometer covered with a silk wick which dips into water. The other bulb is left dry. Water creeps up the wick due to *capillary action* and wets the bulb with the silk wick. Capillary action is the lifting of liquids by means of tubes or tubelike air spaces in fabrics. The liquid water changes into gaseous water (evaporates) and escapes.

As the water on the bulb changes from the liquid state to the gas state, it absorbs (takes in) heat from the mercury in the bulb, causing the liquid in the bulb to contract. The other thermometer bulb, which is kept dry, indicates the real air temperature.

The evaporation of water from the wet bulb absorbs heat from the mercury in that bulb so that it reads lower than the actual air temperature as shown by the dry bulb thermometer. The drier the air, the greater will be the difference in readings between the wet bulb and the dry bulb. This is because, in the drier air, the water on the wet bulb will evaporate faster and therefore absorb heat faster from the mercury. If the air could be saturated with moisture, no water could evaporate from the wet bulb. Then the wet bulb and dry bulb would read alike, and the relative humidity would be 100 per cent.

Now we can see how the humidity of the air affects our comfort. When the relative humidity is low, perspiration on our skin evaporates rapidly, cooling the skin. When the relative humidity is high, the air contains much moisture. Perspiration cannot evaporate rapidly, and the skin is not cooled.

Experiments 7 and 8 deal with relative humidity.

General Problem 7. What Causes Precipitation?

Dew and Frost. — As the sun drops below the horizon, the land begins to cool rapidly. Consequently, when

EXPERIMENT 7

Does an evaporating liquid absorb heat?

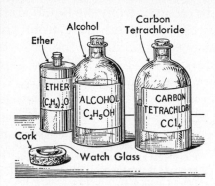

The caution says not to have any flame about while you do this experiment. This is because two of the liquids catch fire easily. Which two?

Be careful when pouring the liquids into the watch glasses not to spill any. Someone with a steady hand should do the pouring, with the watch glass close to the neck of the bottle.

Do you think you could use water instead of any of these liquids and show the same thing? Try it.

WHAT TO USE: — Alcohol; carbon tetrachloride; ether; a large, flat cork; a small watch glass and a little water.

CAUTION: Do not have any flame or fire near by.

WHAT TO DO: — 1. Put a few drops of alcohol on the back of your hand and let it evaporate.

2. Repeat, using a few drops of carbon tetrachloride or ether.

3. Place a few drops of water on the cork. Set the watch glass in the water and fill it with ether. Fan the ether briskly.

WHAT HAPPENS: — 1. Did the alcohol on your hand dry up (evaporate)? Did this make your skin feel cold?

2. How did the other liquids act when used in the same way?

3. Did the ether in the watch glass evaporate? Did fanning make it evaporate faster? What happened to the water under the glass?

CONCLUSION: — Do liquids absorb heat when they evaporate? Explain.

APPLICATION: — Why does fanning make you feel cooler? Why is it colder in a wind than out of the wind?

A LAW: — When any liquid evaporates (turns to the gaseous state), it takes in or absorbs heat.

KEY EXPERIMENT 8

What is the relative humidity of the air?

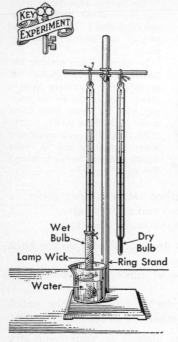

In this experiment you will use the principle you discovered in Experiment 7. Can you repeat that principle?

If you do not have two thermometers, you can get along with just one, although not as conveniently. If you have only one thermometer, use it first to get the air temperature before wetting the bulb. Then put on the wick and use it as a "wet bulb" thermometer.

If you should use ether instead of water to wet the wick, would the mercury in the thermometer be higher or lower than when water is used?

WHAT TO USE: — Two thermometers; a ring stand; a lamp wick; and a beaker of water.

WHAT TO DO: — Place the wick on one of the thermometers, supported so that the wick will hang in the beaker of water as in the drawing.

Hang the second thermometer alongside of the first, as in the drawing.

You have learned that water will rise up the wick due to capillary action. If you observe closely, you will see that this action keeps the bulb of the thermometer with the wick on it wet all the time. This is called the "wet bulb." The other bulb that is dry all the time is called the "dry bulb."

Allow the apparatus to stand a few minutes, and then read and record the temperature of the air shown by the dry-bulb thermometer and record the temperature shown by the wet-bulb thermometer.

WHAT HAPPENS: — Does the wet-bulb thermometer register lower than the dry bulb? What causes the difference?

Use the table of relative humidity in the Appendix to calculate the relative humidity. The directions will tell you how to use the dry bulb and wet bulb readings. These you should repeat in your own words in your written report.

CONCLUSION: — What did you find the relative humidity to be? What principle or law is involved in your finding?

APPLICATION: — What is the relation between health and relative humidity? Between relative humidity and wet things drying?

the air touches the cold earth, it too becomes cooler. The water vapor which the air contains is then condensed to little particles of water on cold objects, such as sticks, leaves of plants, and blades of grass. This *condensed moisture* on the cold objects is called *dew*. You may have shown by experiment in earlier science work how moisture will condense.

Certainly you have seen dew that has formed on pitchers of ice water or on blades of grass.

Warm air holds a larger mixture of invisible water than cold air. But if the air becomes cold enough, some moisture must separate

DEWDROPS

This is how dew appears when looked at through a magnifying lens. Would you believe that early morning "wet grass" could be so beautiful?

EXPERIMENT 9

How does dew form?

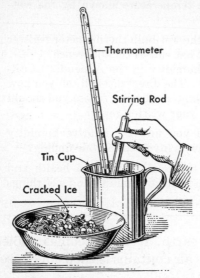

Thermometer

Stirring Rod

Tin Cup

Cracked Ice

In Experiments 7 and 8 you made use of the principle that when liquids evaporate, they absorb heat. This might be stated by saying that when heat is added to liquids, they evaporate. In this experiment, the principle of condensation is used. What is this principle?

What other experiment have you done that uses ice for the same purpose as in this experiment?

WHAT TO USE: — A tin cup; cracked ice; a stirring rod, and a thermometer.

WHAT TO DO: — 1. Partly fill the cup with water at air or room temperature. Put the thermometer bulb in the water. Add ice, a little at a time, stirring constantly with the stirring rod. Do not stir with the thermometer. Why?

2. Watch the outside of the tin to note the first appearance of a film of moisture on the tin surface. At that instant read the temperature of the water.

Repeat the experiment three times.

WHAT HAPPENS: — 1. Did the ice melt? Did the temperature of the water become lower? What caused it to get colder? Why did the temperature not show 32° as in Experiment 4?

2. Did moisture form on the outside of the cup? At what temperature each time? Was the water at the same temperature each time when the moisture formed?

What was the average temperature for the three trials?
Where did the moisture come from?
What was the temperature of the layer of air touching the tin dish when its moisture condensed?

CONCLUSION: — The air temperature at which its moisture condenses is called its *dew point*. What was the dew point of the air during your experiment?
What was the advantage of making three trials?

APPLICATION: — What makes the cold water pipe or water pitcher "sweat" some days in summer more than on other days?
Why do windows in the house "steam" some days and not other days?

from the warm air and become visible. When water separates from air and falls as rain, snow, sleet, hail, or forms dew or frost, the process is called *precipitation*.

The formation of dew is illustrated by Experiment 9. If you have a thermometer at home that will not be harmed by putting it into water, you can do this experiment at home.

If, during the night, the temperature of the earth and the air touching it drops down to 32° F. or below, the moisture freezes as fast as it separates from the air and the resulting ice crystals are called *frost*.

Science Service

FROST CRYSTALS MAGNIFIED

Kabel

FOG OVER A FOREST

Fog is a low-lying cloud made up of tiny particles of water.   Do you think it is possible for this fog to turn into rain or snow?   What other forms of water do you see in the picture?

66

The Birth of a Raindrop. — Rain is common except in the desert. If you live where winters are cold, you are familiar with snow. But many people live where it never snows. Clouds are known to us all. You will understand clouds, rain, and snow better if you know what clouds are, how they are formed, and what causes the moisture of the clouds to fall to the earth.

You have learned that clouds are really particles of water that left the earth because of evaporation.

It is strange, but true, that water vapor in the air will not readily change from a gas to a liquid unless it has something to condense "on," such as a cold dish, window, or leaf as in the formation of dew. In the air tiny dust particles act as so many cold objects on which the water of the air can collect as little drops. Some scientists think that charges of electricity in the air, called *electrons*, also may act as tiny objects for condensation.

Clouds consist of millions of tiny drops of water — so light as to be held up by the air — water particles only about one thousandth of an inch in diameter. Once the water particles are formed, they may grow larger by the condensation of still more water on their surfaces, and finally may become large enough to fall.

A raindrop may be half a million times larger than a cloud particle. The sizes of raindrops vary from one fiftieth of an inch to one fifth of an inch. Raindrops fall

---

FIELD RESEARCH:

With the aid of a large glass bottle with a one-hole rubber stopper, a glass exit tube, an exhaust air pump, a heavy-walled rubber tube and some chalk dust, try forming a fog. The air in the bottle may be cooled by quickly taking out air by means of the exhaust pump, which causes rapid expansion of the air left in the bottle. If the air in the bottle contains dust when the air is suddenly cooled as above, a fog will form. If there is no dust, put in some chalk dust and exhaust again.

more than 10 feet in a second. One inch of rainfall deposits over 100 tons of water per acre.

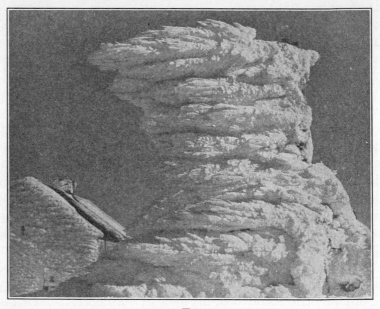

FROST FEATHERS

The wind at the top of Mt. Washington, New Hampshire, has blown these frost crystals into a fantastic yet beautiful formation. The instrument at the top of the picture is used to record heat from the sun.

Drizzle consists of particles of water that are less than one fiftieth of an inch in diameter. They are so small they seem to float along in the air and fall very slowly.

The formation of fog illustrates the need for particles on which moisture can condense.

Why Is the Air Cold at Higher Altitude? — In order to complete our knowledge of how it rains, we must discover what makes the air above the earth get cooler as it rises. You know that there is a general cooling at certain seasons due to the amount of heat the earth receives from the sun's rays. However, it is a local cooling that causes rain, snow, or hail. What causes this local cooling? There are several factors, some of which we can think about now.

A simple law of gases (air is a mixture of gases) will help to answer our question. Do you know what happens when you compress air into a tire with a tire pump? The pump gets hot, but not from friction. It gets hot because in forcing air into the tire, the air becomes hot.

When a gas is forcibly compressed into a smaller space, it gets hot. You remember that temperature really has to do with how fast molecules move about. When a gas is squeezed into a smaller space the molecules are squeezed together and move faster. This makes the gas get warmer. Also when a gas expands, it gets cooler. (Refer to your fog experiment.) When the molecules are allowed more room, they use up some heat and so the gas gets cooler.

Remember, then, that gases become heated when they are compressed, and cooler when they expand. This helps to explain the cooling of air at increasing altitudes above the earth.

Another thing to remember is that the air gets most of its heat from the earth, not directly from the sun. Therefore it is reasonable to expect that air farther from the earth will be colder than air nearer the earth. Of course as you know, heat from the sun warms the earth, but it does not heat the air very much through which it passes.

Warm air expands as it rises above the earth; therefore it cools. If the rising current of warm air contains considerable moisture, the cooling, due to expansion, may cause the moisture to condense and form a cloud. That is just what causes cumulus clouds.

If the expansion is great enough, the cooling may result in the formation of drops of water large enough to fall in spite of the rising current which is able to keep the smaller cloud drops dancing in the air. When a gentle drizzle takes place, it shows that the rising current of air is so slow that even tiny drops can break away from their clouds and fall down through the air.

A SNOWFLAKE

These crystals are always six-sided and no two are ever alike.

Snow and Sleet. — A blanket of snow is made up of snowflakes, just as rain is made up of rain-drops. But is the snow that falls always the same? If you ever made a snow man or a snow fort, or if you are a skier, you know how differently snow packs. Sometimes it is so dry it will not pack at all, and then again it is so wet it makes the best of snowballs.

FIELD RESEARCH:

On a cold, crisp day examine snowflakes with a magnifier. You will marvel at their beauty. It was said by Wilson A. Bentley of Jericho, Vt., who, during his life, photographed thousands of snowflakes, that there are no two alike.

Whenever the air is cooled to a temperature of 32° F., or somewhat lower, its moisture will freeze into tiny crystals. More crystals form on the first crystal, and so a snowflake is built up.

Snow is measured by finding its average depth, but as "precipitation" it is reported in inches of water obtained when it is melted. Some snow is heavier than other snow because it contains less air; in other words, it is more packed. It ordinarily takes about twelve inches of snow to make one inch of water.

Some people think that snow consists of frozen raindrops. That is not the case. Frozen raindrops form what is known as *sleet*. Sleet is also formed when snowflakes melt in the air and become frozen again. While sleet consists of little ice particles, these ice particles differ from hail in their structure and manner of formation.

A SLEET CRYSTAL

Compare this with the central part of the snowflake.

How Hail Is Formed. — While snow and sleet occur in the winter, hail almost always occurs in warm weather. Hail is a feature of thunderstorms and is formed by raindrops being tossed high into the air by the upward currents of air to an altitude where the air temperature is below freezing. There they change to little balls of ice. If the hail drops, it may melt before it reaches the earth, or it may become covered with an additional layer of water condensed on its surface and be hurled up again, causing a new layer of ice to form. In this way a hailstone is made up of layers of ice. When it gets too heavy for the rising currents to keep it up, it falls to earth.

Thinking Things Over. — There are many weather factors that need to be known before one can get a really good idea of what weather is. These factors are all closely interrelated; therefore, a change in one factor affects most of the others.

When you realize the importance of each weather factor and the need to observe or measure it, you can understand why animals cannot be good weather forecasters.

Keystone View

THE EFFECT OF A HAILSTORM

Our next few problems will deal with storms and weather forecasting; so you will need to apply what you know about weather factors. If you are doubtful about your understanding of them, it will be a good idea to make a quick review.

Key Words

air mass	atmosphere	clouds
air pressure	capillary action	cold front
altitude	Centigrade	contract
aneroid	clinical	cyclone

dew   hygrometer   snow
evaporate   mercury   temperature
Fahrenheit   Pascal   thermometer
"fixed points"   precipitation   tornado
fog   rain   Torricelli
frost   relative humidity   velocity
hail   saturated   warm front
humidity   sleet   wind

Key Statements

1. Our senses are poor indicators of temperature.

2. Metals expand at different rates.

3. Mercury and alcohol are used in thermometers because they expand uniformly and because their freezing points and boiling points occur at convenient temperatures.

4. Most solids (including metals), liquids, and gases expand when heated and contract when cooled.

5. The Fahrenheit thermometer scale has 32° for the temperature of freezing water (or melting ice) and 212° for the boiling point of water at sea-level air pressure.

6. The Centigrade thermometer scale has 0° for the temperature of freezing water (or melting ice) and 100° for the boiling point of water at sea-level air pressure.

7. Air pressure (atmospheric pressure) is due to weight of the air.

8. The air pressure decreases as the altitude increases.

9. Air pressure can be measured with a barometer.

10. Wind is caused by the unequal heating of the air.

11. Great masses or blocks of air move across the country from cold regions to warm regions or from warm regions to cold regions.

12. The front edge of the cold mass of air is called a *cold front* while the front edge of a warm mass of air is the *warm front*.

13. Sometimes when a warm front meets a cold front a counterclockwise whirl of air is produced.

14. Great air whirls are called cyclones.

15. Due to the rotation of the earth, air currents are deflected to the right in the northern hemisphere and to the left in the southern hemisphere. This is thought to be the cause of the counterclockwise movement of air in the cyclones.

16. The pressure of the wind increases as the square of its velocity.

17. Relative humidity is the ratio of the amount of moisture in the air to the amount that would be needed to saturate the air at a given temperature.

18. Evaporating liquids absorb heat.

19. Dew forms by condensation of the moisture of the air, when the air is sufficiently cooled by contact with cold objects. Frost occurs if the cold object is below freezing.

20. Rain results from the condensation of the water particles on dust or electric charges.

21. Rising air currents expand and become cooler.

22. Snow is composed of ice crystals formed by the freezing of the moisture of the air.

23. Sleet forms from the freezing of rain or the melting of snowflakes and the freezing of the drop of water which results.

24. Hail is made up of little balls of ice in layers.

Thought Questions

1. What happens when milk in a bottle freezes? Why does freezing water break up rocks?

2. Why does not an alcohol thermometer have temperatures marked as high as 212° F.?

3. Why are the freezing point and the boiling point of water taken as "fixed" points on thermometers?

4. If air pressure acting on the surface of the mercury in the dish holds the mercury up in the tube of a barometer, why does it not push more mercury into the tube since the area of the mercury surface in the dish is so much greater than in the tube?

5. How can a barometer be used to determine altitudes?

6. Why must the top of a barometer tube be sealed?

7. Why is it necessary to remove some of the air from the box of an aneroid barometer?

8. Why does the wind blow?

9. Why will sprinkling a street with water cool the air?

10. Why is dew or frost less likely to form on a cloudy night than on a clear night? Or under a tree than in the open?

11. Why do we use more gas to motor a given distance at 60 miles an hour than at 40?

Projects for Your Science Discovery Book

1. List all the uses of thermometers you can discover.

2. Record the extreme temperatures for your town. Do you believe that summers are cooler and winters warmer than they used to be? Investigate by means of weather bureau reports to find the facts.

3. Keep a daily weather record for two weeks. Make observations at the same time each day. Include reports of wind direction and velocity, temperature, precipitation, and cloudiness.

4. Keep a special record of wind direction for one month to determine the prevailing wind direction of your locality.

5. Make a report on the direction and effects of ocean currents.

6. Make an air thermometer and compare it with a house thermometer.

7. Using Magdeburg hemispheres and an exhaust air pump, prove that the atmosphere exerts a pressure.

8. Make an anemometer (wind meter).

9. Make a wind vane.

10. Make a hygrometer and use it to determine the relative humidity of the air.

11. Find out why water is not a suitable liquid to use in a barometer.

12. To show air pressure, place a pint of water in a gallon tin can and heat the water so that the steam will drive out most of the air. Discontinue the heat and close the opening of the can so that it is air tight. Pour cold water over the can to condense the steam. What happens? Explain.

THROUGH THE STORM

Through dark forbidding skies and high rolling waves, a 63-foot Coast Guard cutter races to rescue the crew of an airplane down in the sea.

TOPIC III

Storm Areas

The winds grow high;
Impending tempests charge the sky,
The lightning flies, the thunder roars;
And big waves lash the frightened shores.

— Prior

Do you know:

1. How large an area a rain storm covers at one time?
2. Whether lightning strikes twice in the same place?
3. What makes the thunder?
4. What high and low pressure areas are?
5. The paths taken by great storm areas across the United States?

General Problem 1. What Are Local Storms?

Local Weather. — When the weather man predicts rain and the day continues fair, do you laugh at the mistake and say, "That is another weather joke"? Or do you realize that the prediction referred to a much larger area perhaps than your home town? Sometimes the mistake is due to the "train being late." Railroad trains run on schedule, and yet they are late once in a while. So it is with the weather. Born maybe in the far north, the Pacific Ocean, or Gulf of Mexico, storms move across the United States in fairly well-defined paths, but not as

well defined as the railroad tracks. Their speed depends
not upon a controlled engine but upon laws of nature
which do not always work on an exact time schedule.

So it is that storms may be late or early. The
"weather," as it moves along, is affected by many local

A THUNDERHEAD

As more and more moisture condenses, the fair weather cumulus clouds
take on a darker threatening appearance. The clouds pictured here foretell
a thunderstorm.

conditions such as mountains, hills, valleys, deserts,
lakes, and forests. These in turn affect the air temperatures and moisture. So it is that, in spite of a forecast saying "fair and warmer," your locality may experience local storms, such as wind storms, violent rains,
excessive heat, or thunderstorms.

Thunderstorms. — The thunderstorm is one of the
most interesting and at the same time terrifying of local
storms. You will recall how cold the rain is which falls

during a thundershower. In fact sometimes hail occurs in such a storm. This tells us that a thundershower is caused by a very sudden and severe cooling of the air above the earth.

Overheating of air in a locality starts a sudden and rapidly rising current of air. You have learned that when air rises rapidly, it cools rapidly. This cooling changes the fair-weather cumulus cloud into a thunderhead.

A thundershower freshens the air because the warm moist air near the surface before the storm is replaced by cool air. The latter pushes its way in because the warm moist air was lighter than the surrounding cooler air. It is one of nature's ways of cooling the air and removing excess moisture from it.

The thundershower is so named because of the noise caused by lightning. It is also called an electric storm because of the electric discharges it produces. Benjamin Franklin, as you remember, discovered the relationship of lightning and electricity by means of his famous kite experiment.

LIBRARY RESEARCH:
Read an account of Franklin's experiment to refresh your memory.

What Makes Lightning? — The cause of the electrical discharge of a thunderstorm is rather difficult to explain without some knowledge of electricity and its action. Experiments 10 and 11 will help you to know something about electricity and what it does.

Have you ever experienced the "shock" of electricity when on a cold day you scuff your feet on a rug and touch another person? If you have, you know that friction causes electricity to form. In Experiment 10 pieces of fur and silk were used to rub on glass, hard rubber, and sealing wax because these substances are especially good producers of electricity when rubbed together.   Many other substances could be used.

FIELD RESEARCH:

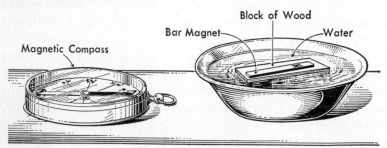

Magnetic Compass

Bar Magnet

Block of Wood

Water

   Secure a bar magnet and a magnetic compass.   Try to discover the similarities of attraction and repulsion between like and unlike electric charges and like and unlike magnetic poles.   What direction does the dark end of the compass needle point when left free?   Place the bar magnet on a block of wood, floating in water.   Does it swing about to any fixed position?   What direction does it point?   Now bring the north-pointing end of the compass needle near the north-pointing end of the bar magnet.   Do they attract or repel each other?   What causes a compass needle to swing in a particular direction?

   The rubbing (friction) doesn't really make the electricity.   Scientists believe that things are actually made up of electricity, that is, electric charges.   In fact the molecules about which you have learned are made up of atoms, and atoms are made up of positive and negative particles or charges of electricity.

   Ordinarily the + and − charges are equal in a body, but friction causes them to separate.   That is why you have a spark.   When the + and − charges are separated they try to get together again, and this they do when the spark occurs.

EXPERIMENT 10

How are electric sparks made?

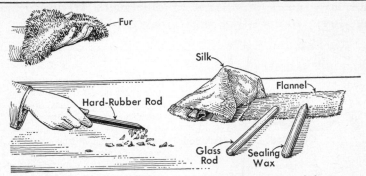

In all the experiments you have done so far you have used the energy called *heat*. In this experiment you will use a different form of energy — electricity.

Most of you can try this experiment at home by rubbing silk, flannel, or fur on hard rubber combs or fountain pens, and by rubbing your feet on the rug. This experiment works better on a cold day when the air is dry; so if it doesn't work well one day, try it on another day.

WHAT TO USE: — Pieces of fur, flannel, and silk; a glass rod; a hard rubber rod; and a stick of sealing wax.

WHAT TO DO: — 1. Rub the fur briskly on each of the rods for a moment. As soon as you stop rubbing hold the rubbed end of the rod near your finger. Repeat the test, using in turn flannel and silk with each rod.

2. Again rub each rod with the fur, flannel, and silk in turn, and each time try to pick up small bits of paper. Notice which combination works best.

WHAT HAPPENS: — 1. Did you hear a slight crackling as you rubbed the rods? Did a spark occur when you held each of the charged rods near your finger? Was there a noise when the spark occurred?

2. Did the rods attract the bits of paper after being rubbed? Which combination seemed to work best?

CONCLUSION: — Did you make electricity by rubbing two substances together? Did the electricity form on the rods?

APPLICATION: — Briskly rub a cat's or dog's fur with both hands. If you feel an electric shock explain why.

KEY EXPERIMENT 11

Are there two kinds of electricity?

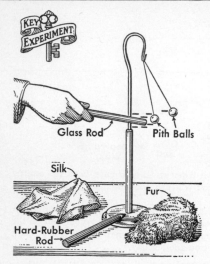

Glass Rod   Pith Balls

Silk

Fur

Hard-Rubber Rod

What kind of energy is used in this experiment? What are you trying to discover that you did not discover in Experiment 10?

The force of gravity is mentioned. While it acts in some ways like electrical charges and like magnetism, it is really different from either one. Can you tell how it is different?

WHAT TO USE: — A piece of fur; a piece of silk; a glass rod; a hard rubber rod; two pith balls — one on each end of a short thread; and a support for the thread.

WHAT TO DO: — 1. Hang the pith balls with the thread over the support so that the balls touch each other.

2. Rub the fur on the glass rod and at once hold the rubbed end of the rod near the balls but without touching them.

3. Repeat, only touch each ball with the glass rod (this is called charging the balls), and then keep the rod near the balls. Now bring the fur near the balls but do not touch them.

4. Again charge the balls with the glass rod rubbed with fur, and then bring the hard rubber rod, which has now been rubbed with the silk, near the balls. Now bring the silk near the balls.

WHAT HAPPENS: — 1. Did the balls touch each other when hanging naturally and not influenced by anything except the pull of gravity?

2. Were the balls attracted to the glass rod at first?

3. After the balls were touched (charged) with the glass rod, were they still attracted to the rod? Did the fur attract them? Did they hang away from each other?

4. When the balls were charged from the glass rod rubbed with fur, were they attracted or repelled by the hard rubber rod rubbed with silk? By the silk?

CONCLUSION: — How many kinds of electricity have you made?

How do they act toward each other? That is, do like charges repel or attract each other?

When electricity formed on a rod, did a different kind form on the fur and on the silk?

When glass and silk are rubbed together, one kind of electricity forms on the glass and another kind on the silk.

When glass is rubbed with fur, the glass is charged with the same kind as the silk had when rubbed on glass. This happens too when rubber is rubbed first with silk and then with fur.

There are two kinds of electricity called positive and negative. Glass is charged with positive (+) when rubbed with silk and negative (−) when rubbed with fur. Hard rubber appears to act just the opposite, negative (−) with silk and positive (+) with fur.

APPLICATION: — Rub a comb or a fountain pen with silk or fur. Hold it near tiny bits of paper to attract them, then if they jump away after a second or two, explain what happens.

So it is that we have two kinds of electricity. The negative charges of electricity are often called *electrons;* so we shall use the word electron to mean negative electricity. The positive charges of electricity are for convenience called *protons.* We shall use this word, too, in our talks about electricity.

A thundercloud is a dense mass of water particles containing electric charges. It is believed that sometimes raindrops get so big that rising currents of air split them into two unequal size drops. When this happens, it is thought that the larger drops lose electrons and so they are left with too great a number of protons. They are said to be positively charged. The smaller drops gain the electrons lost by the big drops and so they are

Wide World

LIGHTNING STRIKES THE EMPIRE STATE BUILDING

Because of the steel construction of this building, the stroke is diffused and carried harmlessly to the ground. For the same reason the steel Eiffel Tower in Paris is never harmed when struck by lightning. These entire buildings are lightning rods.

negatively charged. Protons always tend to attract the unlike electrons to them. If a large number of raindrops become split and then separated into two clouds by the air currents, the electric charge may jump across from one cloud to the other. This discharge is lightning.

Sometimes the charged particles separate so that the upper part of the cloud is made up of the smaller negatively charged particles and the lower part of the cloud of the larger positively charged particles. Then the discharge,

lightning, takes place between the two parts of the same cloud.

If the cloud of larger, positively charged raindrops gets near enough to the earth, the discharge may take place between the cloud and the earth instead of between two clouds.

Chain lightning, which you have seen, occurs when the flash or discharge is from cloud to cloud, and the flash may be several miles long. *The tendency of unlike (positive and negative) electric charges to come together* is measured in *volts*. It requires a charge of a thousand volts to jump one twenty-fifth of an inch through the air. Can you imagine, then, the enormous number of volts represented by lightning when the distance between clouds or between a cloud and the earth may be a mile or more?

What Is Thunder? — When the electric discharge passes through the air, it heats that air very hot. That is why you see the flash. The rapid heating of the air causes it to vibrate, resulting in sound just as a vibrating string produces sound. Also just as the vibrating string sets the air vibrating in waves which reach your ear, so too the air vibration caused by the lightning results in air sound waves that spread in all directions and so reach your ear. The rumbling roar of thunder has an explanation which you can think out for yourself. Start your explanation with the idea of an echo. Give your answer to the class.

Is Lightning Dangerous? — If lightning strikes something, it is quite likely to cause damage, though comparatively few people are injured or killed by it. The greatest damage from lightning is due to fires, especially in forests. This is one of the very few non-preventable causes of forest fires and of fires in general.

Sometimes lightning hits a building and splits it open, knocks down the chimney, or performs other queer tricks. Some places seem more likely to be struck by lightning than others. For example, a barn filled with straw or hay seems more likely to be struck than a house; a tree or a person in an open field, more likely than a tree or person in a wood. Hills, being nearer cloud masses are more likely to be struck than hollows. If you are caught in an open field during an electric storm, lie down.   Do not seek protection under a lone tree.

Lightning
rod

Courtesy General Electric Company

THE SPECIAL LIGHTNING ROD ATOP THE EMPIRE STATE BUILDING

It is probably safer in the center of a room than along the walls.   Inside an automobile with a steel body is a safe place during an electric storm.

Certain it is that if you see the electric flash, you need have no fear, for that particular flash has done its work and is gone.   If you will count the number of seconds that elapse between the time of the flash and the sound of the thunder, you can estimate roughly the distance of the storm.   Here is a scheme for counting seconds sometimes used by photographers:

The light of the flash reaches the eye almost instantly because light travels 186,000 miles a second. The resulting sound travels only about one fifth of a mile a second. By slowly saying the words one thousand one, one thousand two, one thousand three, etc., you can mark off approximately as many seconds as you continue to count.   By counting in this way, you can determine the number of seconds between the flashes and the thunder.   This will tell you how many fifths of a mile away the storm is.

Many devices and schemes have been invented for protection against lightning.   Of them all, lightning rods are best.   Lightning rods properly installed with good ground connections are a real protection to buildings.

They make an easy passageway for the electricity from
the cloud to the earth.   If a discharge is about to take
place near a building equipped with lightning rods, it will
be likely to pass through the rods to the earth without
damaging the building.   It is a law of electricity that an

Courtesy General Electric Company

ARTIFICIAL LIGHTNING

A high-voltage discharge in the Engineering Laboratory of the General
Electric Company at Pittsfield, Massachusetts.

electric current will follow the easiest path — in other
words, the best *conductor*. Lightning rods and wires
connecting them to the ground are good conductors of
electricity.

Scientists are all of the time learning more about
lightning. They construct machines that will produce
great discharges of electricity that imitate lightning.
As they learn more about it we shall be better able to
protect ourselves and our property.

General Problem 2. What Are General Storm Areas?

Cyclones and Anticyclones. — Failure to remember that there are both local and wide area storms sometimes results in weather forecasting being misinterpreted.

The factors which cause local storms are often closely related to the more widespread or general storms; therefore we should become familiar with the characteristics, causes, and results of general storms. We may think also of general or widespread fair weather areas.

These general storm and fair weather areas are often known as cyclones and anticyclones. Like most weather conditions they are the result of unequally heated areas of land. In the center of the cyclone area the air pressure is *low* because of the rapidly rising warm air. Hence they are called *lows*. Cool air rushes in from all sides to push up this expanding warm air. It carries much moisture up with it, and since the air cools as it rises and expands, condensation takes place, often resulting in precipitation.

The air in the cyclone area, as you have learned, is moving counter-clockwise due partly to the rotation of the earth. You should recall that the word cyclone as used here does not mean a tornado. Cyclone is the name given to this great mass of whirling air that may be many miles across, perhaps several hundred miles in diameter. That is why it is called a general storm area.

"What goes up must come down" is quite true even of air. Air that is pushed up because it is lighter than

other air gets cooler as it rises.   It spreads out and falls
back to the earth again.   As this air settles toward the
earth it pushes harder on the earth than the rising air.
As a result the air pressure is higher and so this downward
pushing air is called a *high*.

The air in the *high* is moving in a circular clockwise
direction just the opposite of the air in the *low*.

As you know, when gases are compressed they tend to
get warmer, just the opposite of expanding air.   Air
that is warming up a little does not give up its moisture;
so it is quite natural that this mass of air shall be a fair
weather air.   And so it is.   The area called a *high* is
generally a fair weather area.

Cross-Country Paths of Highs and Lows. — If you
examine a number of weather maps, you will discover that
a *low* is often followed by a *high*.   The air that settles in
the *high* spreads out and pushes toward the center of the
low where it rises, cools, and settles again.   It is a real
circulation of the air caused by unequal heating of the air
in different parts of the country.

The procession of *lows* and *highs* have fairly well defined paths across the country as you can see by studying
the map on page 107.   They may not always follow the
same paths but on the average they do.   There is some
advantage in this fact for the weather forecaster, as you
will learn in the next unit.

Warm Fronts and Cold Fronts. — Great masses or
bodies of cold air move as you know from the north and
northwest down over the United States.   Great masses
of warm air move from the southwest, south, and southeast toward the north and northeast (pages 52–53).   The
front edge of the cold mass is called a polar or *cold front*
and the front edge of the warm mass is called a tropical
or *warm front*.

The *highs* and *lows* described in General Problem 2 are really parts of these cold and warm masses of air.

It often happens that a mass of cold air overtakes a mass of warm air. When this happens, the cold mass wedges in under the warmer air. Perhaps you can remember some day when the temperature dropped several degrees in just a couple of hours. That was caused by the cold front pushing in under a mass of warmer air.

Kabel

COLD LATITUDE

The result of a warm mass of air meeting a cold mass may be snow.

When the warm masses of air come from over the ocean or Gulf of Mexico, called maritime air masses, they usually contain much moisture. Therefore, when this warm mass meets a cold mass, storms often occur resulting in winds and the precipitation of rain or snow.

Most weather troubles are found along the line where cold fronts and warm fronts meet. Back of the front lines the air conditions are fairly stable.

Hot and Cold Waves. — Everyone recalls a long, hot, dry spell or perhaps a few days of continued cold. This is what may happen behind the lines when a cold front and warm front meet and neither gives way. The two fronts just stand still, and whatever air conditions are behind the fronts last as long as they hold their positions.

If the standstill happens when a cold front has moved down quite a way over the country, it may be that the land will be colder than normal, or if the warm front has moved quite a way to the north, the temperatures of some places may be a good deal warmer than normal.

Such a hot wave or spell may linger for three or four days. Locally the moisture sometimes becomes oppressive until, finally, cooling thunderstorms result.

Philip Gendreau

HEAT OF THE DESERT

In the warm dry desert areas of the earth, vegetation is scant.

Climate. — It is natural for us to think of climate whenever we speak in terms of the weather. As in the case of weather, we all know what climate is, but for working purposes we need to agree upon a definition of it. *Climate is the average of weather conditions for a particular area over a long period of time.* The climate of a certain region may be dry, hot, wet, cold, windy, mild, changeable, and so on.

Special climatic conditions are required to produce the various kinds of life. Tropical climates produce abundant plant and animal life; the Arctic regions produce a scarcity of both. Man, of all living things, seems to be the only one who can adapt his living to any of the various climates on the earth.

Our pleasures, crops, industries, and our health, all are closely related to weather conditions. Understanding the weather, its causes and effects, gives man the information to help him plan and adjust his living to nature's laws. Accurate predictions of weather give man an added advantage in his adaptations to life.

Thinking Things Over. — Now that you know about local and general storm areas, you can understand more about the storms that you experience. When you recall that air moves in great masses from cold regions toward warmer regions and from warm regions toward colder ones, you can understand how storms over large areas may be caused. Your knowledge of the occurrence of lows where a polar front and tropical front meet, together with the fact that lows take rather uniform paths across the country, will help you to understand weather forecasting, which is our next topic.

Key Words

anticyclone	general storm area	negative
climate	*high*	polar front
cold wave	hot wave	positive
conductor	lightning	proton
cyclone	local storm area	storm paths
electric charge	*low*	thunder
electron	millibar	tropical front

Key Statements

1. Local storms include electric (thunder) storms, rain, sleet, snow, hail, and windstorms.

2. A general storm area includes the air conditions over a large extent of territory. General storm areas move along rather definite paths across the country.

3. Weather conditions in a general storm area or cyclone are rather constant as the storm moves along.

4. As air rises it expands and becomes colder.

5. Thundershowers (electric storms) are caused by sudden and rapidly rising currents of warm, moist air. Expansion, due to rising, causes sudden cooling of the air, condensation, and precipitation of the air moisture.

6. The rapid heating of the air from an electric discharge causes it to vibrate, which results in the noise called thunder.

7. Lightning is an electrical discharge between near-by clouds or between a cloud and the earth.

8. Properly installed lightning rods on buildings are a protection against lightning.

9. Great masses or blocks of air move across the country. The front of a cold mass is called a polar front while the front of the warm mass is called a tropical front.

10. Storms occur where a tropical front meets a polar front.

11. In a cyclone area the air moves counter-clockwise in the northern hemisphere and clockwise in the southern.

12. Hot and cold waves in the northern section of the country occur in summer when a polar front and tropical front come to a temporary standstill.

13. Climate is the average of weather conditions for a particular region over a long period of time.

Thought Questions

1. Why do hailstones often form during a thunderstorm?

2. What kind of cloud form becomes a thunder-cloud?

3. How big is a raindrop?

4. Why is a person more likely to be struck by lightning when standing in an open field than when standing in the woods?

5. What does the phrase " best conductor of electricity " mean?

6. Tall objects in the open are more likely to be struck by lightning than are short objects. Why?

Projects for Your Science Discovery Book

1. Study U. S. Weather Maps for a two-week period and report on cyclone movements. Sample maps may be obtained for a small charge from the U. S. Weather Bureau, Washington, D. C.

2. From your study of weather maps make a series of warm and cold front lines to show the progress of these air masses.

3. Make a labeled drawing of the formation of a thundercloud, studied from observation.

4. If possible, take air temperatures and relative humidity before and after a thundershower.

5. Investigate the artificial lightning experiments carried on by the General Electric Company at Pittsfield, Massachusetts.

6. Explain why sometimes in the winter you get a discharge of electricity on touching another person who has just walked across a rug or carpet.

7. Prepare a class report on the various climates of the world, including a discussion of their effects on civilization.

Courtesy Esso Standard Oil Company

SCIENTIFIC WEATHER FORECASTING

This new weather balloon ascends to over 60,000 feet, carrying instruments which record the weather. The information gained about atmospheric pressure, temperature, and relative humidity is then sent back to the weather station by automatic radio signals. This data is used by weather experts to make predictions. At a certain height atmospheric pressure causes the balloon to burst, and the instrument box, which is equipped with a parachute, floats back to earth.

Forecasting the Weather

O suns and skies and clouds of June,
And flowers of June together,
Ye cannot rival for one hour
October's bright blue weather.

— Helen Hunt Jackson

Do you know:

1. Why people take summer vacations near the water?
2. How the newspapers get their information about the weather?
3. How to read a weather map?
4. How your health is related to the weather?
5. Whether a lake heats up faster than its surrounding land?

General Problem 1. What Will the Weather Be?

Do You Believe in Weather Signs? — Of course you now know that weather results from natural laws as they apply to gases. Any weather signs then must have natural laws behind them if they have any reliability. In a given locality an observing person soon learns that a certain wind direction indicates good or bad weather. Some clouds are dark with moisture and indicate rain or, if the temperature is low, snow. Other clouds indicate fair weather. A changing air pressure shown by the barometer tells us that the weather is changing.

The flight of birds and habits of insects and small animals are believed by some to indicate changes in the weather to one who is very observing. However, weather signs are not, for the most part, very accurate means of foretelling the weather.

Read the following lines, "Signs of Rain," written long ago and learned by school children almost a hundred years ago, to help them "foretell" the weather. Do you think there are any points in the poem that are true? Compare this method of forecasting the weather with the scientific method.

SIGNS OF RAIN [1]

The hollow winds begin to blow,
The clouds look black,
The glass is low.
Hark how the chairs and table crack!
Old Betty's joints are on the rack.
How restless are the snorting swine!
The busy flies disturb the kine.
Puss, on the hearth, with velvet paws,
Sits wiping o'er her whiskered jaws.
My dog, so altered in his taste,
Quits mutton bones on grass to feast.
And see yon rooks — how odd their flight!
They imitate the gliding kite
And, headlong, downward seem to fall
As if they felt the piercing ball.
'Twill surely rain. I see with sorrow
Our jaunt must be put off tomorrow.

Newspaper Reports. — Many newspapers print weather reports furnished by the United States Weather Bureau. The predictions for a day in advance are based upon: (1) a knowledge of the weather conditions all over the country; (2) exact knowledge of how general storm

---

[1] From a collection of weather doggerel usually attributed to Dr. Edward Jenner and written from memory by a pupil of 1850.

areas travel across the country; (3) upon a knowledge of the air masses and their movements; and (4) the positions of the warm and cold fronts. The forecast is made for a rather large region and, therefore, is sometimes incorrect for a particular locality.

Courtesy United Air Lines

FLIGHT PLANNING

Behind every airplane flight there is scientific teamwork. Weather reports are radioed and teletyped to forecast centers where maps are made. These are then studied by the pilots before the plane takes off.

FIELD RESEARCH:

Study a newspaper weather report and discover the accuracy of the prediction. What weather factors are included in the report?

Radio Reports. — The radio is an important means by which weather conditions can be made known to everyone interested. Forewarning of the probability of violent windstorms, and of the likelihood of killing frosts, is important to mariners and to shippers and gardeners. Airplane pilots are kept constantly informed about weather conditions ahead and whether to proceed to their destination or make for the nearest landing field.

Although daily weather forecasts were not broadcast during wartime, forecasts of unusually severe storms were even then broadcast from time to time.

The Work of a Weather Prophet. — *Temperature, air pressure, air moisture, wind direction, and wind velocity* are factors to be considered in forecasting the weather both of the small local areas and the larger, general areas. To foretell successfully the local weather changes, these factors must be accurately determined, and the observer must know how local conditions are related to the more general weather conditions.

General Problem 2. How Are Scientific Weather Observations Used?

Official Weather Reports. — Scientific weather observations are reported to one of the forecast centers of the United States Weather Bureau. At present there are seventeen General Forecast Centers and twenty-one Airway Forecast Centers. Some of these centers are located at Albuquerque, Chicago, Denver, Jacksonville, Kansas City, New Orleans, San Francisco, Seattle, and Washington. Weather observation stations are located in more than 400 cities and towns of the United States, Alaska, and other possessions, in Canada, Mexico, and Cuba. At most of these stations, weather observers determine all the weather factors each hour and send the information to the nearest First Class Weather Station. First Class Stations are usually located in rather large cities. They use the information to make local weather forecasts.

Four times each day — 1:30 A.M., 7:30 A.M., 1:30 P.M., and 7:30 P.M., Eastern Standard Time — weather stations send their weather information to one of the General Forecast Centers. Here a forecast for a much larger area is made.

Weather stations send their information to the forecast center by code telegraph or teletype. If each weather condition were described in ordinary language, it would take a long message to report the weather. The use of a code makes it possible to send all the information by using number groups. Each number has a special meaning depending upon its position in the message. A coded weather message may look like this:

40530   83220   12716   24731   67220   67228   74542

This code means:

405   is the station sending the report — Washington, D. C.
30   is the temperature of the dewpoint — 30° F.
8   is the amount of cloud — completely covered.
32   is the wind direction — northwest.
20   is the wind speed in knots — 20 knots.
12   is the visibility in miles — $\frac{12}{8}$ or $1\frac{1}{2}$ miles.
71   is the present weather — continuous slight snow.
6   is the past weather — rain.

The message continues in the same way, each number or group of numbers having a definite meaning in the code.

The weather map in many morning newspapers is based on coded weather information sent in at 1:30 A.M. (EST) to the central office at Washington, D. C. The map is sent to the newspapers by wirephoto.

At each weather station the observer determines the weather conditions by instrument or direct observation. Special devices record hours of sunshine, wind velocity and direction, amount of precipitation, if any, air temperature, and relative humidity. The kinds and heights of clouds and their movements are noted, also.

Every day at 10:00 A.M. and 10:00 P.M. at about 100 stations, balloons are sent up to high altitudes. Each balloon carries instruments that send back by radio a continuous record of temperatures, pressures, and humidity. At some of these stations the travel of the balloons is followed by directional radio. Thus wind direction and velocity can be determined at high altitudes. At many more stations kite balloons are sent up and watched by eye to determine the wind direction and velocity at different levels.

These records obtained by balloons, together with the observations at ground level, tell the weather conditions not only at the earth's surface, but also up to several thousand feet above the surface. This additional information makes much more accurate forecasts possible than surface observations alone. Added to the observations by United States Weather Bureau observers, are the weather reports made by air pilots during their flights across the country and oceans.

Thus scientific weather forecasts are much more accurate than local forecasts that depend upon local individual observation. One airline alone may spend $50,000 upon weather forecasting, and the United States and other governments spend millions to collect and distribute weather information.

The Weather Map. — Four times each twenty-four hours the reports received at the Washington Weather Bureau and other forecast centers are posted on a large map of the United States. These reports include all of the weather items you have been reading about and many others. It would take a very large map if this information were to be written out, so a "weather shorthand" has been devised, samples of which are on page 103. There are symbols for all weather conditions.

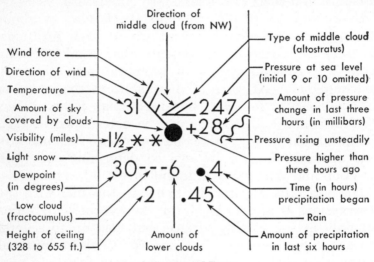

Direction of middle cloud (from NW)

Type of middle cloud (altostratus)

Wind force

Direction of wind

Temperature

Amount of sky covered by clouds

Visibility (miles)

Light snow

Dewpoint (in degrees)

Low cloud (fractocumulus)

Height of ceiling (328 to 655 ft.)

Pressure at sea level (initial 9 or 10 omitted)

Amount of pressure change in last three hours (in millibars)

Pressure rising unsteadily

Pressure higher than three hours ago

Time (in hours) precipitation began

Rain

Amount of precipitation in last six hours

Amount of lower clouds

A STATION MODEL

Only the lines, dots, and figures in the center are put on the weather map. The explanations are given here to explain each symbol. A completed weather map will have dozens of station models like this — one for each station reporting the weather.

Often even these symbols take up too much space, so the Weather Bureau uses many of the code numbers as sent by the stations. The diagram above shows how the weather at one station is represented on the map. Each number and its position around the center dot tells something about the weather at that station.

When all the weather information has been recorded, black lines are drawn through places having the same air pressure. These lines are called *isobars*, meaning equal pressure. The location of cold fronts and warm

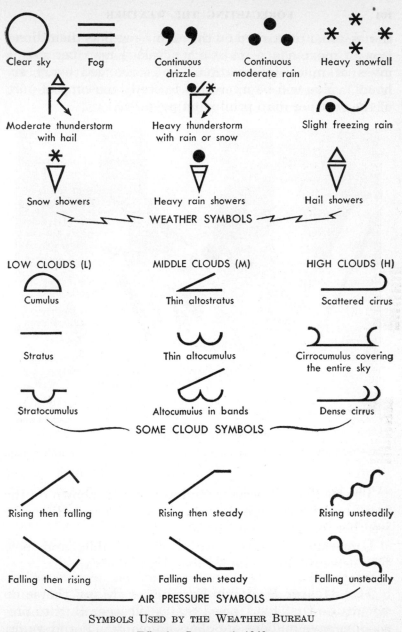

Clear sky   Fog   Continuous drizzle   Continuous moderate rain   Heavy snowfall

Moderate thunderstorm with hail   Heavy thunderstorm with rain or snow   Slight freezing rain

Snow showers   Heavy rain showers   Hail showers

WEATHER SYMBOLS

LOW CLOUDS (L)   MIDDLE CLOUDS (M)   HIGH CLOUDS (H)

Cumulus   Thin altostratus   Scattered cirrus

Stratus   Thin altocumulus   Cirrocumulus covering the entire sky

Stratocumulus   Altocumuius in bands   Dense cirrus

SOME CLOUD SYMBOLS

Rising then falling   Rising then steady   Rising unsteadily

Falling then rising   Falling then steady   Falling unsteadily

AIR PRESSURE SYMBOLS

SYMBOLS USED BY THE WEATHER BUREAU
Effective January 1, 1949

fronts, too, are marked on the map, as well as their direction of movement. It is a marvelous map because it gives so much information. It is changed every six hours. You will be interested to study the copy of part of the weather map printed on page 102.

Courtesy U. S. Weather Bureau

MAKING THE WEATHER MAP

These men are each adding some particular information to a weather map. Later all this will be placed on one map.

The weather forecaster studies the facts shown on the map, and from these data he forecasts or predicts the weather for the next 12 to 36 hours.

Long-range forecasts are most desirable, and now forecasts are also made for five days in advance.

The Master Weather Prophet. — Many people do not realize that the United States Weather Bureau predictions save millions of dollars annually. For example, if food is shipped in cars which are not frostproof, a sudden fall of temperature below the freezing point may spoil a whole trainload of perishable foods. The Weather Bureau publishes the lowest temperatures likely to be encountered for a period of a few days. Hence shippers, by following these reports, know what care to take of perishable material.

FIELD RESEARCH:

If you should find it possible to obtain a weather map, locate your home town and note weather factors as shown by the map at the time the map data were prepared. Look at the weather map again and, supposing the conditions shown should move toward the east, note what changes might occur at your locality in the next twenty-four hours. Bring your prediction to class for discussion.

The shipping and fishing industries receive advance warning of great storms at sea. By "laying by" in some good harbor, untold shipping losses are prevented. Advance information of the approach of a tornado is often given in the tornado section and people are able to protect themselves. Fruit growers and farmers, in general, profit enormously by taking advantage of advance information concerning unexpected frosts. Many individuals call up the "Weather Man" and ask about the weather "tomorrow" in order to complete plans for outings, celebrations, and so on.

As noted on page 100, the Weather Bureau publishes a daily weather map which shows the weather conditions all over the country. Copies of these maps are distributed throughout the larger towns and cities of the United States. The weather maps may be had for a small charge by any citizen who will write to the nearest Weather Bureau and ask that his name be placed on the mailing list. Thousands of postcards stating the probable weather conditions and possible occurrence of frosts and storms are sent out every day all over this great country. The information contained on one of these cards may save thousands of dollars.

These methods of distributing information are supplemented by the radio. The study of the air and general weather conditions made by the United States Weather

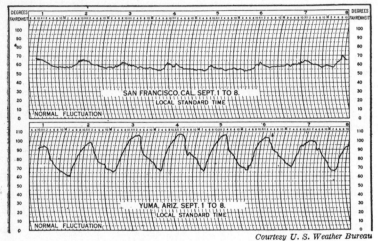

RANGE OF TEMPERATURE

These graphs show continuous daily records of temperature at the stations named, through a period of eight days each. Two types of climate, marine and arid-continental, are shown. The marine type is strikingly uniform.

Bureau has resulted in a vast amount of scientific information available for the use of men who are studying and improving aviation. Without this information the airplane could not have advanced and become such a factor in the day's doings as it is. The success of airplane flights across the Atlantic and Pacific are dependent to a great extent upon weather advice from the Bureau. Knowledge of weather factors and prediction were important aids to Admiral Byrd's successful flight over the South Pole. In the same way, the Bureau's Arctic Project has aided and been aided by the Army Air Forces' weekly weather flights over the North Pole.

The Bureau studies and makes reports relative to weather and rain insurance, the influence of weather on public highways, and other matters of interest and importance. In the summer and fall, special weather forecasts are sent to forest-fire wardens, who are thereby

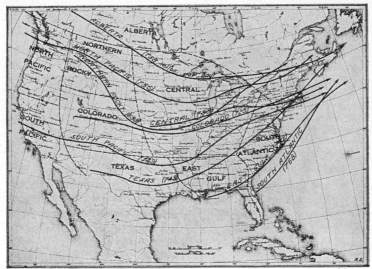

Courtesy U. S. Weather Bureau

ORIGIN AND PATHS OF STORMS

This map shows the average beginning and paths of storms across the United States in January. Where do most winter storms start? In what direction do they move? How fast do they travel?

helped greatly in preparing for a possible fire and its control.

Weather Forecasting as a Science. — In order that you may forecast the weather with considerable accuracy, for twenty-four to thirty-six hours in advance, you should have in mind the following rules:

1. The storm areas (cyclones) proceed across the United States from west to east, usually passing over the St. Lawrence River region. Or the path goes from the southwest to the northeast and

out the St. Lawrence River region.   (See the map on page 107.)

2. On the map, the direction of the wind in the storm area (low) is somewhat circular and opposite to the motion of the hands of a

A WEATHER RECORDER

This kiosk contains various instruments registering different phases of the weather.

clock.   The general direction is along the isobars, crossing them slightly toward the center.

3. Facing the wind, the right hand stretched out at the side will indicate roughly the direction of the storm center.

4. The direction of the wind, together with the position of the storm center, will determine in which of the four quadrants (quarters) of the cyclone the observer is located.   The weather conditions of each of the four quadrants of a storm area are somewhat constant.

5. The barometer reading will indicate the nearness or remoteness of the storm center, if the observer refers to the isobars on the weather map.

6. A changing air pressure indicates the approach or passing of a storm area.   For example, if your town happens to be in the southeast quarter and the storm is moving so as to bring the northwest quarter to you (draw this on your paper), you can predict weather conditions similar to those prevailing in the northwest quarter.   If the storm center has not reached you, you should be able to predict whether the storm center will pass north or south of you and hence what weather you will have.   If you know by study of the map how fast the storm is moving, you can predict when it will reach you.

7. A very slowly falling pressure indicates warmer temperatures. A very slowly rising pressure indicates cooler temperatures.

8. Generally, winds from the east quadrants with falling barometer indicate stormy weather.   Winds changing to the west quadrants indicate fair weather.

9. Weather map pressures are sea-level pressures, therefore the barometer reading of a given locality should be converted to sea-level reading to compare with the weather map data. Since the pressure decreases as the altitude increases, something must be added to convert a local pressure to sea-level pressure. Practically 1 inch should be added for each 900 feet altitude or fraction or multiple thereof. A change of 900 feet in altitude would be equal to about 34 millibars.

General Problem 3. How Are Water and Climate Related?

Weather and Water. — Water and heat are so closely associated as factors in weather making that a student of weather conditions must take them into account when he considers the problems of weather forecasting. When heat is added to water, the temperature of the water rises. The more water there is, the greater the amount of heat required to cause the same rise in temperature. If enough heat is added to water, boiling takes place. Then there is no further rise in temperature as long as any liquid water remains. At boiling temperature the liquid water changes to water vapor or gas.

In nature, the energy from the sun is the source of heat for water and for the land. A given soil has a certain capacity for absorbing water, a fact that every successful gardener well understands. You can see examples of this yourself, any spring or summer day after a shower. In about the same way land, water, and all other substances have certain capacities for absorbing heat. In this respect, water has a greater capacity than any other common substance; that is, it takes more heat to raise a pound of water to a certain temperature than is required by the same weight of any other common substance. The rate at which a given weight of a substance heats indicates its heat-absorbing capacity. The more slowly it heats, the greater its heat capacity.

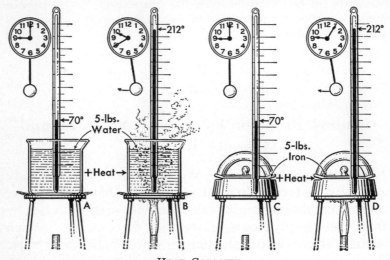

HEAT CAPACITY

Heat capacity is the ability of a substance to absorb heat.

In this diagram both the water and iron start at 70°. They are heated until their temperatures reach 212°.

Which one was heated longer? Which one absorbed more heat? Which one has the greater heat capacity?

Why wasn't a higher upper temperature selected instead of 212°?

Experiment 12 is a very important one because it tells you how to discover for yourself the different effects of heating water and sand.

A pound of iron, a pound of brass, a pound of soil, a pound of air, or any other substance will heat faster than a pound of water if the heat is added at the same rate.

The Heating and Cooling of Land and Water. — Applying your knowledge of the heat capacity of water and other substances, you can understand why land and water heat up and cool off at different rates and you can then understand the cause of land and sea breezes. When the heat (energy) of the sun strikes the land, the land heats up more rapidly than near-by water. The temperature of the land becomes higher than that of the water. This is shown in the drawing on this page. When the sun goes down, the land cools off (loses heat) faster than the water.

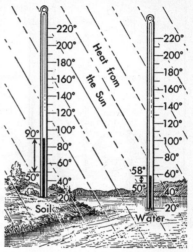

TEMPERATURE OF WATER AND SOIL

When the same amount of heat falls upon water and soil, the soil heats faster. Compare the temperature increases shown in this diagram.

Does this help explain why water temperature at the lake or seashore during the day is lower than the air temperature?

These facts about the unequal heating and cooling of land and water are true not only from day to night, but from season to season. As spring advances, the land away from a large body of water becomes warmer a little faster each day than the body of water. If the body of water is large enough, the summer may be far advanced before the water becomes as warm as the land some distance away.

The air is not heated directly by the energy from the sun but must get its heat from land and water which it touches. For this reason changes in air temperatures over the land and the water correspond to changes in the temperature of land and water. As the summer advances, the water of lake and sea gradually absorbs more and more heat. As fall comes on, the land away from the water quickly loses its heat and the air over it

KEY EXPERIMENT 12

Does water have a greater or less heat capacity than soil?

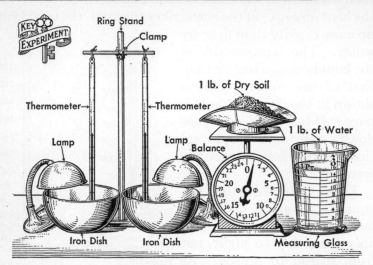

Ring Stand

Clamp

1 lb. of Dry Soil

Thermometer→ ←Thermometer

1 lb. of Water

Lamp   Lamp   Balance

Iron Dish   Iron Dish   Measuring Glass

In this experiment we use heat energy again. What is the source of the energy in the experiment? In nature?

In some other experiments and in this one you measured temperatures. What did you use? What other measurements do you make in th's experiment?

WHAT TO USE: — A pound of water; a pound of dry soil; two iron or tin dishes; two thermometers; two gooseneck lamps with reflector shades and 60 watt lamps; a ring stand and clamp; a balance; and a measuring glass.

WHAT TO DO: — 1. Place the pound of water in one dish and the pound of soil in the other. Set each dish on the table. Support the thermometers so that the bulb of one is in the water and the bulb of the other is in the soil.

Adjust the lamps so that the bulb in each case is the same distance from the top of the soil and the water, about three or four inches. Turn on the electricity and heat the soil and water for fifteen minutes, recording the changes in temperature every two or three minutes.

2. Turn off the lamps and record the cooling temperatures every two or three minutes as before for fifteen minutes.

WHAT HAPPENS: — 1. Did each material receive the same amount of heat? Was it radiant heat, like that from the sun? Which material heated up the faster?
Which was hotter at the end of the fifteen minutes?
2. Which cooled off the faster when the lamps were turned off? What was the temperature at the end of fifteen minutes? Did the materials cool off as fast as they were heated up?

CONCLUSION: — Which material has the greater heat capacity? Explain.

APPLICATION: — Why is water used in automobile radiators?

becomes cooler. On the other hand the heat stored in water is given off very slowly, keeping the air warmer.

Land and Sea Breezes. — The unequal heating and cooling of land and water causes interesting and useful air movements between neighboring land and water. You have learned that air currents move from places of high pressure to places of low pressure. Warm air is lighter and therefore exerts less pressure than the same volume of cold air. Another fact to consider is that air has a very low heat capacity, and therefore heats up rapidly and cools off rapidly. With the help of the drawings on pages 114 and 115 and remembering also that the air gets its heat from the land or the water, you are ready to explain the occurrence of land and sea breezes.

FIELD RESEARCH:
Sometime when you are at the lake, with permission and caution build a small fire on the shore at night and again during the day. Do not try this experiment if there is any wind to speak of.
Each time notice the direction taken by the smoke from the fire.

As the land heats up rapidly the air touching it heats up even more rapidly and becomes lighter because it expands. At the same time the air over the cooler water continues cool and hence heavier than the warm, lighter air over the land. Therefore, the cool, heavier air moves

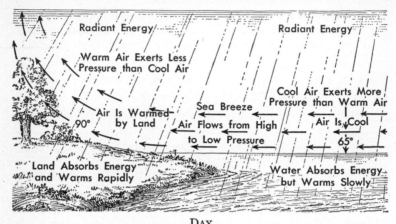

DAY

Because land and water do not heat equally fast, there are often sea breezes from bodies of water during summer days. Explain this diagram.

from the water surface to the land surface and pushes the warm, lighter air up out of the way. The cool air, in turn, becomes warm and is pushed up by more cool air from the sea. The air current thus set up is called a *sea breeze*.

At night the land becomes cool more rapidly than the water, hence the air over the land becomes cooler than the air over the water. In other words, the air pressure is now greater over the land than over the water and an air current moves from land to the water. This kind of air current is called a *land breeze*.

The Growing Season. — The length of a plant-growing season is often determined by the number of days between the last killing frost of spring and the first killing frost of fall.   Crops that require longer time to mature than the time between these two dates are better grown farther to the south where the growing season is longer.

It is important for a farmer or gardener to know the length of the growing season where he lives and the

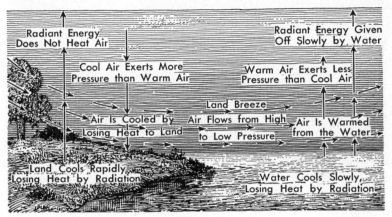

Radiant Energy Does Not Heat Air

Radiant Energy Given Off Slowly by Water

Cool Air Exerts More Pressure than Warm Air

Warm Air Exerts Less Pressure than Cool Air

Land Breeze

Air Is Cooled by Losing Heat to Land

Air Flows from High to Low Pressure

Air Is Warmed from the Water

Land Cools Rapidly, Losing Heat by Radiation

Water Cools Slowly, Losing Heat by Radiation

NIGHT

Unequal cooling of land and water causes land breezes at night during the summer.

Explain how gravity is related to the land breeze shown in this diagram.

crops adapted to it.   It is a valuable study for us as students of science to determine what causes affect the length of a growing season in a given locality.

In your investigation and discussion of the length of the growing season, you will need to consider not only the dates of killing frosts, but latitude, altitude, nearness to or remoteness from large bodies of water, and the length of daylight.   In Alaska, for example, a short growing season is made up for by long hours of daylight.

Crops and Related Industries. — Successful growing of certain crops requires not only special soils, but also a sufficiently long growing season.   In the case of perishable crops, it is natural to expect that canning and

preserving industries will be developed near by.   Likewise, raising of cattle, pigs, and other livestock will
develop to take advantage of products that would otherwise be wasted or shipped away.   It will be a good test
of your understanding if you can describe other examples
of the relation of crops and industries.

General Problem 4. What Adaptations Are Made to Weather and Climate?

Weather and Industries. — No doubt many of
you can recall an occasion when the weather conditions
over a large area were such that crops were completely
destroyed.   Such a case happened in western New York,
during the spring of 1945.   Early in the spring, a spell
of warm weather made the apple trees blossom.   Then
came an unexpected cold spell, and the blossoms were
killed.   Without blossoms there could be no fruit.

Weather conditions all over the country during those
growing and harvesting seasons made the food shortage
a serious problem in its relation to the first World War.
Early in the spring of 1916 a gigantic effort was made
throughout the nation to insure an enormous crop of
food staples to make up the loss of the previous year.
Home gardens sprang up everywhere, and people, generally, became more interested in weather conditions
than ever before.

The experiences people had then with gardens, the
value of the food, the pleasure of helping plants grow and
of defending them against disease and insects resulted
not only in the food supply, but developed a lasting
interest in gardening.   Today more and more people are

finding pleasure, profit, and health in scientific gardening and farming.

Every year agricultural industries are very largely dependent upon weather conditions and every individual is concerned, because this industry furnishes our food.

To a greater or less extent, industries of many kinds are dependent for their success upon certain weather conditions. The *canning industry*, for example, will fail unless conditions are such as to produce an abundance of *fruits* and *vegetables*. The *milling industry* will fail unless there is a sufficient amount of *wheat, corn*, and other *grains*. Also, a second class of industries not directly related to the food supply of the nation is often, to a larger extent, dependent for its raw materials upon the growth of plants and animals. These, too, are affected by weather conditions.

Scientific farming has resulted to some extent in localizing crops to meet the weather factors. For example, crops requiring a longer growing period than is found in the north are grown by the southern planter. Sometimes, however, a northern gardener grows a southern crop under glass, where he can maintain indoor weather conditions to suit his needs.

In other cases, as for example with wheat, some varieties have been developed that will withstand more rigorous climatic conditions than other varieties. Certain kinds of vegetables, such as corn, peas, and beans, have been developed to mature in a shorter growing season than other varieties. These are examples that show how man with increasing knowledge is able to make adaptations to natural conditions which he cannot change.

Practically all industries make some adaptation to weather and climate. Houses and factories are differently constructed in the north than in the south. Stores

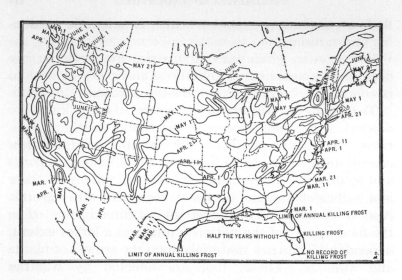

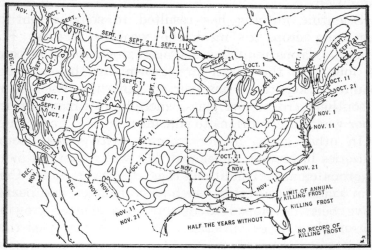

Courtesy U. S. Weather Bureau

LAST KILLING FROST OF SPRING AND FIRST KILLING FROST OF FALL

Some parts of the west have killing frosts as late as June 1 and as early as September 1. Other near-by places have a growing season from March 1 to November 1. Explain the differences.

provide clothing adapted to the climate and season. Ways are discovered to make building easier during the winter months when work is scarce. For example, the chemist has found what to add to mortar and cement to enable it to set and harden without freezing. Roads are built to withstand extremes of temperatures.

Climate and Health. — People with some forms of disease are able to live more comfortably and oftentimes longer in one climate than in another. On the other hand, people who are blessed with good health are able to adapt themselves to almost any kind of climate. Men accustomed to the south can, by wearing suitable clothing and eating the right kinds of food, live and work in the far north. The healthy Eskimo can adapt himself to the southern clime. However, keeping well in localities where the weather is changeable is somewhat more difficult than adapting oneself to extremes of climate.

The body with ordinary exercise loses each hour about as much heat as is given off by the burning of one cubic foot of cooking gas. An ordinary gas burner uses about 30 cubic feet of gas an hour. In half an hour it supplies heat enough to boil a kettle of potatoes. Imagine a class of 30 pupils giving off enough heat to cook a kettle of potatoes in half an hour.

Adapting ourselves to changes of climate or weather as a means of protecting our health is aided by a knowledge of how to control the loss of body heat.

Some heat is lost from the body by *radiation* just as any hot body loses heat. It also loses heat by *conduction* when colder objects touch it and take heat away. When cold air touches the body, it absorbs heat and, if its motion is not hindered, the warmed air is pushed away because colder air pushes in for its share of the heat. This way of taking heat away from anything by a moving or circulating gas or liquid is called *convection*. So the body all of the time loses heat by these three methods: radiation, conduction, and convection.

You have already learned that when liquids evaporate, they absorb heat from objects which they touch. Therefore, when the sweat of the body, which is mostly water, evaporates, it absorbs heat from the body. The water

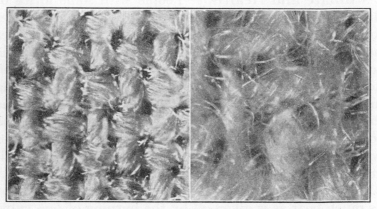

COTTON AND WOOLEN FABRICS (MAGNIFIED)

These pictures show why clothing made of wool is warmer than that made of cotton. Note that the cotton fibers are twisted together tightly and that the wool fibers are fluffy. What relation does this difference bear to the transfer of heat?

vapor thus formed mixes with the air and is carried away by the moving air currents. This explains why you feel colder in a wind than in a sheltered place on a cold day.

Conserving body heat or promoting its loss, as the need may be, by proper use of clothing depends upon our knowledge of how the body loses heat. Winter clothing should prevent, to some extent, the loss of heat from the body. Woolen and silk fabrics are poor conductors of heat. A woolen garment contains many air spaces among its fibers; therefore it retards the loss of heat, because the fibers prevent the circulation of air and so convection losses are prevented. Wool also absorbs moisture and retains it near the skin and so prevents rapid evaporation of sweat.

Summer clothing needs to transmit heat from the body and to reflect heat rays from the sun. Light colors on smooth fabrics of cotton, linen, and silk will reflect the sun's rays. They also contain fewer air spaces than the coarser woolen fabric and so allow freer air circulation, which removes heat from the body. Cotton is a better conductor of heat and so allows heat to escape by that method. Cotton, linen, and silk absorb moisture readily and allow it to evaporate quickly; hence they promote the loss of heat from the body by evaporation of sweat.

FIELD RESEARCH:

Using a hand magnifier, examine samples of woolen, silk, linen, and cotton fabrics to discover differences in weave and air spaces.

Alcohol and the Weather. — Correct clothing, food, rest, and exercise are all necessary to enable a body to adapt itself to ever-changing weather conditions at home and different climatic conditions when traveling. The use of alcoholic beverages is a great handicap to successful adaptation. It may be true that small amounts of alcohol supply a slight amount of heat for the body. But it is also true that alcohol causes the blood capillaries of the skin to become larger, allowing an extra amount of blood to enter. Thus, heat loss from the body is increased, which more than offsets any heat obtained from the alcohol.

The fact that alcohol injures many body cells results in a lowering of general body efficiency, and so it is more likely to be affected by diseases related to weather changes, such as colds and pneumonia. Alcohol is a habit-forming, narcotic drug and like other narcotic drugs should be used only when prescribed by a competent doctor.

Thinking Things Over. — Weather forecasting is becoming almost an exact science, and as such we may expect forecasts to be more and more reliable.

Since weather results from the interplay of cold and warm air it is easy to understand why the laws of gases are important for one to know if he is to try forecasting. You should review these laws, if necessary, and it will help your understanding to try again some of the experiments.

When you try your hand at forecasting be sure to make a record of the prediction and what actually did occur, and then try to explain any differences.

Our next unit for study is "The Heavens." You will discover many ways in which your knowledge of weather will be of help in your new investigation, and your study of the movements of the earth will enable you to understand better how weather is made.

Key Words

adaptations	frosts	radio
cause and effect	heat capacity	sea breeze
climate	land breeze	weather
forecast	pressure	Weather Bureau

Key Statements

1. Scientific prediction of weather depends upon the collection of accurate weather data, or facts, and a knowledge of their cause-and-effect relations.

2. Weather predictions based upon weather signs are not likely to be accurate.

3. Weather forecasting involves a knowledge of the weather factors all over the country.

4. Weather forecasts sent out by the United States Weather Bureau are of great money value to industries of all kinds.

5. Substances differ in their capacity to absorb heat. Water has the greatest heat-absorbing capacity of any common substance.

6. Land, because it has a smaller heat capacity than water, warms faster and cools faster than water.

7. A land breeze (blowing from the land) occurs when the air pressure over the water is less than over the land.

8. A sea breeze occurs when the air pressure is less over the land than over water.

9. The difference in air pressure over adjacent land and water is due to the unequal heating of the air over each.

10. Because of the heat-storing capacity of water, regions near large bodies of water have a longer growing season than regions farther away.

Thought Questions

1. If water has eight times the heat-absorbing capacity of iron, how many pounds of iron would be required to contain as much heat, at a given temperature, as one pound of water?

2. Which would keep a person's feet warm longer, a hot brick or a hot water bottle with an equal weight of water at the same temperature?

3. Explain how the unequal heating of land and water results from their different heat capacities.

4. Why are official weather observations made at a given hour?

5. Why can one not make an accurate weather prediction using only a barometer?

6. How can a frost prediction be made? What factors must be known?

Projects for Your Science Discovery Book

1. List all the ways you can determine in which weather reports by radio are useful.

2. Practice making weather predictions until you become proficient. Keep careful records of the weather factors, your prediction, and the final outcome.

3. Explain why it may be warm and uncomfortable at the seashore in the evening after a warm day. Is the land breeze or the sea breeze likely to be cooler and more refreshing after a warm day?

4. Select a locality near one of the Great Lakes and from Weather Bureau reports determine the latest average date of

killing frost in the spring and earliest average date of killing frost in the fall, within two miles of the lake shore and 25 miles to 30 miles from the shore. What is the average length of the growing season in each location? How is this related to land and sea breezes? Record all your findings.

5. Make a list of the important crops of your vicinity and the industries related to them. Explain the relationships.

6. Discuss the ways in which unusual weather conditions, such as late frosts in spring and too much or too little rain, may determine the abundance or scarcity of food.

7. List the principal occupations in your community and tell how each is related to the weather conditions and what adaptations are made to meet these conditions.

8. List the weather hazards to health in your community and tell how you can adapt yourself to these conditions so as to keep well.

9. At night sink a shallow glass dish in the earth so that the top is level with the surface of the soil. Fill it with water. It should be located where the sun will shine on it next morning.

Early in the morning place one thermometer in the dish of water and stick one in the soil near it.

Note the temperatures of each, and after the sun has shone on them for two hours, again note the temperatures. Explain your observations.

10. Put two shallow dishes of water out overnight in a place where they will receive sunlight in the morning. In the early morning place a thermometer in each and cover one with a white cloth and one with a black cloth. Note the temperatures at the beginning and the end of one hour of the sun's heating. Explain your discoveries.

11. Determine the relation between wind direction and air temperature.

12. Make a study of four different industries to determine their dependence on the weather.

13. Study the effect of weather and climate on six leading crops.

14. Find out how it happens that many fruits, flowers, and vegetables can be grown successfully north of the Arctic circle, in spite of the very short growing season of that region. *Hint:* Consider the influence of sunlight on plant growth; also, the varying lengths of day and night in the Arctic region.

The heavens declare the glory of God;
and the firmament showeth his handi-
work.

Psalm

UNIT II

⟩⟨ THE HEAVENS ⟩⟨

"The Parade of the Planets," "Watch the Sky Parade," and similar headlines in newspapers and magazines during the winter of 1940 called attention to an event that happens only once in about 800 years! Five of the sun's planets visible in the western sky night after night gradually arranged themselves in a majestic line reaching from near the western horizon up into the sky.

Even though we shall not have a chance to see another parade of the planets like that of 1940, every clear night we may see the march of the stars. "In the infinite meadows of heaven blossomed the lovely stars, the forget-me-nots of the Angels."

Who of us has not thought of the evening sky as Longfellow did when he wrote these words? No wonder the fates of men have been related to the stars through superstitions born in admiration! Science helps us to understand the "stars and planets in their courses" and does not detract from their beauty and majesty. It helps us to appreciate all the better the "hand that rules the universe."

To view the universe as a great number of orderly working systems, and to adapt one's living to day and night and to the seasons that are caused by the motions of our planet, require careful study and accurate thinking.

A RADIO TELESCOPE

Ordinary telescopes use mirrors or lenses to focus light from distant objects. This telescope picks up radio waves from the sun. The apparatus follows the sun and records conditions on it which interfere with certain types of radio reception.

126

The Roof of Our Environment

Heaven's ebon vault,
Studded with stars unutterably bright.
— **Shelley**

Do you know:

1. What a star is?
2. What constellations are?
3. How far away the stars are from the earth?
4. Whether the stars control your future?

General Problem 1. What Are Stars and Constellations?

Star-Lore. — Do you think that the stars in the heavens are on the inside of a great hollow globe which turns about the earth? Or do you know that the earth turns, making the stars appear to move?

Long, long ago, before men became scientific, a man named Ptolemy told the people that the earth was the center of the universe and that all bodies in the universe revolved about the earth. To him and to us the earth is the most important part of the solar system.

But Ptolemy was wrong. It is the earth that turns. Even so the ancient people learned many facts about the stars. They knew how to use them for finding directions and for telling time and the seasons. After a while they discovered that stars, planets, the sun, and the moon rise and set because the earth turns. They observed that the stars in the north appeared to move in circles around one particular star which we usually call the North Star but whose real name is "Polaris."

DISTANT STARS

This photograph was made by pointing a powerful telescope toward the constellation called the Northern Cross. The large bright spot in the photograph is one of the stars you can see with your eye alone. None of the other stars is visible without a telescope.

Some of the stars are so arranged as to form interesting shapes or figures, such as the Big Dipper. Not only do the stars that circle about the North Star form figures, but stars in other parts of the heavens form groups, too. Ancient people gave names to these groups and made up queer stories about them. You can see some of these star groups and learn the old stories about them.

For your study of the stars you will need a starry night, the star maps in this book or current magazines, and your Field Research Notebook. The stars and star groups you learn to know will prove to be objects of interest as long as you live. They are not merely fair-

weather friends.   Even though the sky should be stormy,
you will know just where they are, up above the storm.
If you could ride in an airplane above the storm clouds,
you would see them shining.

FIELD RESEARCH:

On a clear, moonless evening in October or November, you and a
friend or two should star-gaze awhile.   Go out into an open field, or on
a hilltop, or out on a lake away from city lights.   Just look, look, look,
until here and there you come to recognize a star, or a group of stars,
by certain characteristics of brightness, position, or color which set
it off from other stars in the heavens.   It will help if you begin your
star-gazing with the last fading twilight so as to see the first star that
is bright enough to show.   One by one other bright stars will appear.
It is easier to learn to recognize the stars this way than when the sky is
filled with "diamonds."   Perhaps someone with you may know the
name of a star group.   Make notes of your first impressions of stars
and drawings of star groups in your Field Research Notebook.

What Are the Stars? — The stars are great *suns* like
our sun, only some of them are much larger.   For example, Betelgeuze (bĕt′el-gûz′) is over a million times
larger than our sun.   But it looks smaller because it is
about 18,000,000 times farther away.   These great hot
bodies send out heat and light as does our sun.   Because
they are so far away, most of the heat is lost before it
reaches us.   But the light comes to us undimmed except
by our own atmosphere.   This light does not *seem* so
bright and widespread as that from our own sun for the
reason that the farther away you are from a glowing
lamp, the smaller it appears and the fainter is its light.

The light from the faintest stars and the light from
the brightest may be compared to the light from a firefly
and the light from a powerful searchlight.

The twenty brightest stars or suns are called *stars of
the first magnitude*, not because they are the largest but
because they are the *brightest* stars.   It is these stars

that are first seen as dusk deepens in the evening. They differ in *size, color* (blue, red, white), *composition,* and *position.* There are about 6000 stars that are bright

THE LICK OBSERVATORY

Notice the dome-shaped roofs on three buildings in this picture. There is a powerful telescope inside each building. Why do you suppose this observatory was built on top of a hill?

enough to be visible to the naked eye although not from one position. Because of misty air, only about 2000 stars are visible to the naked eye from one place of observation. It will be a good test of your eyesight to compare the number of stars you can see with what a companion can see. In ancient times ability to see certain stars was a test one had to pass to become a soldier. With powerful telescopes and by aid of photography countless millions of stars are revealed.

"Look now toward heaven, and tell the stars, if thou be able to number them." (Genesis)

The Milky Way. — Across the heavens, nearly dividing it into two parts, is a broad white path. It is one of the most striking things in the sky and is called the

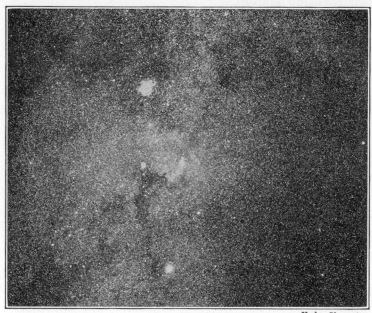

Yerkes Observatory

PHARAOH'S RIVER

An exposure of eight hours through a telescope pointed at the Milky Way produced this photograph. Each white speck is a sun similar to our own sun. The large white spots are believed to be masses of suns.

Milky Way. Ancient Egyptians called it Pharaoh's River, believing it was the river over which the spirits of dead Pharaohs sailed their boats. Until astronomers were able to use high-power telescopes, the Milky Way was thought of as a mass of gas. It is now known to be made up of countless distant stars. The "milky" appearance is due to the fact that the stars of this group are so numerous and distant that their "feeble" lights form only a lacy pattern. A good time to observe the

Milky Way is during the fall and winter evenings when it is high in the sky.   We shall learn later why it is now believed that the stars of the Milky Way are part of a great rotating system.

Yerkes Observatory

THE BIG DIPPER

This constellation is always visible to persons living in the United States. Notice the double star second from the end in the handle.   If you look carefully, you can see these two stars in the sky without a telescope.

The Big Dipper. — Can you see resemblances to kings and queens and to animals as did the ancients when they studied the star groups in the sky?   One ancient race gave us the name "constellations" for these star groups.   One you know is the *Big Dipper*.   Because it is so close to the *North Star* it never passes below the horizon as do star groups farther away from the North Star.   It is called "the Dipper" because its seven stars are arranged in the shape of a dipper, four of them set at the corners of the bowl and three forming the handle. If your eyes are good and the night is clear, you may be able to see a faint star near the second star of the "handle" of the Dipper.   With an opera glass you can see some other stars in the Dipper too faint to see with your naked eye.

The Big Dipper is a good place to start to learn other constellations. Cassiopeia (kăs′ĭ-ō-pē′yȧ) can be seen across the North Star from the Big Dipper. The Northern Cross is higher in the sky than these groups and with Peg′asus can be seen in the summer and fall months. Orion (o-rī′on) can be seen during the winter months.

How Imagination Named the Constellations. —

All of us have let our imaginations form fanciful pictures in the flames of the fireplace, or in the delicate tracery of frost on the window-pane, or in the changing cloud forms of a glorious sunset. In the same way, the Greeks and Romans drew mind pictures on the sky heaven with star groups as outlines. The names of many of their mythological heroes were placed on pictures of the star groups and serve as an interesting record of ancient song and story. The Big Dipper is part of the constellation called by the ancients the *Great Bear*, or, in Latin, *Ursa Major*. Here is one story of its naming:

CALLISTO AND HER SON [1]

In Arcadia lived a beautiful woman, *Callisto*, who had a son called *Arcas*. Juno, the queen of the Greek gods, became very jealous of Callisto because Jupiter, the father of gods and men, was very fond of Callisto and her handsome son. As a mark of her power and envy, Juno changed Callisto into a bear.

Callisto dared not mingle with the other bears in the woods of Arcadia because she retained her human fear of them; and yet she fled from hunters, since naturally they would pursue her at sight and slay her if they could.

One day, however, she caught a glimpse in the distance of her own son Arcas, grown now to splendid manhood. Her love and yearning overcame her, and approaching him with clumsy gait, she

[1] After the story in *Myths and Their Meaning*, by Max Herzberg, in the "Academy Classics for Junior High Schools," published by Allyn and Bacon.

stood on her hind legs and sought to embrace him. But he drew back in mingled wonderment and alarm; and as the bear persisted in following him, he raised his spear and would have killed the strange but terrifying animal.

As the spear-point was about to enter Callisto's breast, Jupiter, looking down from the heavens, saw what was happening and in pity stayed the spear of Arcas. Then he snatched both of them from the earth and placed them as constellations in the heavens. One is a group of stars called the Great Bear, and near by is the Little Bear — Callisto and her son Arcas.

Juno complained bitterly to the gods of the sea at the way Jupiter had treated her rival and her rival's son; and these gods granted to her as a special favor that the Great Bear and the Little Bear should never come into their waters. Hence it is that these constellations constantly circle the pole, but do not sink into the ocean, as do the other stars.

LIBRARY RESEARCH:

Whenever you learn of a new constellation, go to a good book on mythology or to some similar reference book to see if you can discover the reason for its name. This will not only reveal many an interesting story, but will also help you to become better acquainted with the star groups.

The seven stars of the Big Dipper always appear in exactly the same relative position or pattern. While the positions of the stars of this constellation are fixed with respect to each other, the constellation as a whole seems to swing around a point in the northern sky like the hand of a great clock, only in the opposite direction.

FIELD RESEARCH:

Observe the position of the Big Dipper soon after dark in the evening, and again two or three hours later. Repeat the observations several nights later. In your Field Research Notebook record the time of night and dates when you make each observation and make a star map of that part of the heavens, showing especially the Big Dipper. Did you notice that the point in the sky about which it appears to turn is marked by a bright but lonesome star? Did you know that the Big Dipper is always above the horizon in the north temperate zone?

You have probably guessed by now that the lone star about which the Big Dipper appears to turn is the *North Star* or *Polaris*. It is easily found even by beginners by sighting along the line of the two stars which form the outer edge of the bowl of the Big Dipper. (See the star maps on pages 140 and 141.) These two stars are called *pointers*. At a distance from the top of the bowl of about five times the apparent distance between the two stars themselves, you will always find the North Star, a fairly bright, lone star of the second magnitude.

Distances between the stars as they appear in the sky are really measures of the angle you must turn your eyes as you sight from one star to the other. The angle between the two "pointers" is five degrees and twenty minutes. The angle between the pointer nearest the North Star and the North Star itself is twenty-eight degrees. Recalling that there are 360 degrees in a circle, you may be able to estimate angular distances between other stars and constellations.

FIELD RESEARCH:

If you can obtain an old umbrella, open it up and on the inside paste paper stars to represent the Big Dipper. Paste a star about the rod or handle where it goes through the umbrella. This will represent the North Star. Whirl the umbrella counterclockwise and you can illustrate the apparent motions of the stars. Each complete turn will represent 24 hours. Can you also represent the Little Dipper and Cassiopeia?

Finding Other Constellations. — On the opposite side of the North Star from the Big Dipper are five conspicuous stars forming a rather flattened W. These five stars are part of the constellation *Cassiopeia*.

On a clear summer evening look overhead to see six stars in the form of a cross, lying nearly along the Milky Way. This constellation is called by its Latin name,

Cygnus (sĭg′nus), meaning "swan," or by the popular name, *Northern Cross*. It lies in the heavens nearly at right angles to a line from the Big Dipper to the North Star. The bright star at the head of the "Cross" is

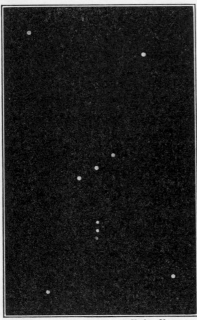

Deneb. The "Cross" is not always above the horizon, as is the Big Dipper. It is visible only during the evening hours of the summer and autumn months. In the fall try to locate Andrŏm′eda, and Pegasus.

The Little Dipper can be seen every month of the year. The North Star (Polaris) is the end star of the handle of the Little Dipper.

The Pleiades (plē′a-dēs), sometimes called the Seven Sisters, are a part of the constellation Taurus — the Bull. Look for the Pleiades during the winter months. The seven stars form a very "little dipper."

Yerkes Observatory

THE MIGHTY HUNTER

Orion is one of the best known of the winter constellations. Rising in the east late in fall, Orion stalks across the sky during the winter. The three stars of the belt and the three that make up the dagger are your clues.

One of the most beautiful winter constellations is Orion, the Hunter. Look for the three bright stars of the "belt" high in the southeastern sky or where shown on your star map. The bright reddish star to the left and above the belt is the great sun Betelgeuse.

The constellations have no scientific importance outside of the fact that they serve as a ready means of locating and naming various stars. For convenience, the astronomer calls the brightest star of each constellation *Alpha*. The Alpha star of the Big Dipper happens to be the one nearest the North Star. The second brightest star is called *Beta*. Often, the Greek letters α, β, and so on are used instead of the words. It must be remembered that the brightness of a star depends mostly upon its distance away from us. The Alpha star of one constellation may therefore be brighter than the Alpha star of some other constellation.

FIELD RESEARCH:

In the fall months try to identify the following stars which are the first to appear as darkness comes on: Vega of Lyra almost overhead, Deneb of the Cross, Arcturus of Boötes, Altair of the Eagle, Antares of the Scorpion, and of course the stars of the Big Dipper and other groups you have studied in the northern sky.

If your observations are made during the winter months, look for Betelgeuse and Rigel in Orion, Aldebaran in Taurus.

Perhaps you have noticed that a particular star with which you are acquainted, Vega for example, is overhead about 9 o'clock in August, but that in September at the same time you find Vega has moved from overhead toward the west. The reason for this is that the stars rise practically four minutes earlier each night; therefore, in a month a star will gain about two hours by your watch. In twelve months a star will gain about 24 hours or one day. So you see a star each August in the same position. However, in six months the star would be overhead about noon, and so you could not see it. Knowing about the early rising of the stars will help you to understand why star maps have the names of the months around the circle.

Star Superstitions. — The movements of stars are governed by the laws of Nature just as all other subjects of her kingdom are. There are some people, however, who do not know this fact.

> Star light, star bright,
> First star I've seen tonight,
> I wish I may, I wish I might,
> Have the wish I wish tonight.

Of course you have said these magic words and wished many a time, but your study of science will convince you that the stars have nothing to do with the outcome of your wishes.

Time was when man thought that his fate was somehow fixed by the stars. The astrologers of old presumed to read their destiny in the stars. This was merely superstition. Even today there are people who study the stars to learn the fate of nations and of men. You will find articles by astrologers in the newspapers. Read them and test the statements scientifically to find if they are true or imaginary. Science has displaced such superstition by a true knowledge of the stars and of their actual relation to our sun and our world.

General Problem 2. How Large Is the Universe?

The Light Year. — How many inches is it from New York to Chicago or San Francisco? You could calculate the distance in inches, but the number would be too large for convenience. The mile is a better *unit of measure* for distances between towns and cities. You would use inches in telling the size of this book, or feet to measure the length or width of your dining room table. In other words, to speak of distances it is very necessary to have a convenient *unit of length*. A few of the common units of length are the *inch*, the *foot*, the *yard*, and the *mile*.

The distances between the earth and the stars are so great that we must have a very special unit of length to measure them. It must be a very long "yardstick" so that we can represent the distance of a star in readable numbers.

Try to imagine a table 186,272 miles long, at the far end of which a boy stands with a powerful electric light. Suppose at a given signal the boy turns on the light. Just one second later the light will reach your eye. It has traveled the full length of the table, 186,272 miles, in a single second.

Light actually travels at this tremendous speed of *186,272 miles in one second.* To get a good idea of this speed, recall that the earth is about 24,000 miles in circumference at the equator. Therefore, 186,272 miles is nearly eight times the distance around the earth. Light, then, can travel in a straight line in one second a distance equal to nearly eight times the circumference of the earth. (For ordinary calculations the even number 186,000 is accurate enough.)

AN ARITHMETIC PROBLEM:

Write down on your paper the number 186,000 and multiply this by 60. Your answer will be the distance that light travels in *one minute.* Multiply this number by 60 (60 minutes in an hour), then multiply by 24 (24 hours in a day), and then by 365 (the number of days in one year), and your answer will be the number of miles that light will travel in *one year.* This will be 5,865,696,000,000. You may have trouble in reading this number unless you recall the order — hundreds, thousands, millions, billions, trillions, quadrillions, etc. This number can be read but is too vast for us actually to sense. It is the distance in miles that light travels in one year in a straight line. This is called the *Light Year.* It is the "yardstick" of the heavens. In round numbers we may use six trillion miles.

How Far Away Are the Stars? — When the astronomer measures the distance between the earth and many stars, his unit of measure is the *light year* — about six trillion miles. It is the distance light can travel in one

The American Museum of Natural History

MAP OF THE WINTER SKIES

To use this map as a guide for the constellations, face south and hold it over your head so that the letter "N" is in the direction of due North.   The map will then show the location of the stars in the heavens.

year.   *Alpha Centauri* is a star of the first magnitude visible in southern latitudes.   It is the nearest bright star that we know, and yet it is so far away that it takes four years and four months for its light to reach us. Another and fainter star in Centauri, called *Proximus Centauri* ("proximus" means "nearest"), is a little nearer.   Light from it takes four years and two months to reach us.   To express the distance of either star in

The American Museum of Natural History

MAP OF THE SUMMER SKIES

The constellations near the North Star (Polaris) are visible in summer as well as in winter. Notice the new constellations that appear in this map and not in the previous one.

miles would involve an inconveniently long string of numbers, and so astronomers use the astronomical unit, the light year, to measure their distances from us.

To help us realize the great distances of stars, astronomers have worked out some interesting comparisons. They tell us that a train traveling at the rate of a mile a minute would require 47,000,000 years to make the journey to Alpha Centauri. To make this journey on a mile-a-minute train, you would need to live 670,000 times the ordinary length of life.

Picture to yourself the fineness and lightness of a spider's web. From an interesting story once told by the late John A. Brashear, a noted astronomer and telescope maker of Pittsburgh, Pennsylvania, we learn that a spider's thread long enough to reach around our earth (24,000 miles) would weigh only a little more than a

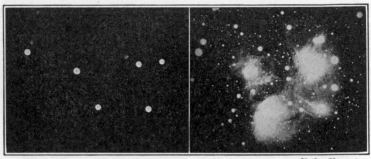

Yerkes Observatory

PLEIADES

The photograph at the left is the cluster of stars called the Pleiades or the Seven Sisters. The star at the upper left is so faint that many persons cannot see it and is sometimes known as the Lost Sister. When a powerful telescope is focused on this constellation, many other distant stars are also seen.

pound and a half, but that one long enough to reach Alpha Centauri would weigh 500,000 tons.

Vega (a blue star of the first magnitude) is visible in *Lyra* (the Harp) almost overhead in the summer and autumn sky. It is the second brightest star in our heavens. It is about 26 light years away or 1,500,000 times farther away than our sun. If it were as near as our sun, it would seem about 50 times as bright. It is known that the axis of the earth is very slowly shifting its direction in such a way that Vega will become the "North Star" in about 12,000 years. The sun with its family of planets is traveling toward Vega about 12 miles per second.

Sirius, the Dog Star, is the brightest star in our heavens. It is best seen in the spring, although it may be seen from December through April. Sirius is only about eight and two-thirds light years away.

In 1893 *Arcturus*, a star of the spring, summer, and autumn, sent forth a beam of light that was used forty years later in 1933 to turn on the lights of the Century of Progress Exposition held in Chicago. Arcturus is about 26 times as far across as our sun, and 86 times as bright. Arcturus is in the constellation *Boötes* (the Herdsman).

The *North Star* (Polaris) is about 465 light years away. It looks bright in spite of its great distance because it is about 2500 times as bright as our sun. Other stars vary in distances from a little more than four to millions of light years away.

Though such distances are hard to understand,

Courtesy The Lick Observatory

A 36-INCH REFRACTOR TELESCOPE

This is the inside view of one of the buildings pictured on page 130. "Thirty-six inches" refers to the diameter of the lens in this telescope.

mathematics, photography, and the telescope enable men to measure the distances of stars with great accuracy. They are measured by determining a star's position when observed from a given point and then noting its position six months later from the same point. From the distance between the two positions and the sizes of the two angles, the distance of the star is calculated.

The more distant the star the more difficult it is to measure its distance accurately. New measurements are constantly being made by astronomers; so, if you find that the distance given for a particular star differs in books of different dates, it may be because new measurements have been determined. Scientists are always trying to make measurements more accurate, and so you must expect new data from time to time.

Red Hot Stars. — Stars are great suns. They are thought of as huge quantities of matter, extremely hot and probably gaseous. The temperatures of the stars vary from 41,000° F. for blue stars and 12,000° F. for those like our sun, to 2800° F. for red stars. Here also new measurements are being made as instruments are improved.

Where one star was known by the ancients, now a million stars tell their stories to the scientist who knows how to study them. The color of the stars has helped the scientist determine their temperature.

Stars Really Move. — While to the naked eye the stars appear to maintain fixed patterns in the sky, yet they do change their relative positions at rates of 10 miles to 20 miles per second. Some move much faster. Arcturus is said to be changing its position at the rate of about 75 miles per second. In 800 years this will change its direction only about the width of the moon; so in our lives it is practically true that the stars do not change their locations.

Meteors, Visitors from Space. — Have you sometimes looked up at the sky on a summer's evening and seen a "star" shoot across the heavens? Millions of these shooting stars, most of them no larger than a grain of sand, are moving about the sun and earth all the time.

But we never see them until they enter the earth's atmosphere. By that time they can do no harm for they are heated so hot by the friction with our protecting atmosphere that most of them are burned up before they reach the earth.

Once in a while a shooting star (meteor) bigger than the others does reach earth. When a meteor actually reaches the earth it is called a *meteorite*. Some of our museums contain great pieces of meteoric rock which have been found in various places in our country. In Arizona there is a huge hole in the ground where a meteor fell thousands of years ago. The rocks on the sides of the hole are burnt, showing how hot the meteor must have been when it struck.

Records of ancient times and those of today tell of great displays of meteors.

Yerkes Observatory

A VISITOR FROM THE SKY

This giant stone, weighing 745 pounds, was found in Arkansas. Meteorites as large as this one are of rare occurrence, but smaller ones which are completely burned before they reach the earth are common. What are meteorites?

In November, 1833, it is recorded that the sky was full of "shooting stars." It must have looked like a Fourth of July celebration. Is it any wonder that primitive man feared such displays, when he could not understand them?

One star in this universe of ours is of more importance to us than all of the others put together. This star is the sun. Its relation to our world and to other planets will be our chief interest as we learn about our next topic — "Our Solar System."

Thinking Things Over. — Probably you have been interested in the stars for several years. You have often looked at the North Star, the Big Dipper, and other stars. By now you should be able to find your way among the stars as each season comes along. Can you show your friends the "forget-me-nots of the angels" and call them by name? But, more than all this, has your study of the stars helped you to realize that our earth is just one tiny part of the great universe? Has the study helped you to appreciate great distances? That even though the stars appear to be alike except in brightness, they really differ in temperature, size, and distance? Does the saying "Hitch your wagon to a star" mean more to you now than before? If your answer is yes to some of these questions, you will be able to appreciate better than ever before the majesty of our Solar System and understand it more thoroughly.

Key Words

Alpha	constellation	North Star
Arcturus	Deneb	Polaris
Beta	light year	Sirius
Betelgeuse	magnitude	star
Big Dipper	meteor	suns
Cassiopeia	meteorite	Vega
celestial	Milky Way	

Key Statements

1. Stars are great suns.
2. The stars appear to be on the inside of a great hollow globe.
3. Stars always appear in the same relative positions or patterns.
4. Certain groups of stars are called "constellations."
5. The stars are far away, the distances varying for different stars.
6. The special unit of length used by astronomers is the "light year," the distance light travels in one year.
7. The stars have nothing to do with one's fate.

8. Superstition about the stars and how they control the life of man is being overcome by scientific truths about the stars.

9. The twenty brightest stars are called "stars of the first magnitude."

Thought Questions

1. How are stars like our sun?

2. By what means do astronomers measure the distances and count the number of the stars?

3. What facts prove that the stars do not rule your fate?

4. Why can you ordinarily see the stars only after dark?

5. How can you locate the North Star?

6. Why do astronomers use the light year instead of miles when telling the distance of stars?

7. Would you give the distance from New York to San Francisco in inches or miles? Why?

8. How have astronomers added to our knowledge?

9. Of what value are the old myths about the constellations?

Projects for Your Science Discovery Book

1. Locate and name at least three stars and three constellations new to you.

2. Draw a map of the brighter stars near the North Star. Indicate the constellations that are visible to you in this region. Allow space to enlarge the area covered by the map. You will be called upon to add to the map from time to time. It will be your *star map*.

3. Locate, observe, and describe the Milky Way.

4. If possible, visit a museum to study meteorites. Make a report on the composition of meteorites.

5. Study recent reports of the Arizona meteoric crater and describe your findings to your class.

6. Look up the biography of one of the great astronomers: Johann Kepler, Pierre Simon LaPlace, Copernicus, Galileo.

7. Locate Cassiopeia by sky observation and place it on your star map. Look up the stories of Cassiopeia and give an account of one to your class.

8. Locate Cygnus by sky observation and make a map of its near-by stars.

9. Locate Vega by sky observation and indicate its location on your star map.

10. Locate Arcturus and show its position on your star map.

11. Locate Pegasus and Andromeda by sky observation. Look up the story of Pegasus and Andromeda and write a story about them.

12. Try to identify the Pleiades with the naked eye. If you have someone with you, find out which of you can see the greater number of stars of the Pleiades.

VALLEY OF THE SUN

Life-giving sunlight streams through dust-laden air, furnishing both strength and beauty to these trees near Yosemite Valley.

TOPIC VI

Our Solar System

The spacious firmament on high,
With all the blue ethereal sky,
And spangled heavens, a shining frame,
Their great Original proclaim.

— Addison

Do you know:

1. How much bigger the sun is than the earth?
2. How life on earth depends upon the sun?
3. Why the earth does not fall into the sun or fly out into space?
4. What causes an eclipse of the sun? Of the moon?
5. What causes a stone to fall?

General Problem 1. Is Our Sun a Star?

The Center of Our Sky System. — Have there been times when you have wondered how big the sun is, how far away it is, and what its purpose is? Is it only to give us light and heat and to serve as a timepiece or does it serve us in still other ways?

Our solar system consists of nine known major planets (and their moons) and over one thousand smaller celestial bodies, all of which revolve in fixed courses around the sun. These planets are at varying distances from the sun and differ from each other in size, color, and the number of their moons. We shall study several of them in some detail a little later, but just now we are concerned with their "guiding star."

Sun Facts. — The sun is a great mass of matter, heated white-hot. The temperature at the center is possibly as high as 40,000,000° F. It is wrapped in dense clouds of hot gases. These surface gases have a temperature of about 12,000° F. The sun is about

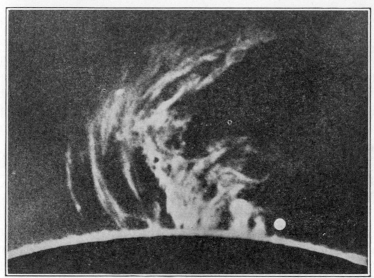

Courtesy Mt. Wilson Observatory

HOW LARGE IS THE SUN?

The curve across the bottom of the picture is the surface of the sun. The white flamelike masses above are made up of hot gases. The gases in this photograph are 140,000 miles high. The earth, represented by the white disc, is tiny in comparison.

870,000 miles in diameter, or nearly 110 times the diameter of our earth. In volume it is 1,300,000 times as large as the earth. It will help you to realize this difference in size, if you will compare the room occupied by yourself with the room that would be occupied by 1,300,000 pupils of your size.

The *force of gravity* tends to hold you to the earth's surface. It causes an apple to fall from a tree. It causes the water in the rivers to flow to the sea. This force of gravity is the force which a heavenly body exerts on objects on or near it. We do not know what gravity is. We only know what it does and how it behaves. The effect of this unknown force extends to the farthest star.

The force of gravity of the earth tends to draw all objects on or near its surface towards the center of the earth. Because of this "drag," you must have strong muscles to jump over a bar three or four feet high. Because of the great mass of the sun the force of gravity at its surface is 28 times as great as the force of gravity of the earth. If you were on the surface of the sun, you would have hard work to jump over this textbook. (Can you give two reasons why no one could live on the sun?)

Another interesting comparison of the force of gravity of the earth and of the sun is that a man weighing 150 pounds on the earth would weigh nearly 4200 pounds, or more than two tons, on the sun. These numbers are given to help you appreciate what an enormous object the sun is — 1,300,000 times as large as the earth.

What Is the Distance to the Sun? — While this great white-hot body is so vast in size as compared with the earth and still more vast as compared with our moon, yet it looks no larger than the moon itself. This is because the sun is so far away. A fast train running day and night could reach the moon in about eight months if such a trip were possible. It would require about 258 years to reach the sun.

Such distances are tremendous, and yet we must try to realize what these distances between the heavenly bodies mean. The average distance of the sun from the earth is about 93,000,000 miles. Traveling at the speed of light, which you remember is about 186,000 miles a second, one could make the journey from the earth to the sun in about eight minutes. Compared with the

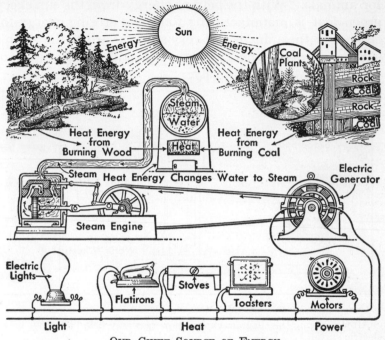

OUR CHIEF SOURCE OF ENERGY

Use this diagram to tell the story of how we get our artificial heat, light, and power from the sun.

distances of other suns or stars about which we have studied, the sun is very close to us. And because it is comparatively close, it effects our lives in many ways.

The Sun as a Powerhouse. — We think of energy to run our machines, heat our homes, and cook our food as coming from burning coal, oil, or gas. We are interested in the great power projects in Tennessee, Hoover Dam, and others. But do you think of the sun as the greatest powerhouse of all? Study the diagram on page 153. Can you think of any other kinds of power we receive indirectly from the sun? The sun sends forth energy which plants use to grow and manufacture food for animals. With the help of energy from the sun every green leaf is manufacturing food and storing energy for the use of the animals. Every square yard of the earth's surface receives energy from the sun at the rate of $1\frac{1}{2}$ horsepower continuously.

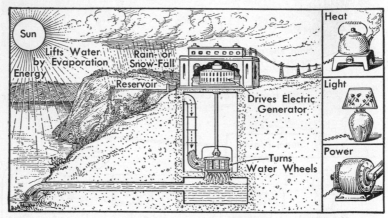

THE SUN AND WATERPOWER

After studying this diagram explain how rain may help boil water on an electric stove.

Tell how sunshine makes it possible for electric trains and street cars to run.

Nevertheless the whole earth receives less than one billionth part of all the energy given out by the sun. Some of the energy of the sun, stored up through the ages in coal-forming plants, is now tied up in the coal. As we burn the coal this solar energy is given off as heat to keep us warm and to supply us power.

Heat from the sun causes the evaporation of water from land and sea into the atmosphere. *Evaporation* is the process by which water changes from the liquid to the gaseous state. It rises into the atmosphere as an

Kabel

THE SPARK PLUG OF THE SOLAR SYSTEM

Clouds, mountains, snow, water, and man — all are possible on the earth because of the energy given off by the sun. Explain how each one is related to the sun.

invisible gas. When the gas cools, the water again becomes liquid by *condensation*, and forms clouds from which the moisture falls as rain or snow. This water cycle carries water from oceans, lakes, and rivers to mountain slopes and hillsides. It flows downward to drive water wheels and turbines, as is shown in the drawing on page 154. Hence water power really comes from the sun. Also certain rays of the sun's energy give us light. This is our sunlight which makes possible so many of our daytime occupations. The sun is the source of energy on which our activities and our very life depend. A great astronomer said: "We are Children of the Sun."

Scientists are trying to discover the cause of the energy of the sun. Is the sun gradually cooling off as a hot iron cools, or are forces at work in the sun itself that serve to produce more energy? The answer seems to be that the sun is producing more energy all the time. But this has not yet been definitely proved.

Sun Substances. — Man has not always known what elements make up the sun. Little more than a lifetime ago the composition of the sun was not known. Now, by means of the *spectroscope* and other measuring instruments in combination with powerful telescopes, photography, and chemistry, much is known, especially of the outer gaseous portion of the sun.

When certain substances are heated very hot and looked at through a spectroscope, various combinations of bright colored lines are seen. Scientists think that the same combinations of colored lines are given off only by similar substances. By applying this principle the elements in the sun are found to agree in kind with those that make up the earth and other planets of our solar system. This is one proof that the sun and its planets were once parts of a single mass of matter.

SUN SUBSTANCES 157

FIELD RESEARCH:
With the help of a physics or chemistry teacher arrange to observe bright colored lines in a spectroscope.

Elements are both metals, such as iron, zinc, and tin, and non-metals, such as oxygen, carbon, nitrogen, hydrogen, and the like. The metals have been easier to

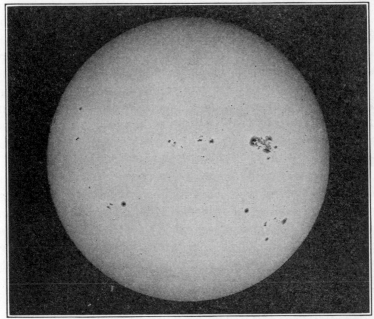

Courtesy Carnegie Institution of Washington

SUN SPOTS

Sun spots are storms on the sun's surface. They appear to observers on the earth as dark spots moving across the surface of the sun. What are some effects of sun spots?

discover in the sun than the non-metals because their lines in the spectroscope are brighter. Magnesium, iron, silicon, and sodium are very common in the sun's outer portion. They are also abundant in the rocks that make up the earth. It is estimated that hydrogen makes up

most of the sun's atmosphere by volume, perhaps 90%
to 95%. Oxygen and helium form 2% to 4%. The rest
is made up mostly by magnesium, iron, silicon, and
sodium.

Helium has an interesting story. It was first discovered in the sun's atmosphere. Some time later an
English chemist discovered that it existed also in the
earth's atmosphere in very small quantities.

During the first World War helium was discovered by
American chemists in some kinds of natural gas. They
found out how to separate it, but at first it was very
expensive. Scientists kept at the problem until great
quantities could be obtained cheaply. The gas helium
is very light and so it is used to fill dirigibles. It will not
burn and is therefore much safer to use for this purpose
than hydrogen.

Sun Spots. — The outer portion of the sun is the
sun's atmosphere and consists of very hot gases. These
gases are made up of molecules which move about constantly. When gases are heated very hot, the molecules
move very fast. Toward the interior of the sun, where
it is still hotter, the violence of the motion probably
increases.

This tremendous disturbance acts like a terrific storm.
In comparison our tornadoes are a mere trifle. These
whirling gases form dark spots in the sun's atmosphere
somewhat as a thunder cloud forms a dark spot in our
atmosphere of our earth. These dark spots are called
sun spots and are a few thousand degrees cooler than
the sun's surface. Sun spots vary from 500 miles to
50,000 miles in diameter.

Just as thunder storms in our atmosphere occur more
frequently at certain seasons and in certain zones, so it
seems that sun spots occur more abundantly in certain

NORTHERN LIGHTS

Visitors to the Hayden Planetarium in New York City find the stars projected on the inside of a domelike roof. This photograph shows northern lights produced in the planetarium. If the partitions of the roof did not appear in the picture, these man-made northern lights could easily be mistaken for real ones.

zones of the sun. Also, the sun spots increase and decrease in number quite regularly, approximately every eleven years. A minimum of sun spot activity occurred in the fall of 1933. By 1937–1938 there was a maximum of sun spots. Again in 1943–1944 there was a minimum number of sun spots observed. The year 1948 completed another cycle as a year of maximum sun spot activity.

During sun spot activity it is believed that electrons are hurled like bullets toward the earth's atmosphere. This may help to explain the northern lights (Aurora Borealis) which are more frequent and brilliant at times of great sun spot activity.

Radio transmission and reception appear to be related to the height of the layer of air called the Kennelly-Heaviside layer. The position of this layer is known to be related to sun spot activity. This helps us to understand why local radio reception is better at times of sun spot activity and why long-distance radio is helped by fewer sun spots. Even one large sunspot, however, seems to have the power to interrupt, or "black out," most of our international radio communication throughout the world.

For many years observers have tried to discover relationships between sun spot activity and the weather. Since the earth's atmosphere is affected by the results of the great electron storms on the sun, it seems possible that our world weather should be affected in some ways by sun spot activity.

General Problem 2.   What Does the Moon Do to Us?

First Stop: The Moon. — "First stop, the moon." This would be the announcement by the stewardess of an imaginary sky ship if we were starting on a visit to members of the solar system. Of all the objects in the heavens the one most looked for, the one about which the greatest number of stories have been written, and one of the most interesting of all is the *moon*. When visible, it is the most con-spicuous object in the evening sky and al-ways attracts our atten-tion.

The moon is strictly our property. It be-longs to our earth and revolves around it once in about twenty-nine days. It is a solid ball about 2160 miles in diameter and is nearly 240,000 miles from the earth. Although the moon is the most con-spicuous object in the night sky, it is, never-theless, a very small body when compared with the sun or any of the planets.

MOONLIGHT

The moon is a cold dead body, but because it reflects light it makes possible such beautiful scenes. The clouds, trees, and water in this photograph are all lighted by reflected light from the moon.

The Light of the Moon. — On a clear night the moon glows with much brilliance, yet it really gives out no light of its own. The moonlight that you see is sun-light reflected from the surface of the moon. All objects that we can see are made visible because light from some source falls upon them and is reflected to our eyes. A black object is black because it does not reflect light that reaches it. If it is really black you only see lighter objects or backgrounds around it. Black cloth does not reflect much light, and a white ball would be invisible

EXPERIMENT 13

How does the moon give light?

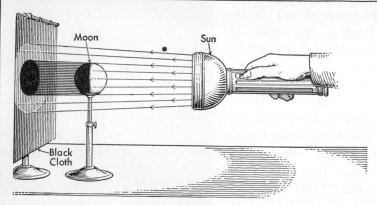

In this experiment we meet another form of energy. We have used heat and electrical energy. Now we use light energy. Light energy really results from heat energy.

The important idea in this experiment is to illustrate what many of you already know — that we can see things only because they are lighted up (that is, illuminated). But do you know if that is how we see the moon? Does the moon make its own light or does some other object light it up?

The sun is several million times larger than the moon, so when a golf ball is used to represent the moon, a flashlight is really very much too small to represent the sun, but it illustrates the principle.

WHAT TO USE: — A golf ball to represent the moon; support for the ball; a flashlight to represent the sun; a piece of black cloth; and a room that can be darkened.

WHAT TO DO: — Make the room so dark that you cannot see the ball when it is held across the room with the cloth behind it. Of course you can do the experiment at night by turning out the lights. Then let a pupil behind the class turn the beam of light from the flashlight on the ball.

WHAT HAPPENS: — Does the ball become light enough to be seen when the beam of light strikes it? What does the ball do to the light?

Does the cloth appear as visible as the ball? Why not?

CONCLUSION: — Do you think the light that enabled you to see the ball in the darkened room originated from the ball or the flashlight?

Why did the ball show light while the cloth did not do so?

APPLICATION: — Explain how light from automobile headlights makes objects alongside the road visible. How do automobile headlights make cats' eyes appear?

against it unless it were lighted up by light falling on it and being reflected from it. If the ball were really black, you would not be able to see it even if light were thrown on it.

If you try Experiment 13 you will be able to prove these statements. Even though you pretty well know in advance how some experiments turn out, it is worth while doing them because you are training yourself in the ways of a scientist. Almost always the experiment will help to clear up doubts or partly understood principles.

High Jumping on the Moon. — How high can you jump? When you jump up from the earth's surface, you jump against the force of gravity. Most people can jump upward in this way only a few feet. On the moon, however, you could jump over a train. This is because the force of gravity exerted by the moon is only about one sixth that of the earth. Therefore, a person could jump six times higher on the moon than on the earth. The 150 pound earth-man who would weigh 4200 pounds on the sun would weigh only 25 pounds on the moon.

Solids, water, and the gases of the air of the earth are held to our earth and prevented from escaping by the force of gravity of the earth. The moon, on the other hand, is so small that its force of gravity is not great enough to hold water vapor or other gases on its surface. That is why today it is a barren waste of rock — airless and waterless. The history of the moon is written in its craters, its long, barren valleys and high rugged mountain peaks. They have remained because there has been no leveling action of rain and snow, rivers, glaciers, and wind.

Temperatures. — Daylight on the moon lasts a little more than fourteen of our days, and the night is the same length. During this long day of two weeks of our time, the rays from the sun, undiminished by any atmosphere, beat upon the surface of the moon. As a consequence of this long-continued heating, it is probable that the temperature of the rocks is raised above the boiling point of water, 212° F., and possibly as high as 244° F. But when the moon turns on its axis so that this same surface is away from the sun, its temperature drops rapidly to about − 250° F. During an eclipse of the moon its temperature fell 335° F.

In like manner, if our earth had no atmosphere, we should be baked by day and frozen by night. Fortunately for us, atmosphere and clouds about the earth act as a blanket which prevents rapid heating by day and rapid loss of heat by night.

A natural law tells us that a warm body or object always tends to lose heat by *radiation* to colder objects or gases about it. For example, when you stand near a fire, the part of you toward the fire receives energy radiated (sent out in all directions) from the fire, while the rest of your body does not receive any. When the radiant energy strikes your body, it is changed to heat energy. The same result occurs when you hold your hand near a hot flatiron. The hot iron gives off energy in every direction. The energy stopped by your hand is transformed to heat and your hand becomes warm. It is radiant energy given off by the sun that is changed to heat when it strikes our earth and moon and helps to keep them warm.

Seeing on the Moon. — Our atmosphere, with its moisture and dust, serves to *diffuse* (scatter) light from the sun. This is what happens when sunlight passes through air with smoke or other dust in it. It is what you see when the light from the head lamps of a car shines through fog. The tiny particles of water diffuse or scatter the light. Since the moon has no atmosphere, the sun illuminates only those objects in its direct or reflected light. Where the light does not strike, there is darkness.

For example, suppose you had a house on the moon, a house with non-reflecting inside walls. In the rooms facing the sun, only those portions in direct line with the windows would receive light. The other portions would be darker than any nights we know. The rooms on the opposite side of the house would receive only that light which might be reflected from surfaces in the paths of the sun's rays.

The moon's surface is not so good a reflector of light as that of our earth. It is about equal to that of ordinary sandstone. Shadows on the moon are very sharp. This is due to the absence of *diffused light.* When there is an atmosphere such as our earth possesses, light is diffused. Thus an object held in a bright light on the earth does not cast nearly so sharp a shadow as that cast by any of the mountain peaks on the moon, which has no atmosphere.

The moisture and dust particles in our air also give us our blue sky and colored sunrises and sunsets. On the moon the sky is black and there are no beautiful sunsets or sunrises.

FIELD RESEARCH:

Hold an object between a bright light and the wall. Do you observe two depths of shadows — one darker than the other? How could there be any light behind the object, if it did not come in from the sides as diffused rays?

Silence and the Man in the Moon. — When a person on the earth speaks, his voice is carried in all directions by wave-like motions of the air much as waves spread from a stone thrown into water. On the moon there must be absolute silence, for there is no air to carry sound.

FIELD RESEARCH:

If there is a physics teacher in your school, ask him to help your class prove that air carries sound. He will need a bell jar, exhaust air pump, and an alarm clock. If the clock is placed in the bell jar containing air and the alarm sounds, it can be heard. If the air in the bell jar is taken out by means of the air pump and the alarm rings, the sound can be heard faintly or not at all, depending on how much of the air has been removed.

On the earth we are conscious of the air because it fans our faces, blows dust into our eyes, carries clouds along with it. It carries sound to our ears. It sometimes tears down buildings and trees. Yet to realize fully all that air means to us, we must bear in mind that without air there would be no sound, places would be either very bright or very dark, and the temperature would be very hot or very cold.

Another curious thing about the moon is that it turns on its axis only once in about twenty-nine days; hence a whole day on the moon is nearly as long as our month. At any one place on the moon there would be continuous daylight for a little more than fourteen days and then utter darkness for another two weeks of our time. Now it happens that because the moon's time of rotation on its axis is nearly equal to its time of revolution around the earth, we see only one side or portion of the moon.

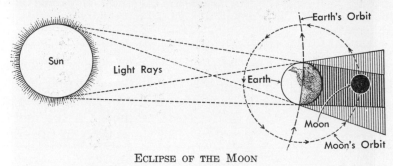

ECLIPSE OF THE MOON

Compare this diagram with the one explaining the eclipse of the sun (page 169). Can there be an eclipse of the moon at any phase of the moon? Explain.

This explains why we always see the same "man in the moon." No one on earth has ever seen the other side of the moon. Actually, 59 per cent of the moon's surface has been observed at one time or another. Forty-one per cent has never been seen.

An Eclipse of the Moon. — Because the moon is visible by the reflected light of the sun, you can understand that if an object passes between the sun and the moon, some of the light will be cut off. The moon will then be only partly visible.

This is just what happens when an eclipse of the moon occurs. It is the earth itself that gets in between the sun and the moon. When the sun, earth, and moon get into a straight line the shadow of the earth falls upon the moon and there is a *total eclipse* of the moon. Study the diagram on this page to understand the positions of the earth and moon during a total eclipse of the moon.

The shadow of the earth frequently covers only a portion of the moon's face, and then we have what is known as *a partial eclipse.* Because the edge of the

American Museum of Natural History

LUNAR ECLIPSE

The shadow of the earth is falling across part of the moon. When the moon and the earth move into a direct line the earth's shadow will completely block the light of the moon.

earth's shadow on the moon's face is always circular, we know that the earth is shaped like a ball, for only a ball can make a circular shadow if it is turning on an axis all of the time.

Experiment 14 tells you how to set up a "moon," "earth," and "sun" and see for yourself just how an eclipse of the moon is caused. Of course you must keep in mind that the objects do not accurately represent the sizes or distances of the sun, moon, and earth, nor will the motions be exact.

An Eclipse of the Sun. — Sometimes the moon gets between the earth and the sun and cuts from our view a portion of the sun's face, causing an *eclipse of the sun.*

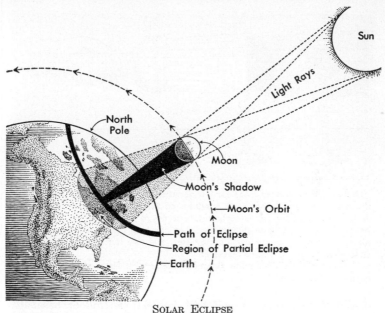

SOLAR ECLIPSE

When the moon moves into position so that it blocks sunlight coming to the earth, there is a solar eclipse. In this diagram, the dark band across Canada and the United States represents the region where there is a total eclipse. How would the sun look to an observer in that region?

The most recent total eclipse of the sun visible in the United States (Idaho and Montana) occurred on July 9, 1945. Not again until July 20, 1963,[1] will another total eclipse of the sun be visible in any part of the United States. The eclipse of 1963 will be visible in its totality in Vermont, New Hampshire, and Maine. In 1970, on March 7, a total eclipse will be visible in Florida. Others will occur in 1979, 2017, 2022, 2045, visible as total eclipses in various parts of the United States.

---

[1] Data from *Science News Letter*, July 30, 1932.

EXPERIMENT 14
What causes an eclipse of the moon?

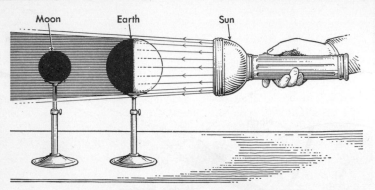

Actually the diameter of the earth is about four times that of the moon, and the sun's diameter is about one hundred ten times that of the earth's diameter. Before trying this experiment, you might draw lines on the blackboard to represent these diameters. Let one-half inch equal the moon's diameter, two inches the earth's diameter, and two hundred twenty inches (how many feet?) the sun's diameter.

This experiment will require patience — several trials to show clearly the eclipse of the moon.

WHAT TO USE: — A golf ball (moon); an indoor baseball (earth); and a flashlight (sun).

(The flashlight is not a true illustration of the sun, for the sun should be many, many times larger than the earth. Also if an indoor baseball represents the earth, the golf ball is much too large to represent the moon proportionally. With these differences in mind, however, these objects will serve for the experiment.)

WHAT TO DO: — 1. Make the room as dark as possible. From behind the class let a pupil turn the light on the golf ball held in front of the class and rather high. Let another pupil slowly carry the "earth" between the "sun" and the "moon."

If the room cannot be made quite dark, it may be necessary to set up the golf ball, baseball, and flashlight as in the drawing on a table.

2. Find a location for the "earth" so that the shadow of the "earth" just covers the "moon." This will represent a total eclipse.

3. Now start over again and move the "earth" so as to cause its shadow to appear first at the right of the "moon" and cross the face of the "moon" from right to left, passing off the "moon" on the other side. The total eclipse occurs when the whole "moon" is covered.

4. Try to find a place for the "earth" so that only a portion of the "moon" will be covered as the "earth" is moved, causing the shadow to cross the "moon" without at any time covering the whole "moon." This represents a partial eclipse.

5. Again place the "earth" so that its shadow covers a part of the "moon." Turn the "earth" on an axis and note the shape of the shadow as the "earth" turns. Is it always circular?

WHAT HAPPENS: — 1. Could you see the shadow of the "earth" on the "moon"?

2. Could you cause the whole "moon" to be covered by the shadow of the "earth"?

3. When the shadow moved across the "moon" was there a short time when the whole "moon" was covered?

4. What did you do to cause the partial eclipse?

5. Was the shadow circular? Did it continue circular in shape as the "earth" turned on its axis?

CONCLUSION: — What causes an eclipse of the moon? Why is the eclipse total sometimes and partial at others? How does an eclipse of the moon help to prove that the earth is round?

APPLICATION: — Explain how the moon might eclipse a star or planet.

Eclipses are predicted by astronomers many years in advance. Not only are the date and year predicted, but the hour, minute, and exact second when they are to start and end. For example, in 1945, the exact path and the width of the shadow of totality were predicted so people could go to that area and be sure of seeing the sun in a total eclipse.   However, clouds hid the sun in some localities and spoiled observations.

Wide World

TOTALITY

The Old Man of the Mountain in Franconia Notch, New Hampshire, looks out upon the total eclipse of the sun in August, 1932.   Explain why so much of this picture is dark.

Of course, the eclipse was seen as a partial eclipse by people all over the United States. The diagram on page 173 shows how the sun could be seen as a total eclipse in some places and as a partial eclipse in others.

As the moon, invisible in the bright light, comes between the observer and the sun it appears through a smoked glass as a dark circular object making a curved nick in the edge of the sun.   As the moon covers more and more of the sun, the world grows dark with a weird disappearing light.   The shadow of the moon moves across the earth at a speed of 2000 miles per hour. Animals prepare for the night, stars and planets shine.   When the sun's disk is all covered, flames of hydrogen and other gases flash from behind and form a lighted corona.

The path of the total eclipse in 1932 was so conveniently located that scientists from all over the world

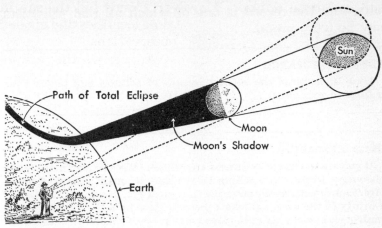

Path of Total Eclipse

Sun

Moon

Moon's Shadow

Earth

CAUSE OF A PARTIAL ECLIPSE

A person in the band marked "Path of Total Eclipse" would see a total eclipse of the sun. The figures in this diagram see a partial eclipse.

Study the diagram, imagine this happening, and then explain how a partial eclipse is caused.

came to America to view the eclipse. Although the eclipse lasted only ninety seconds, the scientists spent months in setting up and testing their equipment and in timing each step of observation. Much new knowledge was to be gained in that brief time, and so not one second must be wasted. As we might expect, such careful planning produced excellent re-

Courtesy Mt. Wilson Observatory

SOLAR ECLIPSE

At the time of the total eclipse of the sun, the moon completely hides the sun. Only the ring of hot gases surrounding the sun can be seen. What would the picture taken five minutes later look like?

sults, and the record is one of which all real scientists may be truly proud.

LIBRARY RESEARCH:

Look up some of the earliest records of eclipses and report your findings to your class.

FIELD RESEARCH:

If you are fortunate to witness an eclipse of the sun, you may try the following: Observe the eclipse of the sun through a smoked glass. Never look directly at the sun with the naked eye, because of the danger of injury to the eyes. Smoke a piece of glass by setting fire to a very small piece of camphor gum placed on a piece of sheet iron or asbestos. Camphor gum burns with a low temperature and produces a very dense smoke. The flame can be extinguished by blowing on it. If you do not have a piece of camphor, you may use a burning candle to smoke the glass.

With the smoked glass through which to look at the sun during the eclipse, you can see the shape of the moon silhouetted against the face of the sun. The shape will be circular. What does this prove?

Another interesting observation to make before and during an eclipse of the sun is to note, as the sunlight shines through tiny openings of the leaves of trees, the shape of the lighted areas where the sunlight falls. Usually these areas are circular in shape, but, during a solar eclipse, the shape is crescent because part of the light is cut off by the moon and the spaces through the leaves are small enough to act like a hole of a pinhole camera to reproduce an image of a bright object.

You will be interested to try Experiment 15 to demonstrate just how the sun is eclipsed or hidden by the moon. Recall also what was said about Experiment 14.

The Phases of the Moon. — Why is the moon full? Why is there a half moon? Have you wondered about these things on clear moonlit nights and tried to think out the answers? They are not difficult to answer, if you will reason carefully about the problem they present. The bright side of the moon is always toward the sun, and since the moon travels around our earth, some of the time the whole lighted face is toward us and sometimes only part is visible. As you read about the phases of the moon in the next paragraph, be sure to refer to the diagram on this page.

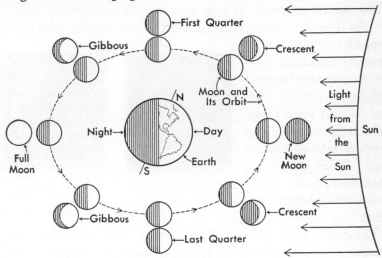

PHASES OF THE MOON

This diagram shows the earth, light from the sun, and two rings of moons.

The inside ring shows what the moon would look like if you were viewing it from some place off in space. Note that half of the moon is always lighted — the half facing the sun.

The outside ring of moons shows the portion of the moon's lighted face you see when on the earth. These are the *phases of the moon.*

The dark portion of the moon (the part you cannot see) is represented by shading in the diagram. According to the diagram, you cannot see the *new moon.* Why not?

These apparent shapes of the moon are called *phases.* The *phases* (shapes) *of the moon* in order of appearance are called: *new moon, first quarter, full moon,* and *third quarter.* These names really tell us how much of the moon's journey around the earth is completed each month. Starting with the thin crescent of the "new moon," the completion of the first quarter of the journey is indicated by a "half moon"; the "full moon" tells us the journey is half over; the "old half moon" that follows the "full moon" marks the finish of the third quarter of the journey. With the next new moon the complete journey has been made and a new one started. The whole journey, as you know, takes nearly 29 days.

As the earth and moon move, the sun, moon, and earth regularly fall into a nearly straight line, with the sun beyond the moon as we look at it. At such times the bright face of the moon is away from us. This phase is the new moon. Usually the moon cannot be seen now.

Courtesy Mt. Wilson Observatory

NEW MOON   FIRST QUARTER

Where is the sun in relation

(Diagram, page 175.) With certain atmospheric conditions, however, the new moon is faintly visible, illuminated by sunlight reflected from the earth. This is sometimes called the "dark of the moon."

As the earth and moon journey on, the sun's rays strike the moon at an angle from our right, and we see a small strip of crescent-shaped light on the moon. This thin crescent is often called the "new moon," but actually the moon is already past the new moon phase when a crescent is seen. When the thin crescent appears on a clear night, we can often see a faint outline of the entire moon. Some people call this the "old moon in the arms of the new moon." This crescent is that part of the moon lighted by rays coming directly from the sun. The faint outline of the rest of the moon is the part lighted by the sun's rays reflected from the earth.

As days pass, a night comes when the sunlight strikes

the moon squarely from our right as we look toward it, and we see the half circle of light (half moon).   The first quarter of the moon's journey about the earth is completed.

When the sun is shining on the opposite side of our earth, leaving us in darkness, you may, at the right time of the month see the full face of the moon illuminated by the light rays from the sun which pass by and beyond our earth and strike the moon. As you stand facing a full moon, the sunshine is coming from behind you, passing a little above or below the earth.

Courtesy Mt. Wilson Observatory

FULL MOON   THIRD QUARTER

to each phase of the moon?

When the sunlight comes from your left as you face the moon and half of its lighted face is visible (half moon), the third quarter of its journey is finished.   Here the sun and moon are again at right angles to each other with reference to the earth.   Whether the moon looks "full," "half," "quarter," or crescent-shaped, actually half of it is lighted by the sun.   You see only part of the lighted surface. This is why the moon appears to change shape, although you know now that it really does not.

If you see all of the lighted surface of the moon, it is circular in shape and called the full moon.   If you see only half of the lighted surface from one side, it looks like a half circle (half moon).   You cannot see the part not lighted.   With the change from "new" to first quarter, the moon appears crescent-shaped.   You can tell where the sun is in relation to the earth and moon because the horns of the crescent point away from the sun.

EXPERIMENT 15

What causes an eclipse of the sun?

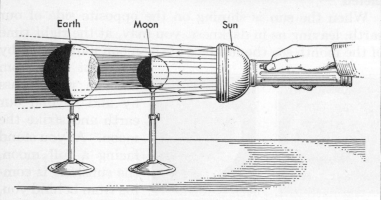

Earth   Moon   Sun

Compare this drawing with that for Experiment 14. In this case it is the smaller body — the moon — that shuts off the light of the sun. That is why the shadow is cone-shaped, making a small shadow on the earth. Notice the darker shadow and the lighter shadow on the drawing. As in Experiment 14, the sizes and distances of the objects are out of proportion. Try to illustrate the distance on the blackboard. Let one-half inch equal 240,000 miles (earth to moon), and one hundred ninety-four inches equal 93,000,000 miles (earth to sun).

WHAT TO USE: — Use the same apparatus as in the preceding experiment.

WHAT TO DO: — Think out for yourself how to arrange the golf ball, baseball, and flashlight to cause a shadow of the "moon" to be cast on the "earth."

WHAT HAPPENS: — Make a drawing to illustrate what happens.

CONCLUSION: — What causes an eclipse of the sun?

APPLICATION: — Using a pencil, an electric light bulb, and a piece of paper, demonstrate the cause of the shadow having a darker and lighter portion.

The Orbit of the Moon. — In making your outdoor observations of the causes of the phases of the moon, the earth on which you stand appears to stand still and the moon and the sun appear to move. Is this what really happens? In the experiment the "moon" was kept in the same place. You stood in the same place while the "sun" was moved. Of course actually the moon and the earth both move. The earth moves around the sun, while at the same time the moon moves around the earth.

The path of the moon about the earth is called the *moon's orbit*. Likewise the path of the earth about the sun is called the *earth's orbit*. The moon's orbit is nearly circular and

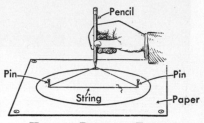

HOW TO DRAW AN ELLIPSE

Be careful to keep your pencil straight up and down. Why?

the earth's orbit is elliptical, that is, one diameter is longer than the other. The actual line of the path forms an *ellipse*, that is, a somewhat oval figure. (It would be well to practice drawing an ellipse, using a string, two pins, your pencil, and paper as in the accompanying diagram.)

The orbit of the moon and of the earth each determine a plane or flat surface like a table top. It happens that the earth's orbit and the moon's orbit are not in the same plane. Instead they are on planes that form an angle with each other. In other words, if viewed from one edge, the plane of the moon's orbit would intersect the earth's orbit plane in such a way that part would be a little below and part a little above the plane of the earth's orbit.

Partial and total eclipses are due to the fact that *the planes of the orbits of the earth and the moon make an angle*

EXPERIMENT 16
What causes the phases of the moon?

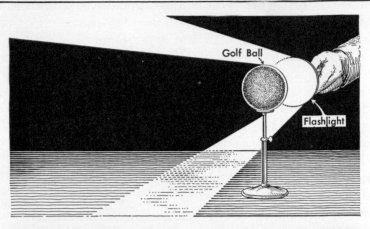

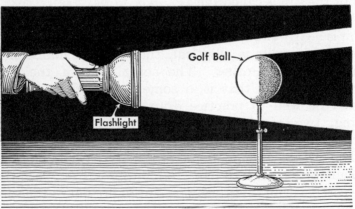

In this experiment you will need to watch carefully to see just how it illustrates the phases of the moon. As the experiment is tried, keep the sun and moon in your mind as you have seen them. Do you usually see the sun at the same time you see the moon? Why?

In all of these experiments with the "sun," "earth," and "moon," keep in mind what kind of energy is being used.

WHAT TO USE: — A darkened room; table; golf ball with support; and a flashlight.

WHAT TO DO: — 1. In the darkened room place the golf ball on its support on a table in front of the class. With the flashlight behind the golf ball, point the flashlight so that the light shines on the ball and toward the class.

2. Keeping the light shining on the golf ball, move the flashlight to the left (counter-clockwise) until it is at the left of the ball and shines on it parallel to the front of the class.

While moving the light, notice how much of the lighted part of the golf ball you can observe — first a narrow crescent and then a half of the ball.

3. Continue moving the flashlight counter-clockwise until it is in front of the class and shines directly on the ball. Again notice how much of the lighted surface is visible.

4. Continue moving the flashlight around the ball, keeping its light falling on the ball until it is at the right of the ball and finally at the place of beginning.

Make a labeled drawing to illustrate each step in the experiment.

WHAT HAPPENS: — 1. What part of the golf ball was lighted? Could you see that part from where you sat? What phase of the moon did this position illustrate?

2. How much of the ball's surface was lighted? Could you see that much or only a smaller portion of it was lighted? What shapes did the lighted portion take? What phase of the moon did this position illustrate?

3. How much of the surface of the ball was now lighted? Could you see all of the lighted surface? What phase of the moon did this position illustrate?

4. Describe what you saw. What phase of the moon did this position illustrate?

CONCLUSION: — How much of the ball's surface was lighted all of the time? Could you see that much of the lighted surface all of the time or only portions? Why?

What is the cause of the apparent change in shape of the moon?

with each other. The varying positions along the horizon of the rising and setting moon are also due to the angle between the planes of the orbits.

Thinking Things Over. — As you think over these facts about the sun and the moon has your mind changed about them in any way? Had you realized how enormous the sun is and how much energy it sends out? More than ever before you must appreciate how living things depend upon the sun. Yet we shall discover still more ways in which the sun is important.

So far your acquaintance with the moon has to do mostly with things that cannot happen on the moon because of lack of air. That makes us realize all the more how important air is on the earth.

The motions of the sun, moon, and earth result in eclipses, but we shall learn that these motions have much greater importance to us than the cause of eclipses.

If you understand thoroughly what you have learned in this topic, you will be more interested in the next topic about the sister planets.

Key Words

atmosphere	illuminate	reflect
eclipse	moon	revolution
ellipse	orbit	rotation
energy	phase	solar system
force	plane	space
gravitation	planet	sun spot
horizon	radiation	telescope

Key Statements

1. The sun is the largest body in our solar system.

2. The planets revolve around the sun in the same direction, all in fixed courses, but at different distances from it.

3. The force of gravity is greater on a large, heavy body than on a small, light one.

4. Directly or indirectly, practically all of the energy used on earth comes from the sun.

5. The sun, the nine known planets, and the many small bodies revolving about the sun make up the solar system.

6. Sun spots are caused by terrific storms in the sun's atmosphere.

7. Radio, Aurora Borealis, and world weather conditions are related to sun spot activity.

8. Moonlight is sunlight reflected by the moon.

9. The moon belongs to and revolves about the earth.

10. The moon is a comparatively small, cold body without an atmosphere.

11. An eclipse of the moon occurs when the earth is directly between the sun and the moon. The shadow of the earth passes over the face of the moon.

12. The shadow of the earth on the moon is circular, which helps to prove that the earth is round.

13. An eclipse of the sun occurs when the moon is directly between the sun and the earth.

14. Eclipses can be predicted many years in advance because scientists know the paths taken by the sun, moon, and earth and how fast they move.

15. The different phases of the moon are due to the different amounts of the moon's lighted portion we see.

16. The four phases of the moon are called new, first quarter, full, and third quarter.

17. The new moon occurs when the moon and sun are in line with the observer, — the sun behind the moon.

The full moon occurs when the sun and moon are opposite each other, — the moon in front and the sun behind the observer.

The first and third quarters occur when the sun and moon are at right angles to each other with reference to the earth.

18. An orbit is the path traveled by a planet or other celestial (heavenly) body around a central object.

Thought Questions

1. What are some of the consequences of the great size and weight of the sun?

2. About how heavy would this book be if the earth were as large as the sun? Or as small as the moon?

3. Explain how the electric energy produced at Niagara Falls or some other waterfall really comes from the sun.

4. If the moon is a "cold" body, how is it that we can see it at night?

5. Does the earth reflect sunlight?   What is your evidence for your answer?

6. Why is the force of gravity less on the moon than on the earth?

7. What would be some of the consequences of no atmosphere on the earth?

8. What causes an eclipse of the moon?   Of the sun?

9. Does the shape of the moon really change?   Explain.

10. What is the difference between "the dark of the moon" and "the old moon in the arms of the new moon"?

Projects for Your Science Discovery Book

1. Make a list of the activities that would be impossible if the earth were as large as the sun, and tell why.

2. List six ways in which you are dependent directly or indirectly upon the energy from the sun.

3. Through a small telescope or powerful field glass observe the moon when it is crescent-shaped and when it is full.   Make drawings of what you see.

4. Observe the phases of the moon over a month's time and record drawings and observations.

5. Learn how to make a pinhole camera to demonstrate the shape of images of bright objects.

Courtesy Mt. Wilson — Palomar Observatories

WINDOW TO THE UNKNOWN

The mighty 200-inch telescope of the Palomar Observatory will reveal unknown wonders in the heavens. What do you think astronomers may expect to find with the new telescope?

Note the two men in the balcony at the left. Their figures give an idea of the size of the Observatory.

The Planets

Soon as the evening shades prevail,
The moon takes up the wondrous tale,
And nightly to the listening earth
Repeats the story of her birth;

While all the stars that round her burn
And all the planets in their turn
Confirm the tidings as they roll,
And spread the truth from pole to pole.
— "Ode" by Joseph Addison

That very law which moulds a tear
And bids it trickle from its source,
That law preserves the earth a sphere,
And guides the planets in their course.
— "On a Tear" by Samuel Rogers

Do you know:

1. How to tell a planet from a star?
2. The names of the planets in our solar system?
3. What a "morning star" is? An "evening star"?
4. What causes the tides?
5. Whether or not there is more than one universe?

General Problem 1. What Are the Family Traits of the Planets?

The Sun's Family. — Anyone who watches the constellations, from night to night, has occasionally discovered a visitor in this or that group. These visitors shine with a clear, steady light in contrast to the twinkle of the surrounding stars, and seem to move

186

across the constellations, sometimes from east to west, sometimes from west to east. Their name, *planet,* comes from an old Greek word meaning "wanderer."

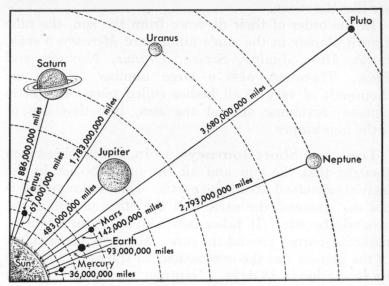

THE SOLAR SYSTEM

How many known planets are there? Which one is nearest to the sun? Which planet do you think is coldest? Do you know which planet is the "earth's twin"? Is there life on Mars?

The real stars of the heavens do not visibly change their positions in relation to each other. That is why they are sometimes called *fixed stars.* The planets, on the other hand, do change their positions in relation to each other and in relation to the stars. The paths (orbits) of the planets are as well known to astronomers as are the orbits of the sun and moon. These men can tell you just when and where you can observe them. Some planets are visible in the summer months, others in other seasons.

Some of the planets look much brighter than the stars, because they are so much nearer and because their sur-

faces are good reflectors of light. All of the planets are
cold bodies and can be seen only because they are illuminated by light from the sun. In this respect the planets
are like the moon.

In the order of their distance from the sun, the nine
known planets in the sun's family are *Mercury, Venus,
Earth, Mars, Jupiter, Saturn, Uranus, Neptune,* and
Pluto. There are also a large number (about one
thousand) of very small bodies called *planetoids* (little
planets) revolving around the sun, but they are of
little importance.

Long and Short Journeys. — In ancient times men
thought that the sun and all the other bodies in the
heavens revolved about the earth. But we know this is
not so. Instead, the earth and the other planets move
around the sun. It takes $365\frac{1}{4}$ days for the earth to
make its journey around the sun. Mercury, the smallest
of the planets and the one nearest to the sun, completes
its revolution in 88 days. Neptune, nearly 2800 million
miles from the sun, requires 165 of our years for one
revolution. In other words, Neptune's year is 165 times
longer than a year on the earth. Pluto, the most recently
discovered planet, requires almost 248 times as long to
make one complete revolution about the sun as does
the earth. These planets are all revolving around the
sun in about the same plane as the earth.

"The Red Planet." — Mars is the planet about
which we hear most. It is about one and one-half times
as far from the sun as the earth, and it takes 687 days for
Mars to revolve once around the sun. This means that
a year on Mars (reckoned in our time) is nearly twice as
long as a year on the earth.

In some respects the earth and Mars are alike. It is
probable that Mars has a thin layer of gases or atmos-

phere. It is known as "The Red Planet" because of the color of light which it sends out. There seems to be plant life on Mars, but just what kind is not definitely known by scientists. Both the earth and Mars are cold bodies, receiving heat and light from the sun. Since Mars is farther from the sun than is the earth, it receives on the average only about as much heat as our polar regions receive. Its surface temperature ranges from 90° F. below zero to about 60° F. above zero. Plant life therefore, if any exists there, must be unlike that of the earth. Since it has less atmosphere than our earth and probably little oxygen or water vapor in it, animal life, if there is any, would also differ from that on earth.

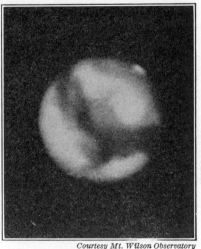

Courtesy Mt. Wilson Observatory

THE PLANET MARS

This view was taken through the 60-inch telescope at Mount Wilson Observatory.

Mars rotates on its axis once in a little more than 24½ hours; so the length of day is not very different from our day. Mars has two moons while our earth has only one.

The King of Planets. — Jupiter is a planet a thousand times larger than the earth. Although Jupiter is 88,392 miles in diameter, it is so far away that it looks like a small star, whereas the moon (2160 miles in diameter), only 240,000 miles away, looks large.

Through a large telescope Jupiter is seen to possess eleven moons which revolve around it as our one moon does about the earth. The moon nearest to Jupiter takes only about eleven hours to make one revolution. Four of these moons can be seen with a small telescope. Galileo discovered them first with his new telescope in 1610.

FIELD RESEARCH:

Secure a small telescope or good field glass. Arrange to steady it on a support. Then when Jupiter is in a good position for observation, try to discover the four moons that Galileo saw.

There is evidence that Jupiter has a dense, deep atmosphere, full of yellow and red clouds. The atmosphere is different in composition from ours in that it contains ammonia and methane. You are familiar with ammonia, as it is used for household cleaning. Methane is a gas that is sometimes formed by decay of vegetation under water. It is given off as bubbles when the mud at the bottom of the pond is disturbed.

For a long time astronomers thought Jupiter was hot; but we now know it is cold. Its surface temperature is about 200° F. below zero. Like the other planets it shines by light which it reflects from the sun.

An interesting fact about Jupiter is that its diameter from pole to pole is nearly six thousand miles shorter than its diameter through the equator.

The flattening of the earth, and of Jupiter, is thought to be due to their whirling motion when they were in a molten state.

The earth, you remember, is 26 miles longer through the equator than through its poles. Jupiter rotates much faster than the earth, once in a little less than ten hours, or about twice while the earth is rotating only once.

Venus. — Venus, the planet nearest to the earth, is a globe about the size of the earth, completely enveloped in fleecy clouds.   It is nearer the sun than the earth, being only about 67,000,000 miles from the sun.   We rarely see it overhead in the night sky, for it never gets very far from the sun.   It appears at twilight in the western sky, or just before dawn in the eastern sky.

American Museum of Natural History

TRACKS ACROSS THE SKY

This photograph was made by pointing a camera toward the moon and letting it stay open for a long time.   The broader track is caused by the moon.   The finer trail above was made by the planet Venus.   These trails show the paths of the two bodies.

When, in its orbit, it is on the same side of the sun as the earth, and nearer to the earth, it shines with great brilliancy.   It is so bright that at times it can be seen for a while even after sunrise, or before sundown.   This was true in the latter part of September, 1940, when it was visible near the old crescent moon for about a half hour after the red sun rose above the horizon.

Alike as Venus and the earth are, their atmospheres are very unlike.   Water and oxygen, so necessary to earthborn creatures, are very rare on Venus. That fact seems to prove that there is no vegetation there, since it is earth's vegetation that supplies oxygen to earth-atmosphere.

Morning and Evening "Stars." — Parading ahead to herald the rising sun, Venus is a sight well worth our getting out before sunup to see. At certain seasons this beautiful planet can be seen leading the sun across the sky. It disappears below the horizon before the sun gets there and reappears ahead of the sun the next morning.

Then the scene changes and Venus follows the sun across the sky and can be seen as the Evening Star soon after sunset. But Venus appears to lose a little in the race every day and so sets later and later after the sun until it becomes a Morning Star again.

Reference to the diagram, page 193, will help you to understand this interesting result. Because Venus is revolving about the sun inside the orbit of the earth, we see it part of the time to the right of the sun, that is, west of the sun. From the earth it seems to precede the sun in its path. Thus it rises ahead of the sun and is a Morning Star. However, a little later Venus appears to the left of the sun, that is, east of the sun. Then it seems to follow the sun and hence sets later than the sun. It is then the Evening Star.

Mercury. — There is another Evening Star which may be seen in the spring, very soon after sunset. It is Mercury, the planet closest to the sun. Mercury is so near to the sun that it is only seen near the horizon soon after the sun sets or just before the sun is up in the morning. In February of 1940 Mercury led Venus, Jupiter, Saturn, and Mars in a sky parade not seen before for many hundreds of years. Perhaps you saw the

Sky Parade of the Planets that year as they formed into line and followed the sun below the horizon. Because of its nearness to the sun, the Greeks believed that Mercury was a close friend of Apollo, the sun-god.

Mercury is considerably smaller than the earth, about the size of the moon. Because of its nearness to the sun and lack of atmosphere, it would be an uncomfortably hot place in which to live. It turns on its axis at about the same rate of speed that it moves around the sun, so that the same side is always exposed to the sun's heat.

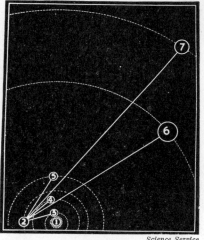

Science Service

SKY PARADE

This diagram shows the positions of the planets in February, 1940. No. 1 represents the Sun; no. 2 the Earth. To an observer on the Earth, the planets were then lined up in this order: nearest the horizon no. 3 (Mercury); above Mercury no. 6 (Jupiter); then no. 4 (Venus); no. 7 (Saturn); and no. 5 (Mars). Which planet was the last to set that night?

Saturn, the Ringed Plant. — One of the most beautiful sights of the heavens through a telescope is Saturn with its famous rings. Saturn is about ten times larger than our earth and about as heavy as an equal volume of cork.

There are three rings around Saturn that make it look so different from the other planets. The middle ring is estimated to be about 16,000 miles wide, while the outside rings are about 10,000 miles wide. But these rings that look flat and thin are really made up of vast numbers of small moons revolving like lines of marching men around the planet. Besides the countless little moons of the rings, Saturn has ten regular moons, whereas our earth has only one.

It takes Saturn about twenty-nine times as long as the earth to make one revolution. And sometimes during that journey the planet is tipped so we see the rings on edge. Most of the time, however, we can see the surface of the rings.

Courtesy Yerkes Observatory

URANUS AND ITS FIVE MOONS

The fifth moon of Uranus, "Miranda," was discovered in 1948. It is the faintest of the five moons here and nearest Uranus. Are scientists sure that all the moons of all the planets have been discovered?

While a year on Saturn is about twenty-nine times as long as a year on earth, day and night are much shorter because Saturn turns on its axis once in about ten hours instead of our twenty-four hours.

Is there life on Saturn? Saturn is more than 880,000,000 miles from the sun. The earth, you know, is only about 93,000,000 miles from the sun. How cold do you think it would be on a planet that is nearly ten times farther from the sun than the earth?

Pluto. — The planet Pluto, the most recent addition to the solar family, was discovered in March, 1930. Its existence and position, however, had been predicted fifteen years earlier by Professor Percival Lowell of the Flagstaff Observatory, Arizona.

Pluto is nearly forty times as far from the sun as is the earth. It is so far away from the earth that it takes from four to five hours for its light to reach us. It requires almost 248 of our years for Pluto to make one revolution about the sun. In size Pluto is thought to be like Mercury.

The story of the discovery of Pluto is similar in many respects to the discovery of the planet Neptune many years previously. About a hundred years ago the planet Uranus was thought to be the most distant planet of the sun's family. However, astronomers and mathematicians knew the paths planets should take as determined from their size, weight, distance from the sun, and other properties. They found that Uranus, for some reason or other, did not move in the particular path they thought it should. Two young mathematicians and astronomers decided there must be another planet outside of Uranus which exerted gravitational forces upon Uranus, causing it to move in a different path than it would otherwise. Therefore, they assumed the presence of such a planet and calculated where it would be. Later the planet Neptune was discovered almost exactly where these young mathematicians had predicted.

However, even the existence of Neptune and the effects of its gravitational force were not enough to explain entirely why Uranus did not travel the path that it should. This led Professor Lowell to assume another planet still farther from the sun than Neptune, and he calculated its position and how it would move. His calculations resulted in the discovery of Pluto.

The discovery of these two planets after their prediction by scientists is an excellent example of the way in which scientists work in making new discoveries. Based on the motions of the planets already known, it depended on the laws of gravitation. It is striking evidence of the accuracy of the method of science.

Merry-Go-Round. — The rising and setting of the sun and the rising and setting of the moon are events of

such common observation as to require no discussion, if
it were not for the fact that their motion is apparent
rather than real.   Have you ever had the experience on a
train or automobile of thinking that a nearby car was

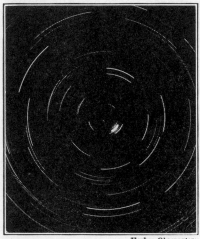

THE MERRY-GO-ROUND

This photograph was made by pointing a camera toward the North Star
and leaving the lens open. The camera
moving with the earth's rotation caused
each star to leave a trail on the film.
About how long was the camera lens
open?

moving when all the time
the movement was that of
your own car?   In much
the same way we can understand the *apparent* movement of the sun, the stars,
the moon, and the planets
from east to west in our
sky.

The earth *rotates* (*turns*)
on its axis from west to east.
Hence an object in the sky
that is comparatively stationary in the sky pattern
is seen first at the point
where the earth and sky
seem to meet in the east.
As the earth continues to
turn toward the east, the
horizon line, where the sky
and earth seem to meet,
changes, and the object appears to move upward through
the sky, until it reaches a position directly overhead.
As the earth turns still farther, the object appears to
move closer to the western horizon.   Consequently the
sun and the moon appear to move, when actually it is
the earth which moves and thus causes the march of these
objects across our sky.

For the same reason, the stars at night appear to rise
above our eastern horizon and march across the sky
finally to sink below the western horizon.   But it is only

an apparent motion, since the earth during our night completes its rotation about its axis.

Planets, being in almost the same plane with the sun and the moon, appear to rise nearly in the same position on the horizon as do the sun and the moon, and they take nearly the same paths across the sky, setting at the western horizon. The stars each have their own parallel paths across our sky. Some, as you know, are above the northern horizon all the time. Of course another lot of stars have their paths above the southern horizon and are seen by people living south of the equator.

FIELD RESEARCH:

Over a period of several months keep track of the place on the horizon where the sun and the moon rise or set. Then try to explain. They do not rise and set at the same places on the horizon at different seasons.

Catching Up with the Moon. — You have learned that the moon not only turns on its own axis, but that it also revolves about the earth from west to east. Therefore, the apparent speed of the moon (which is due principally to the rotation of the earth) is different from that of the stars or the sun, for they do not revolve directly around the earth.

The stars rise about four minutes (exactly 3 minutes 56 seconds) *earlier* each night, while the moon rises about fifty minutes *later* each night. It takes twenty-four hours plus that fifty minutes for an observer at a given place on the earth to catch up with the moon and see it again at the eastern horizon. It is, therefore, fifty minutes later by the clock each night when the moon rises.

FIELD RESEARCH:

Note the times given on a calendar for the rising of the moon each night and compare with your own observations.

General Problem 2. Are There Other Worlds than Ours?

A Task for Your Imagination. — How far will your imagination reach? Are you satisfied to think of our own solar system with its planets or would you like to think on and on and out still farther beyond them into space?

Yerkes Observatory

STARS BEYOND OUR GALAXY

Far out beyond our own galaxy are other clusters or galaxies of giant suns. This is a picture of the galaxy found in the constellation Hercules. Thousands of other galaxies are believed to exist in space.

The stars that you see are suns, many of them thousands of times larger than our sun. Scientists believe that all these suns and many more, too, form a great group, shaped like a huge lens, or perhaps like a wagon wheel, with most of the stars out near the rim. This group of stars, or island universe, is called a galaxy. The diameter of our galaxy is possibly about 200,000 light years and its thickness is about 100,000 light years. If you recall that one light year is almost six trillion miles, it will help you understand better how huge our galaxy is. These dimensions are approximate only, since thus far it has been impossible to measure them accurately. *A galaxy is a great system of suns having an orderly motion and development.*

Our galaxy, whose outer rim is the Milky Way, is thought to be rotating like a great wheel once in about 240,000,000 years. It may contain several hundred thousand million stars. One of these stars is our sun, which is perhaps a third or more of the distance from the hub to the rim of the wheel. On this basis our sun with its family of planets is traveling about 200 miles per second in its journey through space.

But this wheel-shaped system of stars is not the only galaxy. Far out in space, almost beyond the power of the most powerful telescope, are other galaxies. So far away are these other galaxies or star clusters that they look like dim clouds of light, and hence were called *nebulae*, a Latin word meaning "clouds." Beginning as revolving balls of gases, they flung out long wisps or streamers which broke up into thousands of sparkling objects called stars.

The brightest of our neighboring galaxies, the great *Andromeda nebula*, can be seen without a telescope. On a clear moonless night this nebula can be seen by the naked eye if one knows just where to look. It was long considered to be a mass of gas among the stars. Now the astronomers have evidence tending to prove that it is not a mass of gas but a galaxy, 800,000 light years away, and 40,000 light years from side to side. It is similar to our own galaxy in size and grouping of suns. Such thoughts are like stepping out into space and looking back at our own starry system. Where does it all end? No one can say, but it is an interesting task for your imagination. The new 200-inch telescope will disclose new facts about the universe.

General Problem 3. How Has It All Happened?

Theories Change. — The past history of the stars can be inferred only from happenings of the present. As a science pupil you are learning to distinguish fact from theories or guesses. As scientists discover new facts, they often have to change their opinion or theory about the thing they are studying. You, too, must be ready to change your opinions as new facts are learned. As scientific instruments are improved and new ones invented, new facts are discovered.

The use of a very recent invention, *radar*, may soon lead to new facts about the moon, the planets, and possibly the stars and our galaxy. Early in 1946 the United States Army used this instrument successfully in making a contact with the moon. Some scientists believe that radar may become a tool as important as the telescope in astronomy. This new use of radar may change some of our theories about the universe.

An Orderly Development. — In a sense, astronomers are viewing the past from today since the light reaching us today from far-off bodies really started on its way hundreds, thousands, even millions of years ago.

Just as nature's activities today proceed with systematic order that may be expressed as laws, so it is thought that there has always been an orderly development throughout the ages. If this is true, it enables us to reason out the happenings of the past by means of our knowledge of the happenings of today.

To tell the story of the beginning of the universe and its development in a few simple sentences is like trying to paint a great picture with one color or one line. All details and supporting evidence must be omitted. However, as you go on with your study of science you may find the evidence and detail for yourself. Perhaps you will discover the divine guidance in it all.

A SPIRAL NEBULA *Courtesy Mt. Wilson Observatory*

This vast mass of stars looks like a giant pinwheel. Because the streamers spiral out from the center, it is called a spiral nebula. It is another family of suns, a galaxy far out in space.

A Developing Universe.[1] — From the many facts that are known today it may be assumed that the material of all the universe was once a mass of rotating gas, uniformly scattered through space, thousands of millions of light years in diameter. The rate of motion changed,

---

[1] Much of this discussion is based on a lecture, "An Evolving Universe," by Sir James Jeans, published in the *Report of the Smithsonian Institution*, 1931.

which may have resulted in the formation and separation of millions of nebulae at great distances from each other. These nebulae, starting out like fluffy balls of gas, end up as clusters of stars or galaxies. It is known that some 2,000,000 galaxies exist within a distance from the earth of about 140,000,000 light years. Each galaxy seems to be similar in many ways to the nebula in Andromeda and to the galaxy of which our sun is a part.

Sir James Jeans gives our imagination a help to picture this huge array:

"To construct a model, we may take 300 tons of apples and space them at about 10 yards apart, thus filling a sphere of about a mile diameter. This sphere is the range of vision of the 100-inch telescope; each apple is a nebula containing matter enough for the creation of several thousand million stars like our sun; and each atom in each apple is the size of a solar system with a diameter equal to or slightly larger than that of the earth's orbit."

Changing speeds of motions and other forces may have caused a rotating nebula to form with spiral arms thrown out from the central mass. Parts of these arms perhaps formed stars or suns. Possibly our own sun reproduced on a smaller scale the great nebula and in turn threw out arms of gas which broke up into parts which later became the planets and moons.

General Problem 4. What Holds the Universe Together?

Universal Gravitation. — Each one of the billion or more suns has a particular place in its own galaxy and has some relation to all the other suns in that family.

Out beyond, each galaxy has its place and function in a universe which has been described mainly from theories.

The rules which produce this law and order in the universe have been recognized for many, many years by scientists. Early scientists knew that a stone falls to the earth because there is a *force of attraction* between the earth and a falling stone, and that unless they are held apart by some equal or greater force they will come together. You know that to be true from your own experiences.

Archimedes knew this fact, and Galileo knew it. In fact Galileo made a special study of falling bodies and learned that all bodies, large and small, fall at the same rate of speed for each second of time. He found, too, that they fall faster and faster each second. The farther they fall, the faster they fall.

Sir Isaac Newton went much farther in his studies of gravitation and proved to other scientists by means of mathematics and physics that the attraction which the earth has for the stone is a *universal attraction*. By that he meant *every body in the universe attracts every other body.* This is called *Newton's law of universal gravitation.*

All of the suns have an attraction or a pulling force for each other. Our sun has an attraction for our earth and all the other planets, and our earth and all the other planets have an attraction for their moons.

Holding the Earth in Place. — You are now ready to find out how it is that this earth of ours and all the other planets maintain their positions in space while they travel in their orbits about the sun.

To help you to understand the tremendous forces that hold the planets in their orbits, think of what is happening in the drawing on the next page. When you tie an apple to a string and whirl it about your head, you know that as long as the string does not break the apple will continue in its circular motion about your head as a center; but once it does break, the apple will fly off in a straight line.

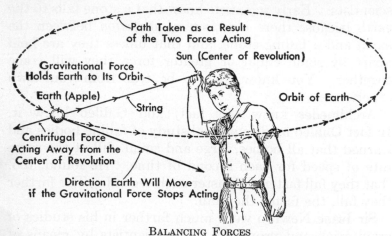

BALANCING FORCES

Have you ever tried this experiment? Tell how the forces illustrated here work opposite each other to keep the earth in its orbit.

In the same manner mud flies from the wheel of a rapidly moving automobile or bicycle. The mud sticks to a slow-moving wheel, and so long as the "sticking" force is greater than the "throwing" force the mud will stay on the wheel. But as the wheel goes faster, the force which tends to throw the mud from the wheel increases and the mud will fly off. The fact that the earth is revolving about the sun gives it a tendency to fly away from the sun just as the mud flies from the rotating wheel.

This force acting away from the center of a rotating body is known as centrifugal force. An opposite force acting towards the center (like gravitation) is known as centripetal force. The earth, revolving around the sun, is therefore acted upon by two balancing forces: one, *gravitation*, tending to pull the earth and the sun together, and the other, the *centrifugal force*, tending to force the earth farther away from the sun. Because these forces are balanced, the earth maintains its position in its orbit.

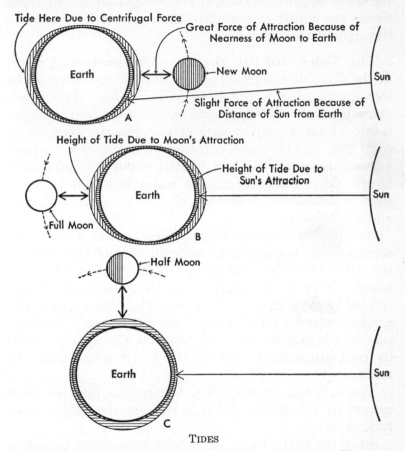

TIDES

A. Both the sun and moon are causing tides on the earth. The moon, being nearer, produces the greater effect.

B. Although on opposite sides of the earth, the moon and sun are still working together to produce the tide shown.

C. The moon and sun are pulling at right angles "against" each other. Note that the tide caused by the moon is greater than that caused by the sun.

Explain why the forces of the sun and moon are added together in B. Why don't they, being on opposite sides of the earth, balance each other?

All the other planets are also held in their places by a balancing of these two forces. Not only are the planets of our solar system held in their orbits by the balance of the force of gravitation and centrifugal force, but these forces are acting to maintain the same orderly balance throughout the universe.

The Tides and the Moon. — One interesting result of the force of attraction and of centrifugal force is the movement of the water in ocean *tides*. The moon attracts and actually pulls the water of the ocean nearest it into a kind of heap or wave crest. See the diagram on page 205. As the earth turns on its axis this wave crest follows the moon but lags behind about 200 miles each hour. Of course, heaping the water in one place must make it shallower in another, and so we have *high tides* and *low tides*.

Another curious fact about tides is that a high tide occurs in the ocean on the opposite side of the earth at the same time that one occurs on the side toward the moon. This is due to the fact that the water, being farther away, is not attracted as much as the earth. The earth is actually pulled away from the water. The high tide on the side far from the moon is also partly caused by centrifugal force pushing the water away from the earth.

The sun, too, causes tides, but not as high as those caused by the moon. That is because the sun is much farther away.

Since the earth turns on its axis once every 24 hours, a high tide occurs at a given place on any ocean about every 12 hours and each high tide at that place is followed by a low tide 6 hours later.

Thinking Things Over. — Can you now appreciate the gigantic scale on which our wonderful solar system is built?   And yet you must not forget that the distances of our planets from each other and from the sun are very small when we consider the distances to other suns in our galaxy.   For example, you have read that Alpha Centauri is over four light years away and that the North Star is four hundred sixty-five light years away. Many suns are hundreds, even thousands, of light years away.   The nebula in Andromeda is nearly one million light years distant.

Your study of our solar system and the billion other suns of our galaxy and of galaxies out beyond reveals to you a law and order in nature almost beyond human under-standing.   As a student of science you value facts and so should develop power to understand this gigantic universe of which

THE NEBULA IN ANDROMEDA

This is one of the two largest and brightest nebulae in the heavens.   The other is the nebula in Orion.

our earth is such a little part.   Small as we humans are, we possess that which is greater, more wonderful, and more difficult to understand than all else in the universe, — minds with which to think, wills to direct our actions, and souls to appreciate the grandeur of the universe.   With all this as a background we can appreciate and understand more than ever before how living things must adapt themselves to life in the solar system, and why our world is probably the only planet to support life as we know it.

Key Words

centrifugal force	Mars	planet
centripetal force	Mercury	Saturn
elliptical	nebula	solar system
galaxy	Neptune	tide
Galileo	Newton	universe
gravitation	orbit	Venus
Jupiter		

define,

tell what

he did

Key Statements

1. The nine known major planets are, in order of distances from the sun, Mercury, Venus, Earth, Mars, Jupiter, Saturn, Uranus, Neptune, and Pluto.

2. Planets change their positions with respect to the stars, but nevertheless follow true courses.

3. The rising, the moving across the sky from east to west, and the setting of the heavenly bodies are apparent rather than real movements. The apparent movement is due to the rotation of the earth from west to east.

4. Celestial bodies are held in their paths by a balancing of the forces of motion and of gravitation.

5. Our sun and the billion or more other suns are parts of a great group of stars called a galaxy.

6. Our galaxy is thought to rotate once in about 240,000,000 years.

7. The nebula of Andromeda is an example of a galaxy beyond our own galaxy.

8. The universe is thought to consist of millions of galaxies in various states of development.

9. Newton discovered the Law of Universal Gravitation: every body in the universe attracts every other body in the universe.

10. Tides are caused by the force of attraction between the moon and the earth and between the sun and the earth.

Thought Questions

1. How can you tell a planet from a star?

2. Does the sun rise, move across the heavens, and set? Explain.

3. The sun is a fixed star, yet its movements across our sky are, in general, like those of the planets. Explain this similarity.

4. What is meant by Newton's Law of Universal Gravitation? What relation has universal gravitation to you?

5. Why is it that high tides and low tides occur with great regularity?

6. Do high tides in any one locality differ in height? Do they differ from one time to another? Explain.

7. What might happen if the forces of nature became unbalanced?

8. Using your ideas of centrifugal force, can you give a more complete explanation of tides?

Projects for Your Science Discovery Book

1. Make diagrams to illustrate the positions of the earth and the moon during high and low tides. There is a time of year when high tides are higher than at other times. How is it explained?

2. Make a list of the names of men and women who have contributed largely to our theories of the development of the universe.

3. Write a story of Copernicus and how his theory differed from that of earlier philosophers.

4. Construct a telescope and try to discover the moons of Jupiter.

5. If you ever listen to a broadcast telling about "space ships" or other means of travel to other planets, try to separate the facts from the fiction.

6. Show how the work of Galileo and that of Newton were endeavors to find the truth.

7. Look up and read American Indian legends relating to the sun and planets.

8. Investigate, through library references, theories concerning life on Mars.

SOMETHING NEW UNDER THE SUN

Scientists have discovered a new use for the huge amount of energy given off by the sun. This experimental house uses the sun as its only source of heat. Notice the large windows. In which direction do you think they face? Would a sun-heated house be practical in all parts of our country?

TOPIC VIII

Living in the Solar System

*And God said, Let there be lights in the
firmament of the heaven to divide the day
from the night; and let them be for signs,
and for seasons, and for days, and years.*

— Genesis 1:14

Do you know:

1. What causes summer and winter?
2. Why there is no winter near the equator except on high mountains?
3. What causes equal day and night?
4. How plants and animals know that the seasons change?
5. Why there is practically no twilight in the tropics?

General Problem 1. How Does the Earth Move?

Revolution and Rotation. — "Revolution" and
"rotation" — do these words mean endless journeys to
you? Our "air space ship" is the earth that hurries
us along around the sun at the rate of about thirty-five
thousand miles every hour. That speed is beyond our
comprehension. Moreover our "air space ship" itself
is turning round and round on its axis once in twenty-
four hours, adding almost another 1000 miles an hour to
our speed. Thus there are two motions — round and
round the axis of the earth called *rotation,* and round
and round the sun called *revolution.*

211

Our earth is not alone in its journey around the sun. There are known to be at least eight other great bodies or planets revolving about the sun in the same direction as the earth. Mercury and Venus have orbits or paths inside that of the earth. Mars, Jupiter, Saturn, Uranus, Neptune, and Pluto travel in circles out beyond the earth.

The revolution of all the planets about the sun is from *west to east*. Imagine yourself looking down upon our great solar system from the North Star. You would see the sun at the center and the planets revolving about the sun in nearly circular paths in a direction opposite to that of the hands of the clock.

If you could look at the earth with a sufficiently powerful telescope from the position of the North Star, you would see it also turning *counter-clockwise*, that is, from west to east. Mars, Saturn, and Jupiter rotate in the same direction as the earth. Uranus rotates in the opposite direction. The rotations of the other planets are not yet positively known.

The Earth's Axis. — A wagon wheel turns about the axle. The axle (axis) of the earth is imaginary. However, the earth turns just as though it had a real axis. You may think of the earth as a spinning top. But it will be different from a real top. If a top is set spinning on a table, its axis will be straight up and down, that is, perpendicular to the table. The top also may spin in just one place on the table. The earth on the other hand spins with its axis at a slant and moves in a great, nearly circular path. The earth, therefore, has two motions — rotation and revolution.

You know that a flat surface like the table top is called a *plane*. The flat surface marked off by the path or orbit of the earth is the plane of the earth's orbit.

The imaginary axis of the earth is inclined (tilted) at an angle of 23.5° away from the perpendicular. It is tipped so that it forms a straight line pointing to the North Star. To illustrate the slant of the axis to the plane of the orbit, first hold a pencil straight up and down on a table top. This position is called perpendicular. Now hold the pencil at an angle to the table. It will then be inclined. Study the diagram on this page.

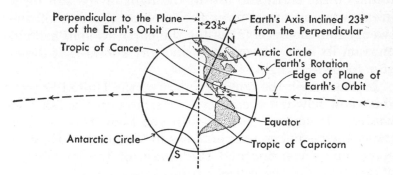

THE EARTH AND ITS ORBIT

If the earth's axis were straight up and down, it would take the position represented by the vertical dotted line.
What are the effects of the inclination of the earth's axis?
What two motions of the earth are shown here?

In the diagram on page 215, Drawing 1 represents the earth with the north end of its axis tilted (inclined) toward the sun. Drawing 2 represents the earth with the north end of the axis inclined away from the sun. Drawing 3-4 represents the earth with its axis at right angles to the sun's rays. Drawing 5 represents the earth as if its axis were inclined 47° away from the vertical. Whatever the position of the earth in its journey around the sun, you must remember that the axis of the earth points always in one direction — toward the North Star.

General Problem 2.   Why Does the Length of Day and Night Vary?

The Effect of Rotation. — As you ride round and round on the earth you are in the light of the sun for a few hours and away from the sun for the rest of the twenty-four hours it takes for the earth to spin around once on its axis.   Every boy and girl knows that darkness follows daylight.

If you live in the northern part of the United States, you know how much earlier it gets dark in the fall and winter.   If you live in the south you know this too, but the change is not so noticeable as in the north.   How all of us long for spring and the return of the long hours of daylight and the warmer sun!

The cause of the change from daylight to darkness is, as you know, the turning of the earth on its axis — rotation.   But do you know why some days are long and some are short?   Let us try to find the answer.   It has to do with the slanting of the earth's axis.

Long and Short Days and Nights. — If the axis of the earth were perpendicular to the plane of the earth's orbit, the length of day and of night would be equal all over the earth at all times of the year.   But since the earth's axis is inclined 23.5° from the perpendicular, a shortening or lengthening of day and night is caused at different seasons, except at the equator.

When the north end of the axis is inclined *toward the sun*, as in Drawing 1, page 215, the days in the northern hemisphere are longer than the nights.   You can tell

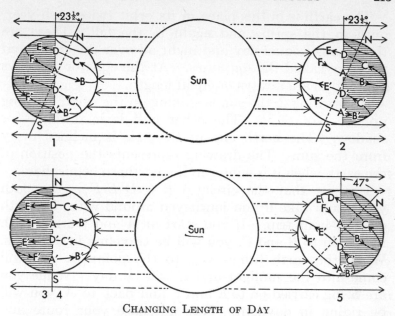

CHANGING LENGTH OF DAY

Diagram 1 represents the earth in its summer position; 2, the winter position; 3 and 4, spring and fall.

Diagram 5 represents what would happen if the earth's axis were tipped at 47 degrees instead of 23½ degrees.

In which diagram (1, 2, 3, or 4) are days longest in the northern hemisphere? What season is this?

Which diagram shows shortest days north of the equator? What season is this?

Where on the earth are days and nights always of equal length?

this is so if you will trace the part of the circle *A–F* that is in the light and compare this with the part in darkness. When the north end of the axis is inclined *away from the sun*, as in Drawing 2, the days in the northern hemisphere are short and the nights are long. When the axis points neither toward nor away from the sun, as in Drawing 3–4, the days and nights are of equal length all over the earth. Riding on the circle from *A* to *D*, one would be in sunshine, and that part of the journey is just the same as from *D* through *E* and *F* to *A*.

The earth is in this place in its orbit twice each year, once in the spring and again in the fall. These are the times of equal day and night all over the earth, and they are called the *equinoxes*. At the equator the days and nights are always of equal length.

In Drawing 2, the sun is shining on the earth, lighting up one half of it. The other half is in darkness or shadow. The north end of the axis is inclined away from the sun. The drawing represents the position of the earth when it is winter in the northern hemisphere.

Imagine that the circle *A–B–C–D–E–F* is the path you would take if you journeyed around with the earth on a 24-hour trip. If you start at *A* and journey with the earth to *B* and *C*, you will be traveling in darkness. When the earth brings you to the point *D*, you will come into the sunlight and it will be day. While you are being carried on to *E* and *F* and back to *A*, you will be riding in daylight. Now measure your route and see how much more of it was in darkness than daylight.

On the same drawing trace a ride represented by a circle in the southern hemisphere. Will the daylight part of the ride be longer than the night? On the equator you would spend just 12 hours in daylight and 12 hours in night.

The difference in the lengths of day and night increases as one travels from the equator toward either pole. For this reason when it is winter in the northern hemisphere, the *north pole* of the earth has night for six months and *south pole* has day for those same six months. When it is summer in the northern hemisphere, the north pole has a six months' day.

Wherever you live, north or south of the equator, once a year you have the "longest day" and "shortest night," and about six months later you have the shortest day and longest night. How many hours long these will be depends upon how far north or south of the equator you live.

In the northern hemisphere the longest day is about June 21, when the earth's axis is slanted most toward the sun, and the shortest day is about December 21, when the axis is slanted most away from the sun.

The six-month night at the north or south pole is not six months of absolute darkness. The twilight and the moon give some light to the polar regions except for about three weeks.

Twilight is caused by the scattering (diffusing) of the sun's rays by dust and moisture in the air. After the sun sets, some diffused light finds its way out over the part of the earth turning from the sun. At the equator twilight is very short, while at the poles it is nearly six months long. (Do you think there can be a twilight on the moon? Why?)

Perhaps you can understand why the lengths of day and night vary by studying the drawings on page 215. However, Experiment 17 will help you to prove the cause of unequal day and night.

General Problem 3. What Causes the Seasons?

Four Seasons. — The revolution of the earth about the sun together with the inclination of its axis causes the change of seasons. To understand the change of the seasons it is necessary to study the transfer of heat from one body to another. We must do this because the change of seasons is due to the way heating rays from the sun strike the earth.

EXPERIMENT 17

What causes unequal lengths of day and night?

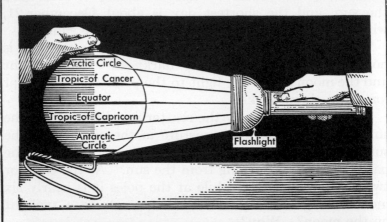

What form of energy is made use of in this experiment? What is its source? In this experiment, as in others for studying the earth, sun, and moon, the sizes of objects do not give an accurate representation of the real things, but with the flashlight and globe you can illustrate the positions of the earth that cause unequal lengths of day and night through the seasons.

In the diagram the rays of light are shown spreading. This is because of the limitation of drawing. Actually the rays from the sun striking the earth are practically parallel.

WHAT TO USE: — A six- or eight-inch slate globe on an axis; a flashlight; and a darkened room.

WHAT TO DO: — 1. Draw a circle on the globe to represent the equator, and parallel circles north and south of the equator to represent the Arctic and Antarctic circles and the tropics of Cancer and Capricorn.

2. Hold the globe in front of the class with the axis in a vertical position. Holding the flashlight in the center of the room, turn the light toward the globe. Rotate the globe slowly and observe how much of each circle is in the light and how much in darkness during one complete turn. Do all places on the earth under this condition have equal day and night?

3. Hold the globe at the side of the room to the right of the class with the axis inclined about 23.5° from the perpendicular and away from the class. Turn the beam of light on the globe. Rotate the globe and, as before, observe the proportion of each circle that is in daylight and in darkness during a complete turn. Notice if the equator circle is equally divided by light and darkness.

WHAT HAPPENS: — 1. How many degrees from the equator should each of these circles be drawn to truly represent those on a map?

2. What proportion of each circle was lighted? (Half, more than half, or less than half.) Were one or more of the circles equally divided by light and darkness? Which ones?

3. What part of each circle was lighted? (Half, more than half, or less than half.) Was any circle equally divided by light and darkness? Which one?

CONCLUSION: — What is the effect of the inclination of the earth's axis on the lengths of day and night?

APPLICATION: — Would the differences between day and night be greater or less if the axis were inclined more than 23.5° from the perpendicular?

When energy leaves a hot body, it goes out in all directions in straight lines like light rays. The energy is said to be *radiated* (page 164). You know that if you are facing a fireplace, the energy radiating from it strikes

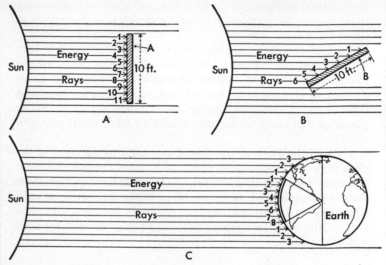

WHY DIRECT RAYS ARE HOTTER THAN SLANTING RAYS

How many heating rays strike the block A? block B? After studying these diagrams can you explain why slanting rays are not as warm as direct rays?

you in front but does not warm your back. If you would warm your back, you must turn it towards the fire. In the same way, only that part of the earth which faces the sun is able to absorb its rays of energy, and be warmed by them. When some energy rays are absorbed by a substance, heat is formed. So we may speak of the energy rays which are thus absorbed as heating rays. Remember that only energy rays which reach the earth can heat it.

While heating rays actually go out in all directions from the sun, we are interested only in the parallel heating rays which strike the earth. The sun is so far away that all the rays that reach us are practically parallel, that is, going in the same direction.

If you hold your hand broadside to a hot body, more heating rays will strike it than if you hold it edgewise, and you will feel more heat. To picture this condition we can use lines as shown in the diagrams on page 220. When block *A* is upright, eleven of the parallel heating rays strike it, but if it is tipped as in *B*, only six rays strike it in spite of the fact that the block is the same length in both cases; only its position has been changed. In other words, more heating rays strike an object when it is held broadside or perpendicular to the rays, than when it is held either edgewise or in a slanting position.

In part *C* of the diagram equal lengths of the earth's surface are marked off to show that more lines of heating rays are intercepted by that part of the earth most nearly perpendicular to them than by any other part of the earth.

You know that the earth receives energy from the sun. You also know that changes in the amount of energy received by any part of the earth result in a change of temperature for that part. And you know that the change from summer to winter temperatures and from winter to summer temperatures is gradual and slow. About six months is required for either change.

The different seasons, then, are caused by gradual changes in temperature of any one part of the earth. Another important fact about the seasons is that they follow one another in an orderly sequence. The change of the seasons, therefore, must be due to orderly processes causing regular changes in the *amount of heat* the earth receives from the sun. Our problem, then, is to determine what causes these variations in the amount of heat received by the earth under different conditions.

We should discover also why the seasons always come in the same order.

Experiment 18, if carefully followed, will help you to understand what causes the changes in temperatures about which you have been reading.

BARE BRANCHES

Seasons result from the varying number of daylight hours and the varying degree of directness with which the sun's rays strike the earth.

The following brief statements about the change of seasons should be easily understood by you, after you have tried the experiment.

When the earth is in position *A*, the northern hemisphere is inclined 23.5° away from the sun. The sun's rays, therefore, strike the northern hemisphere in a slanting direction, and so the northern hemisphere receives less heat than where the rays are more direct.

When the earth is in the opposite position in its orbit, as at *C*, the northern hemisphere is inclined 23.5° toward the sun. The northern hemisphere now receives more direct or perpendicular rays of the sun and is warmer than when it received the slanting rays.

When the northern hemisphere is slanted away from the sun, it is winter in the northern hemisphere and summer in the southern hemisphere. When the north

FOLIAGE AND FRUIT

After the more direct rays of the sun have sent increasing warmth and energy to the winter earth for a period, summer appears.

end of the earth's axis slants toward the sun, it is summer in the northern hemisphere and winter in the southern. Between the two extreme positions the earth moves to positions resulting in spring and fall. The seasons follow one another gradually and with unfailing regularity.

When asked the cause of summer, some people who have not studied science say it is because the earth is nearer the sun. As a matter of fact that is not true. When it is summer in the northern hemisphere, the earth is actually about 3,000,000 miles farther from the

KEY EXPERIMENT 18

What causes the changes of seasons?

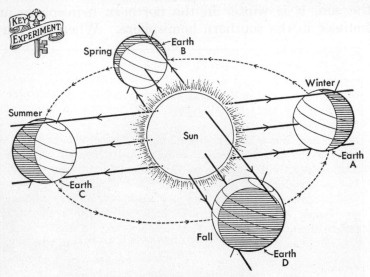

Why do you think this experiment is called a "Key" Experiment? Is it because it is important for each of us to understand what causes the changes in season?

In this experiment we shall use light energy to make things visible, but it is really heat energy that has to do with changes in seasons. Keep this fact in mind. Also, you will remember that sizes and distances are not as they really are in the solar system. Therefore, we shall be able to illustrate only the principles involved. One principle to keep in mind is that energy rays heat a surface more if they strike it at right angles than if at a slant. Another fact to keep in mind is that the axis of the earth always points in the same direction — toward the North Star.

We understand that the change of seasons is due to changes in the amount of heat the earth receives from the sun; so our problem is to demonstrate why the amount of heat does change from time to time.

WHAT TO USE: — A small mounted globe and a frame of three parallel wires to represent heating rays; an object to represent the sun.

WHAT TO DO: — 1. Set the globe so that the axis is perpendicular to the wires representing heating rays, and so that rays (wires) reach each pole, but with the axis inclined 23.5° away from the vertical toward the north as in *D*. Slowly turn the globe one complete turn.

2. Set the globe so that the axis is inclined 23.5° away from the vertical and so that the north end of the axis leans *away from* the top heating ray as in *A*. Rotate the globe as before.

3. Keeping the axis pointed in this same general direction, move the globe counter-clockwise in a circular (really elliptical) path to position *B*, where the axis becomes perpendicular to center ray and the other rays reach both poles as in *D*. Rotate the earth.

4. Again move the globe counter-clockwise to position *C*, keeping the axis inclined 23.5° but leaning toward the top heating ray, and pointing in the same direction as before. Rotate the globe.

5. Continue the swing counter-clockwise to the original position *D*, where again the axis is perpendicular to the rays and rays reach each pole. Rotate the globe.

6. Repeat parts 1, 2, 3, 4, and 5, but with the axis not inclined.

Note: — Repeat each of the above again and again until you know exactly what happens in each case.

WHAT HAPPENS: — 1. Where are the heating rays perpendicular to the earth's surface, as it rotates? Where are they slanting? Where are they most inclined to the surface? How does the rotation of the globe affect the direction of the rays at any place on the earth?

2. Where now do the rays act perpendicularly to the surface? Where do they strike the earth on a slant? What part of the earth receives the most slanting rays? Does any part of the earth fail to receive any rays at all in this position? What part? How does the rotation of the globe affect the direction of the rays on any part of the surface? Compare with position *D*.

3. Compare with the result in *D*.

4. Compare your observations with those in *A*. Where now do the rays act perpendicularly to the surface? Where

do they strike the earth on a slant? What part of the earth receives the most slanting rays? What part of the earth receives no heat? How does the rotation of the globe affect the direction of the rays on any part of the surface?

5. Compare conditions now with what happened in 1.

6. If the axis were always perpendicular to the rays, would the amount of heat received by any part of the earth change from one time to another at any place in the orbit?

CONCLUSION: — How does the inclination of the earth's axis affect the amount of heat received by the northern and southern hemispheres?

How does the inclination affect the heat received at the equator?

How does the rotation of the earth affect the amount of heat received at any one location in its orbit?

How does the revolution of the earth affect the amount of heat received by the northern and southern hemispheres? At the equator? In different positions in the orbit?

What season in the Northern Hemisphere is represented by A?

What season is represented by B?

What season is represented by C?

What season is represented by D?

APPLICATION: — Why does the temperature fall at a given place on a clear day as the sun sets lower and lower?

sun than it is in winter. You now understand that the cause of seasons really depends upon how slanting the heat rays are and how long the days are. Compare the heating effect of Sun 1 and Sun 2 in the diagram on the next page.

When the rays are slanting and the days are short, the earth is not heated as much as when the rays are more direct and the days are longer. These conditions result because of the inclination of the axis, the revolution about the sun, and the rotation of the earth.

The Equinoxes. — Since the axis of the earth always points in the same direction, it follows that as the earth travels around the sun it reaches a position where the north end of the axis slants away from the sun. This

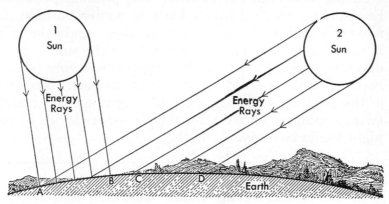

HOW THE SUN'S POSITION AFFECTS THE AMOUNT OF HEAT THE EARTH RECEIVES

When the sun is nearly overhead (Sun 1), its rays heat the land from A to B. When the sun is nearer the horizon, the same amount of heat is spread over a much larger area — from A to D.
Which season does Sun 1 represent?
What time of day does Sun 1 represent? Sun 2?

position accounts for the cold of the winter season in the northern hemisphere. (*A* in diagram, page 224.) When in the opposite position with respect to the sun, the northern hemisphere receives its greatest heat, producing the summer season. (*C* in diagram, page 224.)

Now as the earth swings from the first to the latter position, it gradually moves to a place along its orbit where the north end of the axis slants neither away from nor toward the sun. (*B* in diagram, page 224.) In this midway position, when both ends of the axis are equidistant from the sun and both receive the same amount of heat, it is the spring season. On the first day of spring, were it not for the bending of the sun's rays by the earth's atmosphere, day and night would be equal all over the earth. The date (about March 21) when this occurs is called the *spring (or vernal) equinox.*

As the earth swings from its summer position (northern hemisphere) on its journey back to winter position, it reaches a place midway in its orbit where again the axis is tipped neither toward nor away from the sun. (*D* in diagram, page 224.) The time when this occurs (about September 21) is called the *autumnal equinox.* Because of the bending of the rays of light, day is actually about twenty minutes longer than night; otherwise day and night would be of equal length.

FIELD RESEARCH:

The axis of Venus is nearly vertical. What effect would this have on the seasons of Venus as compared with the seasons on earth?

General Problem 4. What Adaptations Do Living Things Make to the Seasons?

Plants. — Outwardly plants show the effects of changing seasons in various ways. With the oncoming winter, some wither and die after the fruiting season; others drop their leaves and prepare for a period of inactivity; still others die in the portions above the ground, leaving a bulb or root to start new growth with the return of the growing season. Even in the tropics, where the seasonal changes are less extreme than in the north or south, plants must provide for resting periods.

Curiously enough, while plants do not have the power of moving from place to place, their seeds are distributed widely by means of water, winds, birds, and other animals. In this way plants may travel far. However,

A WINTER HOME

Bears prepare for winter by storing foods as fat in their bodies. Then they sleep in their dens all winter. This bear has selected a hole in a tree for its den.

a plant once rooted must be adapted to its environment or perish. Some are adapted to a shorter or longer growing season, to dry or wet weather. Plants show wonderful powers of adaptation in this respect.

Animals. — Animals, too, prepare for the winter by laying up food and by growing heavier pelts. Some *hibernate* or rest during the cold season and waken for renewed activity with the spring.

While animals can move from place to place they generally are adapted to a particular environment and are not likely to wander far. Many kinds of birds, however, migrate great distances to find an environment suited to their needs at nesting time.

With the approach of winter, birds of the north lands migrate southward to lands where food to their liking is available. They return the following spring to raise a family. No one really knows why birds migrate except to find the necessary food.

Man is free to travel as he wills, by boat, train, automobile, and airplane. Man journeys from the torrid zone to the polar regions or flies across the seas. He can adapt his eating, clothing, and shelter to any climate and to any season.

Thinking Things Over. — As you have been studying this topic and trying the experiments, have you thought how you have had to adapt or fit your plans to the changing seasons? Have you considered to what extent the change of seasons affects your life more or less than that of boys and girls who live farther north or south of you?

A remarkable thing about the seasons is their regularity. The change of seasons not only provides resting periods for plants and some animals, but provides desirable changes for human beings. To be sure these changes result sometimes in hardships, but on the whole they are beneficial.

When thinking of the adaptations of plants and animals to changes in seasons and other factors, such as the weather, we must not think that these adaptations are made as a result of thinking it over or of possessing advance knowledge. Plants and animals do not do things with a purpose or reason, as you are learning to do. You have intelligence which enables you to think and plan for the future.

Plants and animals, including man, prepare for the certainty and precision with which the seasons follow one another. Each group in its own way plans ahead for the coming season with confidence that the laws of nature will continue to operate in the future as in the past.

Key Words

axis	heating rays	rotation
circle	hemisphere	season
degree	migrate	spring
ellipse	orbit	torrid zone
environment	perpendicular	tropics
equinox	plane	twilight
galaxy	polar regions	vernal
	revolution	

Key Statements

1. The earth revolves about the sun from west to east.
2. The earth rotates on its axis from west to east.
3. The orbit of the earth about the sun is elliptical.
4. The axis of the earth is inclined 23.5° away from the vertical. It always points in the same direction (toward the North Star).
5. Day and night are caused by the rotation of the earth, and their lengths vary on account of the inclination of the earth's axis and its revolution about the sun.
6. The change of seasons is a result of varying amounts of heat received by the earth's surface.
7. Variations in the amount of heat received by the earth's surface from the sun are caused by the revolution about the sun of the earth with its axis inclined at 23.5°.
8. Rays of energy from the sun are parallel and heat more strongly when they act directly (perpendicularly) than when they act at an angle.
9. The motions of the earth are regular, hence the heat received by the earth varies in an orderly manner, which in turn results in an orderly sequence of the seasons.
10. Winter occurs in the northern hemisphere when the earth is in such a position that the north end of the axis is inclined away

from the sun. At this time it is summer in the southern hemisphere. When the north end of the axis is inclined toward the sun, the seasons are reversed.

11. Spring and fall occur when the earth is in such a position that both the north and south poles are at the same distance from the sun and receive the same amount of heat.

12. About March 21 and September 21 the days and nights are of equal length. These dates are called the *vernal* and the *autumnal equinox*.

13. Plants and animals including man adapt their habits to the changing seasons.

Thought Questions

1. The earth is farthest from the sun when it is summer in the northern hemisphere. Why, then, is it summer?

2. Why must the inclination of the earth's axis be considered when examining the cause of unequal days and nights?

3. How would the apparent motion of the sun, moon, and stars be affected if the earth turned from east to west on its axis?

4. What would be the effect on the variations in the length of day and of night if the axis of the earth inclined 47° away from the vertical? How would the seasons be affected?

5. What evidence can you give from personal observations that plants and animals anticipate the change of seasons?

Projects for Your Science Discovery Book

1. Draw a diagram to represent the sun and earth and use arrows to show the direction of the two motions of the earth.

2. Make a study of the migration of birds, finding out how far and how fast they fly, where they go, and why. Do any birds live the year round in the same environment, adapting their habits to the changing seasons?

3. Make a study of the shelters used by man in the tropics, in the temperate zone, and above the Arctic circle. Compare them as to building materials, construction, and warmth.

4. Make a study of the diet of man in each of the three zones mentioned above.

5. Locate and record the points on the horizon of your locality where the sun rises and sets on the longest day of the year, on the shortest day, and on the two days having day and night of equal

length. Represent the horizon by a circle and mark the locations and date them. Stationary objects (to be labeled), such as trees, corners of buildings, fence posts, telegraph poles, and chimneys, may be used to mark the location on the horizon where the sun rises and sets. Two such objects should be discovered that are in a straight line with the positions of rising and setting.

6. Darken the room, and with your flashlight and an old tennis ball, with a knitting needle stuck through it to represent the earth on its axis, demonstrate how rotation causes day and night.

7. Do you regulate and conduct the affairs of your life as dependably as nature does hers? Describe some things in nature that are good examples for you to follow.

8. Using graph paper, plot the time of the rising and setting of the sun for a month. Start with the longest or shortest day of the year or one of the two days when day and night are equal. You may wish to make the record for a whole year. An almanac will give you the time of rising and setting of the sun.

9. Using graph paper, plot the time of the rising and setting of the moon for a month.

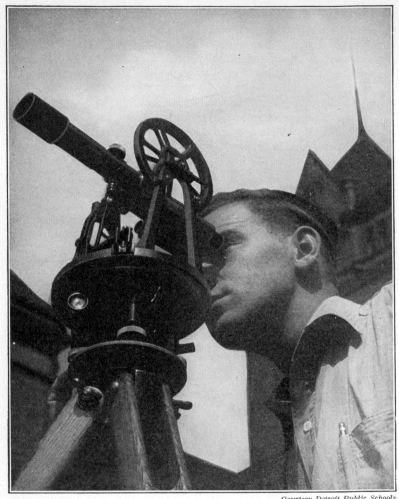

USING A TRANSIT

A new street, a housing project, a new railroad, bridge, or tunnel — before any construction is started, its exact location must be determined. The transit is one instrument used by surveyors and civil engineers for "laying out" position.

The pilot of an airplane 40,000 feet high, and the captain of a ship in the vast Pacific must also know their exact position. How can their navigators find it?

Earth Measurements

I'll put a girdle round about the earth
In forty minutes.
— **Shakespeare**

Do you know:

1. The names of two important imaginary circles north of the equator and two south of the equator?
2. How many degrees there are in a circle?
3. How to describe the location of a place on the earth?
4. Why it becomes light in Boston before it does in Chicago?
5. Why a navigator uses a clock?
6. Why daylight-saving time affects us?

General Problem 1. How Are the Imaginary Circles of the Earth Used?

Meridians and Parallels. — In order to be able to describe the exact location of places on the earth, it is marked off by great imaginary circles which run around the earth intersecting at the north and south poles. At right angles to these is another group of circles which includes the *equator* and many imaginary smaller circles around the earth, parallel with the equator and north and south of it.

THE "AVENUES" AND "STREETS" OF THE WESTERN HEMISPHERE

What are the real names of these imaginary lines?

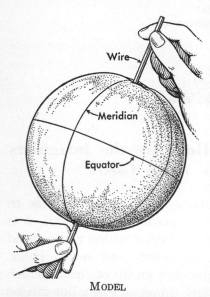

MODEL

Make a model, as described in the Field Research, to help you understand "meridian" and "equator."

The great circles which intersect at the poles run north and south and may be thought of as the avenues of the earth. These are the *meridians*.

The equator circle runs east and west around the middle of the earth at right angles to the meridians. It may be thought of as the "Main Street" — East and West. Smaller circles parallel to the equator, called *parallels*, may be thought of as the numbered streets, 1 to 90 north and south. Street 90 to the north would be the North Pole. The *parallels* get smaller and smaller toward the pole where the circle is merely a point which locates the end of the earth's axis. Thus every part of the earth is laid out with imaginary streets running east and west (the parallels) and imaginary avenues running north and south (the meridians). The part of the earth north of the equator is called the Northern Hemisphere (half sphere), and the part south of the equator is called the Southern Hemisphere.

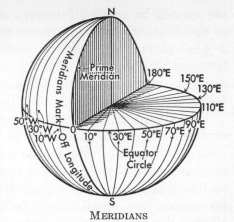

MERIDIANS

Here you see the "avenues" of the world.

Notice that these "avenues" run north and south on the earth's surface and that they all meet at the North and South Poles.

FIELD RESEARCH:

Take a tennis ball with a wire passing through the center to represent the earth and its axis, and with a pencil draw several great circles intersecting where the wire comes out of the ball. These circles will represent *meridians*.

Draw one great circle halfway between the ends of the axis with its plane perpendicular to the axis. It will represent the earth's *equator*.

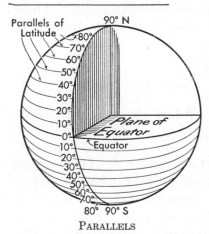

PARALLELS

The "streets" of the world run east and west. Which "street" is the longest?

Can you think of any reason why these imaginary lines are called *parallels?*

The meridians mark off the distances around the equator and parallels, as is shown in the diagram, and since a circle for convenience is divided into 360 degrees, let us say that the meridians divide the equator and parallels each into 360 equal lengths or arcs called *degrees*.

Also, the parallels may be spaced so as to divide each meridian circle into degrees. Since parallels north and south start with the equator circle, they are spaced to mark off degrees north and degrees south of the equator. Since between the equator and the pole is one quarter of a great circle, there are 90 degrees between the equator and the pole. Let us therefore mark the meridians into 90 spaces (degrees) both north and south of the equator. See the diagram on page 237.

The length of the arc, or part of the circle, which represents a degree on the circle of the equator is longer than the length of one degree on any parallel. This is so because the farther north or south one goes, the smaller such arcs become. Every circle is divided into 360 degrees no matter how small it is. In other words, the length of one degree in miles measured along the equator is greater than one degree measured along a parallel. It can be seen, then, that the parallels mark off *equal spaces or distances* north and south of the equator as measured along the meridians, while the meridians mark off *equal numbers* of spaces *or* degrees on each parallel. These spaces vary in length as the circle is large or small.

General Problem 2. What Are Longitude and Latitude?

The Prime Meridian at Greenwich. — Our modern town which has a Main Street may also have a Main Avenue from which other avenues east and west are located and numbered. The equator circle, as you know, is our Main Street of the earth, and so the meridian which passes through Greenwich (grǐn'ij), England, is our Main Avenue and is called the *prime meridian*.

In *Greenwich*, a borough of London, England, there was erected long ago a great observatory with a fine telescope and other astronomical instruments. By 1884, the business of the world had grown so huge that the need for a standard or *prime (first) meridian* was very great. A group of representatives from twenty-six

Keystone View

THE ORIGINAL GREENWICH OBSERVATORY

In 1946 the staff and equipment of this famous building moved from London to Hurstmonceaux, England. City smoke and city lights at night were the cause for moving. Now in the clearer air and still on the prime meridian, precise observations are once more possible.

nations met at Washington, D. C., to decide the question. The majority agreed that since the Greenwich Observatory was the center of investigation in such matters at that time, it would be fitting to name the meridian which passes through Greenwich, the *prime meridian.*

For reckoning purposes, any other meridian would serve just as well as this one for a starting point, but to avoid confusion, it is necessary to have one generally-used prime meridian. All east or west astronomical calculations and earth measurements are, therefore, based on reference to the Greenwich prime meridian.

Recording Locations. — The degrees east and west from a prime meridian are called degrees of *longitude*. The degrees north or south of the equator are called degrees of *latitude*. For convenience in reference, the meridians are numbered east and west from Greenwich, that is, from 0° to 180° each way; the parallels are numbered north and south from the equator, that is, from 0° to 90° each way. For the purposes of greater accuracy, each degree is subdivided into 60 equal parts called *minutes*; and each minute, for still more accurate work, may be divided into 60 equal parts called *seconds*.

Therefore, to give a very accurate location of any spot on the earth, all you need to say is that it is so many degrees (minutes, etc.) east or west longitude, and so many degrees (minutes, etc.) north or south latitude. These data mark the spot where the meridian and the parallel cross each other.

The half of the earth that lies between the prime meridian and 180° west longitude is the western hemisphere, while that part between the prime meridian and 180° east longitude is the eastern hemisphere. Of course 180° west longitude and 180° east longitude come together at the same meridian just halfway around the earth from the prime meridian at Greenwich, England.

General Problem 3. How Are Longitude and Time Related?

Telling Time by Longitude. — In these days of radio everyone knows that a broadcast in London may be heard in Philadelphia at the identical minute, but that the clocks in Philadelphia tell you that time there is five hours earlier than the time told by Big Ben in London.

Acme

CONVOY DUTY

The officers on this destroyer are checking their position. The officer in the center is taking the bearing of an object with relation to the compass, while the signal man at the right blinks out a message to another ship.

At two o'clock we can tune in on eastern football games beginning at two, and at five o'clock we can listen to Pacific Coast games which also begin at two. Why is this? What makes the difference in clock time between places for events that may be heard at the same time in two localities?

One thing you may not have thought of is that when there is a difference in time by the clock, one place is always east of the other, London is east of Philadelphia; New York is east of San Francisco.

Perhaps you are saying to yourself, "That's easy. The sun rises earlier for places east than it does for places west." That is true and that is the secret of the relation of longitude and time.

Let us examine the problem a little, but first you must be sure you know just what the words "latitude" and "longitude" mean.

When you recall that the earth makes one complete rotation on its axis in twenty-four hours, it must be evident that a point, where you live for example, on the earth will turn through an angle of 360° in twenty-four hours. In one hour the earth will rotate 15°, which is one twenty-fourth of 360°. Every 15° change in longitude is, therefore, equivalent to one hour's change in time. That is to say that a place 15° farther west will have sunrise one hour later than the place where you live.

If 15° change in longitude is equivalent to one hour's (60 minutes) change in time, then one degree change in longitude is equivalent to four minutes' change of time (60 minutes divided by 15). On the basis of this relation of longitude and time, it is possible to calculate the difference in time between any two places if we know the difference in longitude.

You know that a person to the east of you will see the sun before you do each morning. In other words, when you see the sunrise, people to the east of you have already seen it and perhaps have had their breakfast and gone to work. When it is six o'clock with you, it will be later than six o'clock — perhaps seven or eight o'clock — with the people living east of you. Therefore, if you want to know what time it is by the sun in a locality east of you, add to your sun time the difference in time indicated by the difference in longitude. For example, suppose it is six o'clock by the sun where you live; then a friend living 10 degrees east of you would have sun time forty minutes later (10 × 4 minutes). It would be forty minutes past six there.

Philadelphia is 75° west of London; therefore, clock time in London is 5 hours later than clock time in Philadelphia (75 divided by 15 equals 5).

If the earth were flat, like a table, and the sun rose above the east end, everyone for the whole distance west would see the sun rise at the same instant. That this is not so is one proof that the earth is spherical and turns on its axis.

Different Kinds of Days. — Do you know what the *zenith* is? It is the point in the heavens directly above your head. As you move, the zenith will be a correspondingly different point in the heavens. If you pointed a telescope toward a star on the line which passes exactly north and south through your *zenith* of the heavens, and then noted the time when the same star crossed the line again the next night, exactly 23 hours, 56 minutes, 1 second would have elapsed. This star-measured day is called a *sidereal* (sī-dē're-al) *day*. It is practically four minutes shorter than a mean solar (sun) day. Hence, the stars rise four minutes earlier each night. Star time is told by a specially made instrument called a *sidereal clock.*

You know that the length of our days and nights varies, owing to the motions of the earth and to the inclination of its axis. But do you know that because of these facts and because the orbit is elliptical the total time from noon to noon, called a *solar day*, is nearly one minute longer on December 21–22 than on September 17–18? Since solar days vary even so slightly in length, the average of the 365 solar days is taken and is called a *mean solar day.* The hours are counted from 0 to 24. It is the day used by astronomers and is sometimes called the *astronomical day*.

The ordinary day by which we run our business, our schools, and our pleasures is called the *civil day*. It is the same length as the astronomical day, but it begins at midnight and ends at the next midnight. The hours of this civil day run from 0 to 12 and repeat. These are clock hours. (What is the meaning of the word "civil" as used here?)

Courtesy U. S. Naval Observatory

PHOTOGRAPHIC ZENITH TUBE

This instrument at the United States Naval Observatory in Washington, D. C., is used to determine the exact instant a star crosses the meridian. Measurements of time determined in this way are then compared with the standard clocks at the Observatory. The records of the clocks are kept day by day, but the clocks are never corrected. In this way the rate of error is known for each clock and it is possible to predict the exact time.

Standard Time. — Actual sun time is different for every point of longitude. That is, the actual time of sunrise and the time of sunset are different for every place east or west of your house. This is because the earth is constantly turning from west to east. A little thought will show that it would be very hard to conduct the world's business if all our clocks were run on sun time. For example, suppose in your town the time of sunrise were called 7:00 o'clock and a train left your home at 7 A.M. going westward. You would then have to make a special timetable for your train showing the differences in longitude for all places between your town and the train's destination, if you wished to determine at what local sun time the train would arrive at its destination.

In order to escape the nuisance and confusion that would result, if all places went by sun time, *standard time* has been adopted. Standard time is the exact sun time on the seventy-fifth meridian, which passes very nearly through Philadelphia. For all places north or south of Philadelphia and lying on this same meridian, sun time and standard time are the same.

If you live east of the Philadelphia meridian, a clock set for sun time will be some minutes ahead of a clock set for standard time. If you live west of the meridian, a clock set for sun time will be slow or behind standard time. To avoid such great differences between sun time and standard time, the whole country is divided into *standard time zones* — Atlantic Standard Time, Eastern Standard Time, Central Standard Time, Mountain Standard Time, and Pacific Standard Time zones.

Time Zones. — A strip of the United States, running north and south for a certain distance on either side of the Philadelphia meridian, uses the sun time of the Philadelphia meridian. That is to say, all clocks in that strip are set to agree with the clocks in Philadelphia. The time for this section is known as Eastern Standard Time.

A second strip, lying directly west of this section, is marked off as a Central Standard Time zone within which the time is one hour earlier than in the Eastern zone. When it is 7 o'clock in the Eastern zone, it will be 6 o'clock in the Central zone.

The third zone includes the mountain region of the west, where the time is called Mountain Standard Time. West of the third zone lies the fourth zone, and here the time is called Pacific Standard Time.

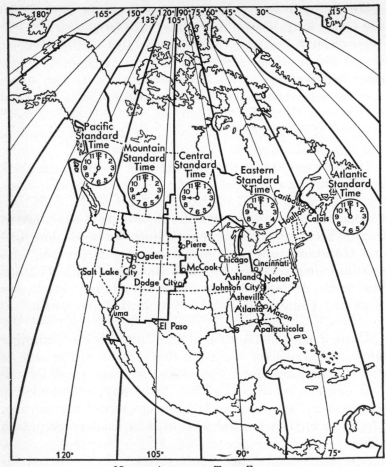

NORTH AMERICAN TIME ZONES

Pick out the meridian passing through the approximate center of each time zone. Account for the irregular boundary lines between the zones.

How many hours difference in time is there between New York and San Francisco? Which zone do you live in?

A small strip of eastern Maine and parts of Canada are east of the Eastern zone and lie in what is called the Atlantic Standard Time zone. The boundaries of these time zones are shown in the diagram above.

By this scheme of time zones any place in a given zone may keep its clocks on standard time and yet not be more than one half hour ahead or behind sun time.

FIELD RESEARCH:

Obtain timetables of the principal transcontinental railroads and a map of the United States. From the timetables determine the boundary cities of the time zones. Mark these places on your map. Connect the boundary cities by lines, and you will have approximately mapped the time zones.

Check the accuracy of your zone boundaries by the time zone map on page 246.

If the time zones were exactly placed, they would have meridians 15° apart as boundary lines. But for business and transportation reasons it is convenient to designate certain principal cities as fixing the boundary marks for the different zones. Railroads especially benefit by such an arrangement. It is not strange, then, that in your study of the map, you have discovered that the boundary lines between the time zones do not coincide with the meridians.

A general standard time has been adopted for all continents, and the prime meridian of Greenwich, England, is the meridian from which the standard time of the world is determined. This is called *Greenwich mean time* and is abbreviated G.M.T. World wide radio program managers make use of G.M.T. in arranging for world broadcasts.

The International Date Line. — It was a Sunday evening at seven forty-five when Bill, listening to his radio, heard Sidney: "This is Australia, one forty-five Monday afternoon." Where Bill was it was Sunday evening, while in Sidney it was the next day, Monday. Bill was used to this situation because he was a "radio bug." Perhaps you also understand how it could be Monday in Sidney and Sunday in the United States. If you do not, you will be interested to learn why. If you will look at a map of the world, you will see that Sidney is on the other side of the International Date Line.

The key to understanding what happens at the International Date Line, which is 180° west of Greenwich and 180° east of Greenwich, is to remember that the earth turns from west to east so that the sun rises later and later as one travels westward. You remember one hour of time equals 15° change in longitude. Traveling 180°, therefore, is the equivalent of 12 hours change in time.

A Mr. Brown, traveling west from Greenwich or any other place, would have to turn his watch back one hour for each 15° he traveled toward the west. When he got halfway around the world he would have lost 12 hours, and if he continued on around the world he would lose another 12 hours, or one whole day, without a date line.

Suppose when he returned to his starting place he met Mr. White who had been going around the world as he had, only from west to east. Mr. White would have gained a whole day. Mr. Brown lost a day and Mr. White gained a day — what a predicament! The two travelers had started at the same time and returned at the same time, but now they found themselves two days apart.

To do away with this confusion the 180th meridian, halfway around the earth each way from Greenwich, has been selected as the International Date Line; so when Mr. Brown crosses the date line he just adds a day which he would otherwise have lost, while Mr. White loses a day which he would have gained if there had been no date line.

The International Date Line does not follow the 180th meridian exactly but is arranged so that it does not cross any large inhabited islands. What a queer thing it would be to live on an island crossed by the International Date Line! It might run down the middle of a street. If so, a person living on the east side of the street would lose a day if he went to the other side, while a person living on the west side would gain a day if he crossed to the east side.

General Problem 4. How Can Navigators Find Their Way?

How the Navigator Keeps His Course. — Navigators of ships and planes are often out of sight of land for long periods of time. They must, therefore, be able to determine their direction and exact position at any time by other means than the observation of familiar landmarks.

The mariner and the pilot use special compasses to maintain sailing directions. However, direction alone does not tell position. For this reason each must know his exact latitude and longitude at given times in order to be sure that he is holding to his course. Knowing his location, the navigator can, with the aid of the sun, the stars, and direction-pointing compasses, continue on his course. He can determine his latitude from the stars on cloudless nights or from the sun on cloudless days.

You remember the earth is laid out in imaginary streets and avenues like a town. The stars and the sun are really marks in the sky, and the navigator has a map on which these sky marks are drawn.

The North Star, an Important Sky Mark. — Let us try to understand how the North Star aids the navigator.

The angle formed by a line drawn from your eye to the North Star and the line of your horizon is the same for everybody on your same parallel of latitude. If you went north from your first position, the angle would get larger. If you went south, the angle would be smaller. That would be true for any other person also.

H. *Armstrong Roberts*

SHOOTING THE SUN

The officer is using a sextant to find the altitude of the sun. After making certain corrections for the time of the year and subtracting from 90°, he determines the latitude.

You can very easily determine your latitude by merely measuring the angle the North Star makes with the horizon lines.

Strictly speaking, you should stand at the center of the earth when looking at the North Star to determine its altitude, but the star is so far away that it doesn't make any practical difference in your measurement.

Thus the latitude of any place in the northern hemisphere can be determined by measuring the angle of the North Star above the horizon.

Experiment 19 is an interesting project for a clear evening when the moon is not bright. Read the experiment carefully so that everything will be ready for you to make your observations when the clear night comes.

Latitude from the Sun.

— If you have ever noticed the shadow of a telephone pole at morning, noon, and night, you know that the shadow is shortest at exactly noon by the sun. In other words noon sun time occurs when the sun is highest in the sky. Not only does this help a navigator to determine exact noon wherever he is, but by measuring the angle of the sun above the horizon at that instant he can calculate his latitude. The angle in degrees subtracted from 90° gives approximately the latitude.

Due to the inclination of the earth's axis and the revolution of the earth about the sun, the altitude of the sun at exact noon varies with the day of the year. Hence for accurate results by this method a correction is made by navigators.

The navigator uses an instrument called a *sextant* to determine the altitude of the sun at exact noon. When the sun shines he looks through the sextant to read the angle the sun makes with the horizon at the instant the sun reaches its highest point. Making a slight correction for the time of the year, he reckons his true latitude.

FIELD RESEARCH:

Try to determine the approximate latitude of your home by measuring the altitude of the sun at noon.

Use the same materials listed in Experiment 19 and a magnetic compass. Follow the same procedure as in Experiment 19. At exact noon the shadow of a plumb line on a horizontal surface (top of box leveled) will point north.

The compass should be laid on the box so that the shadow falling across it will tell you when it is approximate noon. At that instant you should mark the angle of the sun direction with the horizontal and vertical lines on your paper. Since the magnetic north and true north vary at different locations, the compass will give you only the approximate north and therefore only approximately noon.

The angle in degrees substracted from ninety is approximately your latitude. Compare the determination with the results obtained by use of the North Star method.

EXPERIMENT 19

What is the latitude of your home?

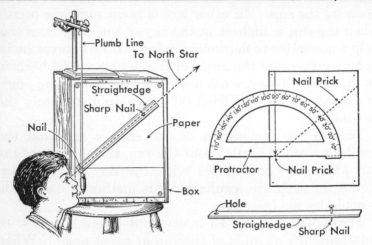

To do this experiment you will need to make careful preparations in advance. It will be a good project to make the apparatus in the school shop if you have one.

Here again you will make use of light energy. A principle involved is that light travels in straight lines. Think that over. Suppose light did not travel in straight lines, how could you do the experiment?

WHAT TO USE: — A plumb line and support; a good-sized box to which is tacked a paper marked with a right angle whose sides are horizontal and vertical; a narrow straight-edged stick fastened to the box at the vertex of the right angle by a nail through a small hole near the end. The stick will swing about the nail. Near the other end of the stick pass another sharp nail so that only the point sticks out. When this nail is pressed slightly it will make a prick in the paper underneath; a high stool; a carpenter's square; a protractor; and a flashlight.

WHAT TO DO: — On a clear night place the stool where there is a good view of the North Star. Set the box on the stool with the paper toward the east and pointing north. Hang the plumb bob from the support so that it swings free.

Adjust the box so that the vertical side of the right angle on the paper will be exactly in line with the plumb line.

Now with your eye in the position as shown in the diagram, sight toward the North Star, and adjust the stick so that the nail in the far end is exactly in line with the North Star. The two nails act as sights. When they are in line with the North Star push on the upper nail to make it prick the paper underneath. Now take the paper into the light and draw a line through the two pricks so that it intersects the horizontal line.

Lay the protractor against the horizontal line with its center mark at vertex of the right angle. Then read the angle made by the star direction line and the horizontal line. This angle is the altitude of the North Star and is equal to the latitude of the place where the observation is made. For the sake of greater accuracy you should try the experiment several times and take the average of the several angles for your result.

CONCLUSION: — What is your latitude? Is it north or south?

APPLICATION: — What is the length of the longest day and of the shortest day at your latitude? Use the apparatus to measure the "altitude" of some other star.

Finding Longitude. — The navigator carries with him a ship's clock, or *chronometer*, set so that it agrees exactly with a master clock at Greenwich Observatory. By means of radio the accuracy of this clock is checked regularly.

If the navigator sailing westward wants to know his longitude, he determines when it is exact noon, or, if at night, he may determine the time from the stars. From the difference between the time shown by his chronometer, which is sun time at Greenwich, and the time by the sun or stars he can calculate his longitude, for he knows that for each hour's difference in time he has changed his position 15°.

Having determined the latitude from the sun or the North Star or some other star (for which the data are known), and having determined the longitude by means of the difference of time, the navigator can locate the position of his ship upon a map which he always carries with him.

Thinking Things Over. — Exact measurement is necessary in science if we are to know with real accuracy about many things. When you buy a pound of butter you expect it to be weighed accurately. This means that the scales used must be accurate, that the grocery man knows how to use it properly, and that he reads it correctly.

So it is with scientists. They must have good measuring instruments, use them properly, and record the data honestly.

Using instruments and numbers sometimes makes a problem more difficult to understand, and sometimes it helps one to understand the problem better.

Your study of earth measurements should help you to understand better how astronomers are able to tell exactly when an eclipse of the sun or moon will occur and where they can be seen. You will appreciate better how they tell the exact time of the beginning of spring, summer, winter, and fall. And most important of all, you should understand better how navigators find their way over the water and through the air.

Key Words

chronometer	latitude	sextant
compass	longitude	sidereal day
diameter	meridian	solar time
equator	noon	standard time
equivalent	parallel	telescope
Greenwich	prime meridian	zenith

Key Statements

1. Places may be located on the earth by stating their latitude and longitude. Latitude is the distance in degrees north or south of the equator. Longitude is the distance in degrees east or west of a prime meridian.

2. Fifteen degrees of longitude is equivalent to one hour of time.

3. Standard time zones are established for convenience in comparing the times of different localities.

4. The north latitude of a place equals the angular altitude of the North Star above the horizon. The latitude of any place also equals the angular distance between the zenith and the sun at high (exact) noon, with allowances made for the position of the earth in its orbit.

5. Longitude is determined by the difference in time between standard time at Greenwich, England, and mean solar time at the place involved.

6. The International Date Line lies approximately along the 180th meridian. When crossing the line going east, one day is added; when going west, one day is lost.

Thought Questions

1. Why is it helpful to be able to give the position of a place in terms of latitude and longitude? How else could one describe the location of a city? A ship at sea? An airplane in the air?

2. Why are 15 degrees of longitude equivalent to one hour of time?

3. Why is it necessary to have a prime meridian?

4. Why is the plan of standard time zones better than that of having every place go by sun time?

5. Referring to page 247, in which United States Time Zone was Bill when he heard Australia?

Projects for Your Science Discovery Book

1. From a map read the latitude and longitude of five places, based on the standard (Greenwich) prime meridian. Now on your map read the position of your home town in latitude and longitude, using the 75th meridian as your prime meridian. Record your results.

2. Make reports of news items that indicate the importance of the radio in navigation of the sea or air.

3. Read in *Skyward*, page 191, what Commander Byrd says about the importance of chronometers and their accuracy in connection with his North Pole flight. Make a report of your reading.

4. Discuss the advantages and disadvantages of daylight saving time.

5. To determine the true north from the sun, set up a stake about four feet tall where the ground is level. Make sure the stake is exactly vertical. When the shadow of the stake is shortest, the shadow is pointing due north.

6. Having determined the true north by the shadow cast by the stake, compare with it the magnetic north direction as indicated by a compass. About how many degrees from the true north is the magnetic north?

7. Learn to determine the north and south direction, using a watch and the shadow of a match or slender stick. Hold the watch in a horizontal position so that the hour hand points toward the sun; that is, so that it is in line with the shadow made by a match or slender stick held exactly vertical.

When the watch is in this position, the north and south direction is a line halfway between the hour hand and the figure twelve.

8. Make a sun dial in a sunny place on your lawn and learn to tell time by it.

9. If you would like to make a sun dial, a cross staff, a quadrant, or a real telescope, consult such books as *Starcraft* by Barton and Joseph, published by Whittlesey House, New York.

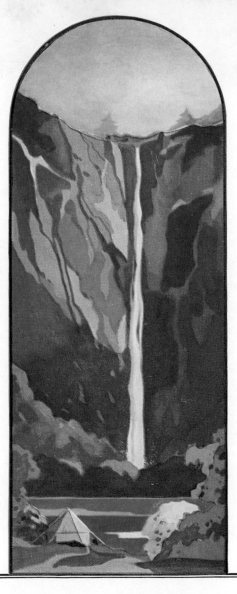

Pure water is the best of gifts
That man to man may bring.
Lord Neaves

UNIT III

≫‖ WATER ‖≪

"Water, water, everywhere, nor any drop to drink." Those words would be most fitting if one were at sea and had no drinking water. Most of us, however, never know what it means to become thirsty almost to death. Fortunate it is indeed that water is so plentiful.

And when we think of water as one of nature's most useful servants, its journeys from leaden clouds to the mountain tops, down the slopes to the rivers, lakes, and oceans, and then being drawn up into the sky again, we marvel. We marvel that in all these changes not a drop is wasted.

Then our thoughts turn to the many and varied uses of water — how it causes deserts to bloom, factory wheels to turn, how it makes plant and animal life possible, how it helps to make the human family clean and healthy, and finally how it adds to our comforts and pleasures. We can scarcely grasp its importance.

A. Devaney

WATER

Snow, ice, and liquid water can be seen in this picture. Still another form of water is here, but you cannot see it. What is it?

What can you see in this picture that suggests some uses of water to human beings and other animals?

Characteristics and Uses of Water

It's but little good you'll do, watering last year's crops.

— George Eliot

Do you know:

1. What is the most abundant substance on the surface of the earth?
2. How much of your body is water?
3. How to tell water from other liquids?
4. What the three states of matter are?
5. Whether water or air is more important?

General Problem 1. Where Is Water Found?

The Abundance of Water. — Water is the most abundant compound on the surface of the earth. What does the word "compound" mean? A *compound* is any substance that can be separated into simple substances called *elements*. Substances, therefore, may be either elements or compounds. (An element, you recall, cannot be changed readily into simpler substances. It is a simple substance itself. Of course elements are made up of molecules, and molecules are made up of atoms. Atoms are made up of positive and negative electric charges.)

You will realize how much water there is in the world, when you learn that three fourths of the earth's surface is covered with water — water as oceans, rivers, lakes,

Kabel

"The breaking waves dashed high
On the stern and rockbound coast."

and ponds. The ocean averages four or five miles deep with its greatest known depth nearly seven miles, near the Philippine Islands. To this vast amount of water we must add all the water held in the atmosphere, the solid water or ice of the polar regions, and the water contained in food and living things. Your body is about two thirds water. Most foods also contain much water. For example, Experiment 20 on the next page will tell you the approximate amount of water in a slice of bread. Most other foods also contain large amounts of water, as the following table suggests:

Food	Per Cent Water
Beef	73.8
Beets	87.5
Cabbage	91.5
Lettuce	94.7
Milk	87.5
Oranges	86.9
Rice	12.3
Tomatoes	94.3

You can check these figures by using the procedure described in Experiment 20. Why might your figures vary slightly?

General Problem 2. What Are Some Properties of Water?

What Are Properties? — You know what water is like, for you have seen it and used it all of your life. But can you describe water exactly, using scientific words? All substances are described or recognized by means of their characteristics or *properties*. Your friend has certain characteristics or properties by which

EXPERIMENT 20

What percentage of water does bread contain?

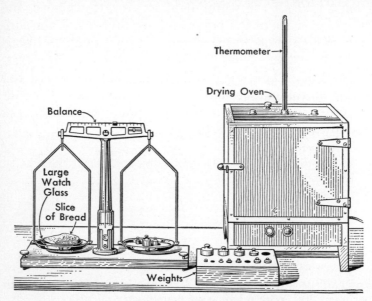

Before you start this experiment, recall what causes evaporation of water. What form of energy will you use? Where will you get the energy?

What kind of weights are suggested? (Metric weights.) You will find the weights of the food before and after heating in grams and tenths of grams. You could use ounces and fractions of ounces, but the metric weights are more convenient if you have them. The gram is the weight of a little cube of water that measures a little less than half an inch on each edge. It is called a cubic centimeter. A cubic centimeter is much smaller than a cubic inch.

WHAT TO USE: — A drying oven, or oven in domestic science room or at home; a thermometer; a slice of bread; a balance and weights; and a large watch glass.

WHAT TO DO: — 1. Heat the oven to 220° F.

2. Weigh the watch glass accurately, and then the watch glass and bread together. Record both weights as below.

3. Place the watch glass and bread in the oven and keep

the temperature at 220° F. for thirty minutes. Remove, cool, and weigh the watch glass and bread again. Record this weight.

CAUTION: If the bread is heated much hotter than 220° it will scorch or burn. This will spoil the experiment. Why?

4. Replace the glass and bread in the oven for fifteen minutes, maintaining the temperature of 220° F. Take out, weigh again, and record the weight. Repeat this heating and weighing until the bread no longer loses weight. Use the last weight for your calculations.

WHAT HAPPENS: — 3. Did the bread become dry? Did it look burned? If so, it was heated too hot and your data will be incorrect.

4. Did the bread lose more weight in second or third heating? Record data as follows:

Before heating:
    Weight of watch glass   ____
    Weight of glass and bread   ____
    Weight of bread   ____
After heating:
    First weight, glass and bread   ____
    Second weight, glass and bread   ____
    Final weight, glass and bread   ____
    Weight of bread alone after heating   ____
    Weight of water lost   ____
    Percentage of water lost   ____

$$\left(\frac{\text{weight of water lost}}{\text{weight of bread}} = \text{percentage of water} \right)$$

CONCLUSION: — What evidence have you that heating the bread drove off water?

What percentage of water did the bread contain?

Note: Some other food might be substituted for the bread. Also satisfactory, but less accurate, results can be obtained by drying a piece of bread in the oven at home (not toasting). If the weights before and after drying are known, the percentage of water can be calculated.

APPLICATION: — How could you prove that plants are partly water?

EXPERIMENT 21

Is water composed of two gases, hydrogen and oxygen?

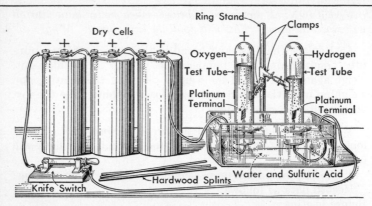

It is interesting to think that in nearly every experiment we must use some form of energy. What form of energy must you use in this experiment? What is the source of the energy?

WHAT TO USE: — Three to five dry cells or a battery charger; two test tubes; a large dish; two pieces of rubber insulated wires each about 18 inches long; platinum or copper foil terminals; hard wood splints; a knife switch cutting one of the wires; a ring stand and two clamps; and dilute sulfuric acid.

WHAT TO DO: — 1. Fill the dish with water to which a few drops of the sulfuric acid have been added.

2. Connect the dry cells in series (positive to negative, etc.), and run a wire from the end positive pole into the water.

The ends of each wire should be fastened to the platinum or copper terminals. This is to give more surface than the wire alone.

Arrange to run another wire from the end negative pole into the water, keeping switch open.

If a charger is used, connect it to a lighting socket and place the end of one wire at one side of the dish and one at the other. Do not let them touch either in or out of water.

CAUTION: Do not handle both battery wires at the same time while the current is turned on.

3. Fill two test tubes with water and invert each under the water in the dish. Clamp one test tube to the ring stand over one wire end terminal, and the other over the other terminal.

4. Close the switch. This completes the circuit from the battery through the positive wire, through the water and out the negative wire.

Observe at which terminal, + or −, the gas forms faster and about how much faster?

5. When the tubes are partly full of gas, take each one out and test the gas in it with a glowing splint (test for oxygen)· Collect more gas in each tube and test with a flaming splint (test for hydrogen).

Does the gas from the positive terminal pop when tested or did the glowing splint burst into flame? The negative?

When not collecting gas, disconnect the battery or charger.

WHAT HAPPENS: — 4. Were gases formed at each wire terminal? What color were they? In what proportion did the gases form?

Did gas form faster at the end of the positive or the negative wire or terminal? How much faster?

5. Describe each of the tests made with the gas formed at each terminal, indicating whether the terminal was negative or positive. Was hydrogen formed at the + or − terminal? Oxygen?

CONCLUSION: — Judging from the properties of the gases formed, what do you think they were? What was the proportion? Does this suggest a reason why the chemist represents water as H_2O?

you recognize him; so there is really nothing new about the use of the word "property" in this sense.

By a property of water is meant a characteristic that is present in every sample of water. A property of any substance is a characteristic which helps us to distinguish that particular substance from all other substances. For example, sulfur is yellow. The yellow color is a property of the sulfur and helps us to distinguish between sulfur and a piece of coal which is black.

In science work you frequently have need to examine a substance and tell several of its properties, because one property is usually not enough to make your identification certain. Useful things to know about a subtance are its color, taste, odor, boiling point, and freezing point. It is also useful to know whether a substance is hard or soft, whether or not it will dissolve in water, whether or not it will burn, and so on. Knowledge of these and other facts about a substance enables you to describe it accurately.

The properties of water which you have studied so far are called *physical properties* because we can recognize them by the use of our senses. We have learned that water, if pure, is odorless, colorless (in small quantities), tasteless, boils at 212° F., and freezes at 32° F. There are other properties of water, however, which are shown only by a study of how it reacts with other chemicals. Such properties are called *chemical properties*.

It is interesting to prove by Experiment 21 that water is composed of two elements, the gases hydrogen and oxygen. Would you be surprised to discover that the gases take up much more room than the water and that there is twice as much hydrogen as oxygen? Try Experiment 21.

Water Is a Solvent. — When we call water a *solvent* we mean that water will dissolve some materials. That water *dissolves* oxygen from the air and minerals from the soil is common knowledge to pupils studying science. But do you know that the ability of water to dissolve substances is a property on which all life depends? For example, plants would die if water in the soil could not dissolve certain minerals. Your food would do you no good if it were not changed so that it can be dissolved by the water in the blood. It is only when food is dissolved in the blood that it can be used by the body.

Not only does water dissolve many substances, but it is equally important to know that water dissolves different amounts of different substances. It is important, too, that some substances do not dissolve in water.

You can prove that substances differ in solubility in water by trying Experiment 22. It is an especially important experiment.

FIELD RESEARCH:

Test various common substances that you know are practically insoluble in water as follows: Grind each to a fine powder and place a very small amount in half a test tube of water. Shake thoroughly. Does it disappear? If not, heat the tube of water. Does it now apparently dissolve?

Now make a list of ten substances which you think are readily soluble in water. Make your selection, so far as possible, from materials used at home. Test your materials to prove their solubility.

What Is a Solution? — *A solution is a clear, even mixture of a substance and water* (*or any liquid*). The mixture will not change if allowed to stand without evaporating, nor can the dissolved substance be separated from the water by *filtering*. According to our definition, gases and liquids, as well as solids, may be used to form solutions with water. The dissolving liquid is the *solvent;* the substance dissolved is the *solute*. Substances vary in their solubility in water. Those which cannot be dissolved are *insoluble*.

The words in italics may be new to you but will be easy to remember if you make solutions and use the words to tell what you do and what happens. It is

KEY EXPERIMENT 22

Are some substances more soluble in water than others?

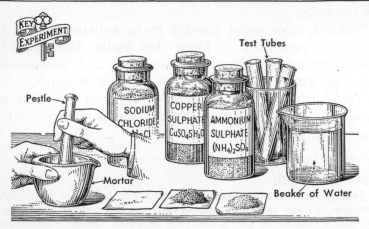

You have two new pieces of apparatus in this experiment. What are they? This is another "Key" Experiment. Why do you think it is so important?

What kind of energy do you use to grind the materials to a fine powder? It is mechanical energy. How many forms of energy does this make that you have used? Try to name them.

Why is it best to grind the material to a fine powder? To discover the reason you might try it without grinding.

When the substances are dissolved, feel the tube to see if the liquid changed any in temperature.

WHAT TO USE: — Table salt; copper sulfate (blue vitriol); ammonium sulfate; three test tubes; a mortar and pestle; and a beaker of water.

WHAT TO DO: — 1. Grind samples of each substance to a fine powder. Put equal amounts of each material (about one half inch in depth) into the three test tubes respectively. Add to each test tube an equal amount of water. Shake the contents of each tube for two minutes, and allow to settle. Observe closely whatever happens.

2. Notice if there is any change in temperature in any of the tubes.

268

3. Make a labeled diagram of each test tube and contents before and after shaking.

WHAT HAPPENS: — 1. Did all of each substance dissolve? Describe.

2. Did the temperature of any of the tubes change? If so, which one changed the most?

CONCLUSION: — Do substances differ in solubility? State the evidence proving your statement.

APPLICATION: — Why does ocean water contain more salt than lime in solution?

much simpler, for example, to use the word *solute* if you know what it means than to use a whole sentence.

Substances dissolve faster if they are finely divided. Not only do they differ in their solubilities in water, but for each substance there is a limit to its solubility. This was shown when you added too much sugar to your cocoa. In spite of stirring, some sugar remained in the bottom of the cup. The water of the drink had dissolved all the sugar it could at that temperature. The cocoa (mostly water) was *saturated* with sugar. Compare this use of the word *saturated* with that on page 59. We shall learn later that the temperature of the liquid also affects the solubility of a substance.

Heat and Solution. — Not only do substances vary in their solubility in water, but the solubility of a given substance varies with the temperature of the water. Generally, solids are more soluble in hot than in cold water, while gases are less soluble in hot than in cold water. Does this latter statement explain why cold water from a faucet, after standing until clear, gradually becomes filled with air bubbles as it becomes warm? Try it.

EXPERIMENT 23

Are certain solids more soluble in hot water than in cold water?

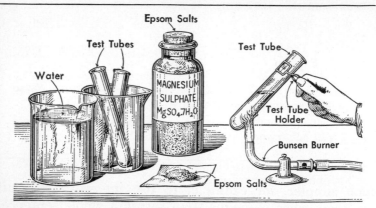

Before you start this experiment, think over some of your experiences with dissolving substances. Perhaps you already know the answer to the problem. If you think you do, then this is a chance to prove whether or not you are correct. Another thing, if you have means of weighing the Epsom salts, you can find out how much difference there is.

WHAT TO USE: — A Bunsen burner; test tubes and test tube holder; water; and Epsom salts (magnesium sulfate).

WHAT TO DO: — 1. To half a test tube of cold water add very small amounts of the Epsom salts and shake thoroughly after each addition until no more will dissolve.

2. Now heat the solution nearly to boiling temperature and add more of the salts, a very small amount at a time, as long as the salts continue to dissolve.

3. Pour off some of the hot clear solution into another test tube and cool it rapidly.

WHAT HAPPENS: — 1. Did the cold water dissolve some of the Epsom salts? Did the cold water dissolve a limited amount only?

2. Did the hot water dissolve more than the cold water? Was there a limit to the amount the hot water would dissolve?

3. Did crystals separate from the water when the hot solution became cold?

CONCLUSION: — Were the Epsom salts more soluble in hot or cold water? Give proof for your decision.

Note: Water that, at a certain temperature, has dissolved as much of a substance as it can dissolve is called a *saturated solution.* Did you make a saturated solution in your experiment? Explain.

If you wish, you could try the above experiment, using Glauber's salts (sodium sulfate) or powdered blue vitriol (copper sulfate) instead of Epsom salts (magnesium sulfate). Table salt (sodium chloride) is just about as soluble in cold as it is in hot water. It is an exception to the rule.

APPLICATION: — Explain the formation of the lime deposits of hot springs called *travertine.*

Courtesy U. S. Coast Guard

THE ICEBERG PATROL

What two states of water do you see here? What other state is present but not seen?

Does this also explain why hot cocoa dissolves sugar faster than cold cocoa?

If you can do Experiment 23, you can prove that certain substances dissolve more in hot water than in cold water. However, this does not prove that all substances act the same way.

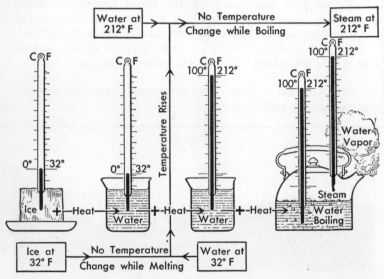

ICE, WATER, AND STEAM

Heat causes water to change from one form to another. Notice that some heat is required just to melt ice, without changing its temperature.

At what temperature can water be heated without changing its temperature? What happens to the water?

States of Water. — Water may exist as a solid (ice), a liquid (water), or a gas (steam). This is not a new fact to many of you. It needs to be recalled now because we shall try to learn what happens to cause water and other substances to change from one state to another. Water can be changed from a solid to a liquid and then to a gas by adding heat. Moreover, by taking heat away (cooling), the gas can be changed first back to the liquid state, and then to the solid state. Study the diagram on page 272.

The temperature at which solid water (ice) changes to liquid is called the *melting point* (melting temperature) of ice. The temperature at which water changes most rapidly to steam is called its *boiling point*. No two substances have the same melting and boiling points. These are physical properties that help to identify a substance, if it is pure, because a pure substance has a fixed boiling point and freezing point. (Look up the melting and boiling points of iron, tin, zinc, lead, paraffin, sugar, chocolate, and butter in the tables to be found in the Appendix.)

Courtesy National Pressure Cooker Company

A PRESSURE COOKER

Foods cooked in pressure cookers retain their flavor better and cook more rapidly than those in ordinary kettles.

We know that when a gas like steam is changed to a liquid by cooling, the process is called *condensation*, and when the liquid is changed to a solid (ice) by further cooling, the process is called *freezing* (solidification). The freezing temperature of water, 32° F. (0° C.), is the same as the melting temperature of its solid form (ice).

The temperature at which water boils is affected very much by changes in air pressure. As the pressure increases, the temperature must be raised higher to make the water boil. The lower the pressure, the lower the boiling point.

People living at high altitudes where the air pressure is low find that the boiling temperature of the water is too low to cook some foods quickly. One way to overcome this difficulty is to use a boiler with a cover that fastens on tightly. This causes steam pressure to increase in the boiler, and therefore the temperature is raised. Can you suggest another way of raising the boiling temperature in case you do not possess a "pressure cooker"? You will find the Laboratory Research described below helpful in understanding the effect of air pressure on the boiling point of water.

LABORATORY RESEARCH:

To find out whether the atmospheric pressure in your science room is standard.

Suspend an accurate all-glass thermometer so that the bulb is just immersed in a flask like the one used in Experiment 4. It should be about ¼ full of water. The flask should be placed on a wire gauze on an iron tripod. Heat the water to a brisk boil, and observe and record the temperature of the water as indicated by the thermometer. Let the water cool a few minutes and heat again to boiling. Observe and record the boiling temperature again. If the two determinations agree very nearly, take the average as the boiling temperature. If they do not agree, make a third and fourth determination, if necessary.

From the table of boiling temperature and pressures in the Appendix, find the pressure corresponding to the boiling temperature just recorded. Standard atmospheric pressure (page 46) is indicated by 30 inches (760 mm.) or 1015.9 millibars. What should the boiling temperature be at this pressure?

What is your altitude? How does altitude affect atmospheric pressure, and how does this affect the boiling temperature of water? What other factors might be responsible for the boiling temperature determined? Try to state a relation between the boiling point of water and altitude, and explain why the relation exists.

The boiling and freezing points already given are for pure water at standard or sea level pressure. Water containing a substance such as sugar, salt, alcohol, or glycerine in solution has a different boiling and freezing temperature from that of pure water.

LABORATORY RESEARCH:

Secure an accurate all-glass thermometer, a Bunsen burner, a beaker or glass, a tripod, wire gauze, and some salt or sugar.

Determine the boiling point of water taken from the tap. Next add and dissolve about ¼ as much sugar or salt as you have water. Now determine the boiling point of the solution. Is it the same or higher or lower than that of the water alone? Try to determine the boiling point of maple syrup.

If you live in a region where winters are severe, you are familiar with the practice of adding alcohol, glycerine, or other substances to the water in the automobile radiator in order to prevent the water from freezing. You can test that scheme by carrying out the following investigation:

LABORATORY RESEARCH:

Make a freezing mixture of equal parts of coarse salt and finely scraped ice.

Place the mixture in a tight wooden box, such as a crayon box, and set the box in a pan to catch any water that may leak out.

Secure five accurate all-glass (chemical) thermometers, five test tubes, some salt, and some denatured alcohol. In one test tube put water from the tap; in the second water plus ⅛ as much salt; in the third put water and twice as much salt as in the second. Prepare the fourth and fifth tubes as the second and third, but use alcohol in place of the salt.

Place a thermometer in each tube, and set the tube in the freezing mixture. Shake each tube occasionally. Record the temperature at which the contents of each tube begins to form ice crystals, that is, begins to freeze.

Tell what you did, and the freezing temperature of each solution if it froze. Explain.

Can you now explain why water in a radiator is protected against freezing by the use of alcohol? How do different amounts of alcohol affect the freezing point of water?

General Problem 3. Are the Uses of Water Related to Its Properties?

Uses of Water. — The uses of water depend upon its properties. Water is used in the digestive juices of the body to dissolve substances. Water also must dissolve minerals from the soil to be of most use to the plant. Because water can dissolve oxygen, it is fit for fish to live in; because water is liquid at ordinary temperatures, it is suitable for boating; because it will freeze at a convenient temperature, it is available for use in refrigerators. With these suggestions, you should be able to make a long list of things that depend upon the properties of water. What would happen —

if water could not be frozen

or

if ice could not be melted

or

if the boiling point of water were lower than the temperature of your body

or

if the atmospheric pressure did not affect the boiling point

or

if water would not evaporate?

How Water Does Work. — The cutting and carving of rocky gorges, mountains and valleys, hills and plains have made the earth a beautiful place on which to live. How uninteresting it would be if the surface of the earth were absolutely level and dry, barren of everything that water in the air, in streams, lakes, and oceans, and in the soil makes possible!

Running water turns wheels of industry. The energy of falling water, transformed by electric generators into electrical energy, provides endless helps and conveniences.

Water used for travel and transportation has played a part of vast importance in the life and development of our country. Civilization and progress have followed the water courses. Explorations and discoveries on land have progressed along the waterways. Read of the voyage of Hendrik Hudson up the river that bears his name, and how the French went up the St. Lawrence, through the Great Lakes, and down the Mississippi.

Philip D. Gendreau

ENFIELD GLEN IN NEW YORK STATE

For thousands of years water has been at work carving gorges and waterfalls. What type of rock is shown here? Explain the step formation of the waterfall.

First settlements have nearly always been made on the main water courses. This was so because in those early days the waterways offered almost the only ready means of transportation.

Later, the people inland drew their produce to the nearest water course for transportation to a settlement. Canals for water transportation were built. Read the story of "Clinton's Ditch," a canal from Troy to Buffalo,

New York, completed in 1825, or the story of the Panama Canal and its importance. Schools and churches were established at centers along the waterways, and so, little by little, education and culture increased.

McLaughlin Aerial Surveys

THE RIVER AND THE CITY

How has the Hudson River helped in the development of Albany?

Industries of various kinds sprang up and still the waterway held its own. When, however, the demand for greater speed in transportation developed, railroads were ready, but even these in the beginning followed the water courses. Now that science has given man so much control over the forces of nature, he tunnels mountains, bridges ravines, and builds airships that carry men and materials over or through mountains, valleys, and oceans.

Water for Drinking. — Your discoveries about the properties of water have to do with pure water. Pure

water, in the mind of the chemist, means water with
nothing at all dissolved in it. It is called *chemically
pure*. However, chemically pure water does not occur
naturally, and can be made only with difficulty by the

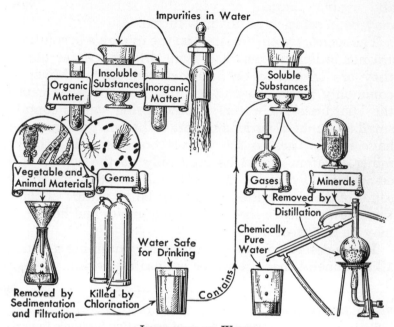

IMPURITIES IN WATER

Although water is a colorless, odorless, and tasteless substance when
relatively pure, one drop may have dozens of impurities in it.

This diagram shows some of the impurities often found in water, and
how they may be removed.

Which of the impurities shown here are harmful?   How are they removed?
Must drinking water be "chemically pure"?

chemists. Since the use of water for drinking is of
greatest importance, we must investigate the impurities
of water to determine whether or not they are harmful
and, if they are, how to remove them.

Water from a health standpoint may be safe to drink
and yet not be chemically pure. All natural water

contains impurities. They may or may not be harmful to man. They may even be beneficial, as, for example, water with certain minerals dissolved in it. The common impurities in water are both *inorganic* (mineral) and *organic* (animal or vegetable) substances. They may be in solution or not in solution.

The *soluble impurities*, that is, the minerals in solution, are not ordinarily removed from drinking water unless they are known to be injurious to health. Minerals commonly found in solution in water are what cause the "hardness" of water. Some spring waters contain small amounts of various minerals that may or may not have special uses to the body. So-called "healthful" mineral waters should be used only on the advice of a competent physician. The diagram on page 279 shows some of the impurities that may be in water. Follow the arrows to learn the kinds of impurities and how they may be removed.

In the deserts are pools sometimes containing so much alkali mineral that the water is unsafe to drink.

FIELD RESEARCH:
Devise and demonstrate a method of separating insoluble impurities from water.

The *organic impurities* commonly found in water consist of parts of vegetable and animal matter, and living *organisms* such as *bacteria*. These may be objectionable or even dangerous. Decaying vegetables and animal tissues may give rise to odors and tastes which are disagreeable, but the greatest objection to them is that they serve as food for the growth of bacteria, some of which may be harmful. If a few typhoid germs or other disease germs get into the water, they may multiply very fast, and the disease may be transmitted to people who drink the water. Great typhoid epidemics have usually been traced to the milk or water supply. However, the bacteria found in water are for the most part harmless.

Certain *algae* in the water give out oil that imparts a fishy taste to the water. While this is not injurious, it is objectionable. The growth of algae may be prevented largely by dissolving an extremely small proportion of copper sulfate (blue vitriol) in the water of the lake or reservoir. Small fish aquaria frequently show a variety of algae growing on the side walls or on stones in the water. In your aquarium, you should not try to prevent the growth of the

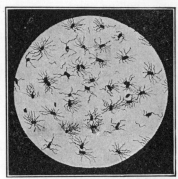

Courtesy Parke, Davis and Company

BACTERIA IN WATER

algae with copper sulfate, for you would be likely to use too much. Moreover, the algae are food for your snails.

Thinking Things Over. — Perhaps you have not learned very much that is new in this topic, but it is often necessary for us to restate and reorganize what we know in order to solve new problems. That is good scientific procedure.

We realize now not only how abundant water is but how important it is to us. Knowing the properties of water, we are in a position to use it to greater advantage.

With our knowledge of the properties of pure water and of the impurities that may occur in water from natural sources, we can investigate intelligently sources and treatments necessary to provide us with safe drinking water. The next chapter will deal with those problems.

Key Words

algae	element	pressure
bacteria	freezing point	property
balance	hydrogen	pure
boiling point	impurities	soluble
characteristic	insoluble	solute
compound	melting point	solution
dissolve	organic	solvent
drying oven	oxygen	transportation

Key Statements

1. Water is the most abundant compound on the earth's surface.

2. Nearly all organic matter contains water.

3. Water can be identified by its properties.

4. Pure water is colorless, odorless, and tasteless; it freezes at 32° F. and boils at 212° F., at normal (standard) air pressure.

5. Many of the uses of water depend upon its remarkable solvent property.

6. Substances vary in their solubility in water, and the solubility of any substance varies with the temperature of the water.

7. At any temperature, water is saturated with a substance when no more of the substance will dissolve in the water.

8. Some substances dissolved in water cause the boiling point to be higher and the freezing point to be lower than normal.

9. The boiling point of water is lower than normal with low air pressures, and higher with high air pressures.

10. Water serves for transportation.

11. Drinking water which contains impurities can be purified.

Thought Questions

1. What property of water makes it possible for fruit, vegetables, or bread to dry out?

2. Given samples of two colorless liquids, one of which is water, how could you determine which one was water?

3. How can you prove that water dissolves oxygen?

4. How can you prove whether a sample of water contains anything in solution?

5. How can you determine whether a solution of sugar and water is a saturated solution?

6. What is meant by *condensation?*

7. What is meant by *solidification?*

8. What is meant by *pure water?*

9. Does it require more or less time to boil an egg on a mountain than it does at sea level?   Why?

10. Try to name a use of water that does not depend upon one or more of its properties.

11. Why may water for drinking need to be purified?

12. Is water safe for drinking necessarily chemically pure water?

Projects for Your Science Discovery Book

1. Make a list of five common substances and write an accurate description of each.   See if your classmates can recognize the substances from your descriptions.

2. From a geography map and a history book, contrast the development of an early seaport town with that of some early inland settlement.

3. Make a report on what happens when a solution of salt is allowed to evaporate slowly.   Try a solution of alum or sugar.

4. Prove by experiments (describing each process carefully):

   a. That ordinary water contains dissolved air.

   b. That soils contain water.

   c. Whether granulated sugar contains water.

5. Perform an experiment to illustrate the water cycle in nature.

6. Report on the part water has played in the development of your own home town.

7. Determine the boiling point of carbon tetrachloride.

8. Place ice with a little water in one beaker, and ice with a little water and some salt in another beaker.   Determine the temperature of each after a few minutes.   Does this explain why salt and ice are used in freezing ice cream?

Courtesy Bureau of Reclamation

FRIANT-KERN CANAL

The Friant-Kern Canal is one of the first completed sections of the California Central Valley Project. This irrigation system is bringing an increased supply of water into the Valley, turning it into a fertile agricultural region. When the entire Project is completed, it will be one of the largest water conservation projects in the world.

The Water Supply

They could not drink of the waters of Marah,
for they were bitter.

—Exodus 15:23

Do you know:

1. Where your drinking water comes from? Whether it is rain water, spring water, or well water; whether it comes from a river or from a natural or artificial lake?

2. How your water supply may become polluted?

3. How fresh water can be obtained from sea water?

4. How the community supply is safeguarded against harmful impurities?

5. How science is able to prevent disease by proper treatment of drinking water?

General Problem 1. What Are the Sources of Water Supply?

For Rural Districts. — Those who live in small villages, on country estates, or on farms usually must provide their own water supply. They must have springs or wells or cisterns to furnish water for the various and many uses of the household and farm. These sources must supply an adequate amount of water all the year round or hardships must be endured.

Some water sources may be better than others. Are springs dependable? Is well water safe and sure? Is cistern water good to drink?

You have learned that one very important property of water is its ability to dissolve minerals. Because of this, spring waters and well waters are likely to contain mineral matter in solution. Minerals may give water a taste that is undesirable, although they may not be harmful to health. The minerals may necessitate the use of extra soap, or they may clog the pipes or deposit lime in the tea-kettle.

Keystone View Company

AN ARTESIAN WELL

In an artesian well the water flows above the level of the land. The water in this artesian well is believed to come from the mountains seen in the distance.

Cistern water, on the other hand, is rain water collected from the roof of the house and is more economical for use with soap because it contains few mineral impurities. Rain water may be dirty and have an objectionable odor because of the material washed from the roofs.

Springs and Wells. — Water from rain and snow soaks into the soil and feeds springs and wells. Water that flows through the soil and rock is called *ground water*. Ground water flows slowly and so dissolves minerals from the soil and rock. Wells that are fed by springs and springs that come to the surface may supply water generously through dry seasons. The important point is whether their source of supply is below the level of the dry weather *water table*. Water that soaks into the soil rock pores or crevices passes on down to fill similar spaces at varying depths below the surface of the ground. Below a certain depth, depending upon the altitude and climate of the locality together with the

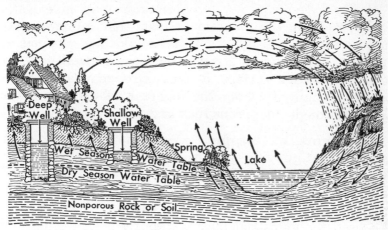

WATER SUPPLY AND THE WATER CYCLE

How is the water cycle related to the supply of water in the wells? Which of these wells will go dry during a drought? Why does a deep well usually give a more steady supply of water?

character of its underlying rocks, the underground water collects in fairly large quantity. The surface of this underground body of water is the *water table*. This does not mean that there is always an underground lake on which a boat might be used, but rather a mass of soil with water standing in the lower part.

FIELD RESEARCH:

It will help you to understand what is meant by *water table* if you will fill a jar with clean sand and then add water until the surface of the water rises part way up in the sand.

Just as the surface level of an ordinary lake is higher during rainy spells, so the surface (water table) of the

soil-filled underground lake (ground water) is higher
during wet spells or seasons. If the water that feeds
an open spring or well spring comes from a level lower
than the dry weather water table, the spring will not
"go dry."

In studying the diagram on page 287, observe that
the water table is not level like a lake, but uneven or
waving, following to some extent the general contour
of the ground surface above. Ground water flows
slowly by gravity from the higher levels to the lower
levels through the porous rock and soil.

Problems of Supply. — A community, large or
small, must provide itself with an adequate supply of
water that is safe for drinking. Wells, rivers, reservoirs,
and lakes are each used depending upon the population
and location of the community. Much of the water will
be used for industrial purposes, but since safeguarding
the health of its people is the duty of a community, care
of its water for drinking is most important.

The problems to be solved by a community in relation
to its water supply are:

1. *How can an abundant water supply be obtained?*
2. *How can the water be safeguarded from contamination
at the source?*
3. *How can the water be brought to the community?*
4. *How can the water be made safe for drinking?*
5. *How can the water be sent into every home?*

An Abundant Supply. — The smaller communities
may supply their needs from deep wells. A tank is
usually placed on a near-by hill or on a tower, and water
from the well is pumped into it. From such a reservoir
the water will run downhill through pipes to the homes.
This is called distribution by gravity because gravity
pulls the water downward.

Some communities pump water from a convenient
river into large reservoirs. River water is especially
liable to contamination from industrial wastes and
sewage materials and usually contains a large amount
of solid material. This necessitates special equipment

Acme

A PUMPING STATION

This huge pumping plant raises water over a mountain ridge to a point
where it will flow by gravity to the City of Los Angeles. This city goes
240 miles to the Colorado River to obtain its water supply.

and machines to purify the river water. The reservoirs,
if practical, are placed at an elevation above the town
so that the water will flow by gravity. If there is
not a good hill near by, large pumps are used to force
the water through the pipes.

A very desirable source of water is a natural or an
artificial lake or reservoir situated so as to collect the
drainage water from a forested watershed and located
at an altitude above the community. The fewer the

homes and barns on the watershed or drainage area, the less will be the chance of contamination with human or animal wastes which may contain disease germs.

Large inland lakes furnish an abundant supply of water to cities on their borders. However, since even this water may be polluted with industrial wastes and with sewage, and since the lake may be at a lower altitude than the city, expensive pumping and purifying equipment must be provided. Usually the water is taken through pipes that reach out into deep water. The water is transported to the city through large pipes called conduits (kŏn'dĭts).

In the United States the Atlantic belt in general has an adequate water supply. Reforestation has been necessary in some localities to preserve or increase this supply and to prevent excessive soil erosion. As new sources of water supply have been required for large cities, lands of watersheds have been purchased, buildings removed, and millions of trees planted.

The great area drained and watered by the Mississippi River is rich agriculturally because of the water supply. However, much of the western third of our country must depend upon transporting water great distances from natural and artificial lakes to water its famous gardens and farms. Many a garden spot would soon change back to its desert condition if it had to depend upon local rain and snowfall for its water. In these great open spaces of the west, precious water changes barren lands to fields of berries, large fruits, garden truck, and flowers as fine as any that nature can give when water is at hand.

In the Snake River Valley of Idaho, more than 200,000 people now live where all was barren land until man improved the water supply. One hundred and fifty years ago the Los Angeles district had a few thousand population with scarcely enough water to grow their crops. By means of water brought 240 miles from the mountains, far across the Mojave Desert, more than 2,000,000 people are now supported and great quantities of fruits and vegetables are raised and shipped to all

Courtesy U. S. Bureau of Reclamation

HOOVER DAM

Dams such as Hoover Dam, once called Boulder Dam, in the Colorado River, make possible electrical power, recreation, flood control, and water for irrigation projects.

parts of the United States and to other countries. As the population and industries of the west increase, new water supplies will be needed. One proposal is the production of fresh water from sea water. However, present methods for making sea water drinkable are too expensive. Scientists must find an inexpensive method of removing the salt from thousands of gallons of water daily.

Another problem related to water supply is the rate of soil erosion. In the southwest, cattle and sheep grazing has resulted in enormous areas losing the cover crop that resisted erosion by flooded rivers. Such an area may be called a "dust bowl" because through lack of water and vegetation the wind removes vast quantities of soil. The flood waters carry great quantities of silt from the slopes and fill the river channels. Hence each flood overrides more land and thus increases the barrenness. Flood control by means of dams and storage lakes and the re-establishment of the cover crop are necessary to check the destructive soil erosion. Feeding by herds of animals must be regulated to prevent further destroying of the cover crops that still remain. Our government and private scientists are studying the causes of erosion and devising methods of preventing it so as to conserve the good top soil.

LIBRARY RESEARCH:

In your library look up about one or more great water supply projects of the west or the T.V.A. of Tennessee. Report your findings to your class.

Flood control projects do much more than control the runoff of water. The reservoirs furnish water the year round for all needs. They provide power to drive electric generators so more people may have its benefits. The reservoirs (artificial lakes) are stocked with fish. People who lived on flooded land are moved to better lands for gardens and farms.

General Problem 2. How Is Water Brought to the Home?

From the Natural Source to the Reservoirs. — The science principles involved in transferring water from the source to a conveniently located storage place are practically the same regardless of the source of the water or the size of the community served. In all possible cases reservoirs are placed at an altitude higher than the community so that gravity may be used to

GRAVITY WATER SUPPLY

When the source is at a higher altitude than the place where the water is used, gravity provides an efficient means of transporting water. Water in this huge conduit is being carried four and a half miles by gravity.

force the water through water mains into the water pipes of the houses, and to produce enough pressure to cause the water to flow rapidly from all faucets.

In like manner, if the water sources are at a still greater altitude than the reservoirs, the force of gravity can be used to cause the water to pass through conduits down through the valleys and over the hills to the reservoirs, providing that no hill is higher than the level of the water at the source. The alternative to this

KEY EXPERIMENT 24

Does water exert a downward pressure and does its pressure vary with its depth?

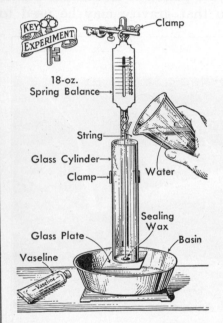

Clamp

18-oz.
Spring Balance

String

Glass Cylinder

Clamp

Water

Sealing
Wax

Glass Plate

Basin

Vaseline

Be sure you can read the marks on the spring balance accurately before you begin the experiment. You might want to use the balance first to weigh a few small objects for practice.

What two forces acting in opposite directions do you use in this experiment?

WHAT TO USE: — An 18-ounce spring balance; a glass cylinder (3 in. $\times$ 12 in.) with ground end; a glass plate, 2 in. square; sealing wax; string; vaseline; basin; a ring stand; and two clamps.

WHAT TO DO: — 1. Fasten the string to the center of the glass plate with sealing wax.

2. Smear vaseline on the glass plate around the wax.

3. Fasten the cylinder in a vertical position, with the basin underneath.

4. Pass the end of the string up through the cylinder and fasten it to the hook of the balance.

5. Fasten the balance to a movable support on the ring stand.

6. Adjust the position of the balance so that the glass plate is held up against the cylinder by a force of 4 oz.

7. Add water slowly to the cylinder and note the depth when the weight (downward pressure) of the water is just enough to push the glass plate away from the cylinder.

8. Readjust the balance so that it shows a 6-oz. pull. Add water as before, noting the depth required to push down the plate. Make several similar trials.

WHAT HAPPENS: — 7. Did water stay in the cylinder at first? What held it in? When a certain depth was reached, did the water push out at the bottom? Why?

8. Did the depth of water required to push out the plate vary with the force exerted by the balance? Did the balance measure the downward pressure?

Make a labeled diagram to illustrate each trial.

CONCLUSION: — Briefly, what did you prove? Give the evidence which you think is proof of your statement.

What was the relation between the downward pressure and depth?

APPLICATION: — Why cannot a person dive more than a few feet into water?

---

gravity system is a *pumping system*. The pumping system requires more complicated and costly equipment, making it less economical than the gravity system.

The Gravity System. — You know that water runs downhill by gravity. You know also that if the water in a stream is blocked or dammed, the water will fill up and overflow the dam, if indeed it does not push the dam out of its way. Water stored in this way exerts a pressure or push to get through the dam. This pressure is due to the force of gravity tending to pull the water down its course to lower levels. The deeper the water the greater the downward pressure. By Experiment 24 you may prove to yourself that water exerts such a pressure. The experiment is important because it will show you how a gravity system works.

If you were successful with the experiment, you proved that water does exert a downward pressure and that the deeper the water, the greater the downward pressure. Downward pressure is caused by gravity and so is called *gravity pressure*.

A cubic foot of water (approximately $7\frac{1}{2}$ gals.) weighs 62.5 lbs. In other words, water in a tank one foot square on the bottom would press downward with a force of 62.5 lbs. if the water were one foot deep. If the depth should be increased to 2 ft., the pressure on the bottom (one square foot in area) would be 2×62.5 lbs. or 125 lbs. It would increase by 62.5 lbs. for each foot of depth. (What would be the pressure per square foot if the water were 60 ft. deep?)

Water pressures are generally stated in pounds per square inch. If you know the pressure per square foot, how can you calculate the pressure per square inch?

Besides exerting a downward pressure, water exerts a lateral or sidewise pressure also. Experiment 25 will show you how we know this.

FIELD RESEARCH:
Examine the plans for a dam. Explain why it provides for stronger construction at the bottom than at the top.

Now that you know that water presses downward and sidewise, you will not be surprised to learn that it presses upward also. You know that if you push a piece of wood under water and let go of it, it comes to the surface. The water pressure pushes it up. Perhaps you have discovered that a stone seems lighter under the water than out of it. This is because the water exerts an upward pressure on it. At any point in a liquid the pressure is equal in all directions.

EXPERIMENT 25

Does water exert a lateral (sidewise) pressure?

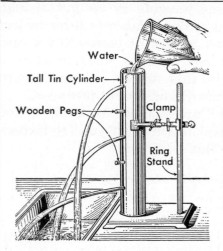

One question you might have in mind is: Does the shape (round with straight sides) have any importance? That is, would a square or oblong tube work all right? Suppose the sides bulged like an egg or water pitcher? What is one important condition? Which of the two forces used in Experiment 24 is used in this one? Would it make any difference if you used some other liquid? What difference? Why?

WHAT TO USE: — A tall tin cylinder closed at the bottom or tin can with three to five holes in line from top to bottom, and wooden pegs to fit the holes. One hole should be near the top, one near the middle and one near the bottom.

WHAT TO DO: — 1. Put the cylinder or can in a sink. Place the little wooden pegs in each hole and fill the cylinder or can with water.

2. Quickly remove all the pegs. Add water to keep the can full.

WHAT HAPPENS: — 2. Did the water spurt out of each hole? Did it spurt out of one hole farther than from any of the others? Which one?

CONCLUSION: — What caused the water to spurt out the side holes? Why did it spurt out farther from some than from others?

APPLICATION: — Why are dams built thicker and stronger at the bottom than at the top?

297

You can prove that a stone or piece of metal is lighter in water than in air by tying the stone to a piece of string with the other end fastened to one end of a balance or lever. With the stone hanging in air put enough weights on the other end of the balance or lever to just balance the stone. Then lower the stone into a dish of water. It now will not need as much weight to balance it. This proves that water has an upward pressure as well as downward and lateral pressures.

You have heard that "water seeks its level." You should now be able to explain why. If you try Experiment 26, you will prove this statement.

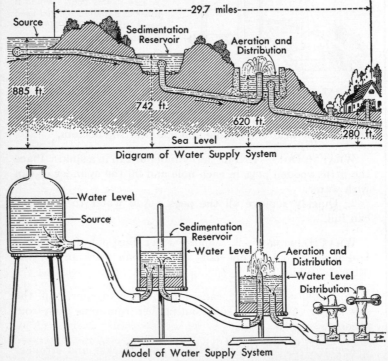

Diagram of Water Supply System

Model of Water Supply System

You can make a model water supply system like the lower one. Explain each part in the above diagram and model.

EXPERIMENT 26

Does water seek its own level?

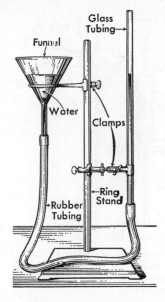

In what ways is this experiment similar to Experiment 25? Look back to Experiment 25, page 297, and figure out what you could add to make it illustrate that water seeks its own level. What force is acting on the water in both experiments?

WHAT TO USE: — Funnel; rubber tubing; glass tubing; and a ring stand with clamps.

WHAT TO DO: — 1. Set up the apparatus as in the drawing so that the water can run from the bottom of the funnel through the rubber tubing into the glass tube held upright.
2. Gradually fill the funnel with water.

WHAT HAPPENS: — 1. Does the water run into the glass tube?
2. As you continue to add water to the funnel, how does the height of the top of the water in the tube compare with the top of the water in the funnel?

CONCLUSION: — Consider what you have learned about water pressure and try to explain what you have demonstrated in this experiment.

EXPERIMENT 27

How does a model gravity water-supply system work?

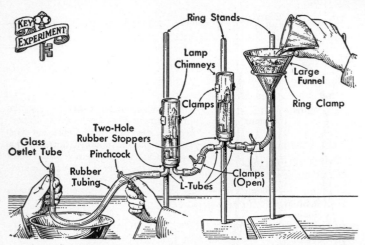

Another "Key" Experiment. Why is it important? What difference would it make with the water spurting from the tube at the left, if the container (reservoir) at the right of the hand in the sketch were higher? What force caused the water to flow through the apparatus?

WHAT TO USE: — A large funnel; three pieces of rubber tubing; two straight-sided lamp chimneys with two-hole rubber stoppers or corks to fit; three ring stands and clamps to hold the chimneys; one pinchcock; two clamps; a pointed glass outlet tube drawn to a small opening; and four "L" tubes. One "L" tube should have the long end drawn out to a small opening.

WHAT TO DO: — Study the diagram (page 298) of an actual gravity system used by a large city and set up a model as represented by the diagram on this page.

When all is connected and the clamps (representing valves) properly closed, fill the large funnel (representing a lake) with water. Open the "valves" and allow water to flow (1) to the first chimney representing the sedimentation reservoir, (2) then into the city reservoir chimney which contains a fountain (pointed "L" tube), and (3) finally out through the pointed exit tube.

WHAT HAPPENS: — Does the water run (flow) from the funnel (lake) to the sedimentation and then to the city reservoir? Why?

Did the water form a little fountain from the pointed tube in the second chimney (city reservoir)? Why?

How high does the water spout from the pointed outlet tube? Does it illustrate the principle that water seeks its level?

CONCLUSION: — State how and why gravity causes the water to pass from the lake to the city reservoir.

What causes the water in the conduits to go over hills?

Explain the height to which the water was forced from the outlet tube from the city reservoir.

APPLICATION: — What is the result of the difference in altitude between the reservoir and the tall buildings?

Now you can understand that a gravity water-supply system is an application of the principles of water pressure with which you are now familiar, namely, that water seeks its level because of gravity pressure; gravity pressure always occurs in water since the force of gravity is always acting; water exerts a pressure sideways and upward as well as downward. These pressures increase with the depth of the water.

It is well enough to talk about a gravity system, but you will understand it better if you can build a model of such a system. Experiment 27 will help you do this.

FIELD RESEARCH:

Using the altitudes given in the diagram (page 298), calculate the pressure per square inch at the first reservoir and at the city reservoir.

EXPERIMENT 28

How can compressed air be used to supply water at higher levels?

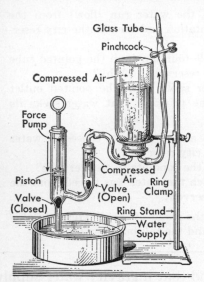

Glass Tube
Pinchcock
Compressed Air
Force Pump
Piston
Valve (Closed)
Compressed Air Valve (Open)
Ring Clamp
Ring Stand
Water Supply

What kind of energy is used to work the pump represented in the picture? Where does it come from? What kind of energy is sometimes used on the farm to work the force pump?

When the piston is raised, water comes up around the valve. What causes the water to rise in this way? What force causes the water to flow out of the "tank" when the tube is opened? What kind of energy does that represent?

WHAT TO USE: — A model force pump; a wide-mouthed bottle (12 oz.); a two-hole rubber stopper to fit the bottle; two glass "L" tubes and rubber tubing; a pinchcock (faucet); a glass tube drawn to a small opening at one end (nozzle); a dish for water; and a ring stand and large clamp to hold bottle.

WHAT TO DO: — Set up your model as illustrated. Place water in the dish (to represent a well or cistern) and operate the apparatus.

WHAT HAPPENS: — Observe how the air in the bottle (tank) is compressed when you pump and how it expands when you allow water to flow from the nozzle. This can be observed by the change in water level in the bottle. Where does the force come from that compressed the air?

CONCLUSION: — In a water system of this kind, what forces the water through the pipes to the faucets?

How does this differ from the water pressure in a gravity system?

What relation do you think exists between the pressure of the air in the tank and the height to which the water will be forced?

APPLICATION: — If you can arrange for it, you will be interested to visit a fire house and find out how the pumper works.

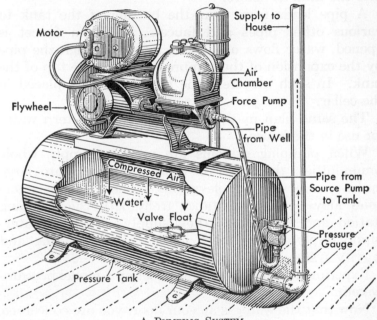

A PUMPING SYSTEM

The motor in this system automatically turns on and pumps water when the water level in the tank drops. As the water is pumped into the tank, air is compressed. Why? What forces the water up into the supply pipe?

Pumping System. — Many people, living outside a community water-supply system, install a private pressure system like the one illustrated on this page. A

motor-driven pump forces water from the well into a tank containing air. As the water is forced in at the bottom, the air is compressed into smaller space above the water. The pump continues to force the water until the air pressure becomes 40 lbs. to 50 lbs. per square inch, as required. The motor is then automatically stopped. When the air pressure in the tank drops, as water is withdrawn, to about 20 lbs. per square inch, the motor automatically starts and more water is pumped into the tank as before.

A pipe leads from near the bottom of the tank to various other pipes and faucets. When a faucet is opened, water flows out, being forced through the pipe by the expansion of the compressed air in the top of the tank. In such a system the tank is usually placed in the cellar.

The same plan may be used to supply cistern water for use in the house.

When pumping systems are used to supply whole communities, the water is usually pumped into large tanks or reservoirs on elevations. These storage reservoirs may be some distance from both the pumping station and the homes they supply. Such a water-supply system is really a combination pumping and gravity system. (Explain.)

Experiment 28 tells you how to set up a model pressure system.

Now that the water is at your door, you are concerned with its distribution to various parts of your house. You are also concerned with its safety from the standpoint of your health. Therefore, the next few sections will help you to discover facts about your home water system, how the water is made pure and safeguarded for your use, and how you may further protect your supply and thereby your health.

General Problem 3. How Is Water Distributed and Controlled in the Home?

Plumbing. — Water must be brought into the house and waste water taken out. In communities with a common supply system, the water is brought to the house through water mains and distributed through small pipes. Water and sewage wastes are disposed of through waste pipes which empty into special disposal tanks or into city sewers. Plumbing has to do with water and waste piping in the house.

Water Faucets. — Faucets are an important part of your water system. They must be simple in construction and easy to repair. The faucet has a valve that may be opened or closed by turning the handle at the top of the post or stem. Most people find it desirable to have a faucet open and close without very many turns of the handle. One type of faucet is in general use. It is made in various shapes, but a little investigation will disclose that they are all about the same.

FIELD RESEARCH:

If you can get an old water faucet from your plumber, take it apart and compare the parts with those shown in the figure. Put the faucet together and work it.

During your investigation try to discover what makes a faucet leak and how to repair it.

Note: If you try to repair a leaky faucet at home, be sure the water is first turned off in the basement, or below the sink or washbowl where the faucet is located.

Self-Closing Faucets. — In public buildings, including schools, where water is supplied for the convenience of the public, it is wise to use a self-closing faucet. The Fuller faucet, shown below, is self-closing. Some self-closing faucets have a coil spring fastened to the post. When the faucet is opened, the spring is tightened up, and when the handle is released, the spring closes the faucet. A sanitary type faucet, that is at the same time very convenient, is a gooseneck faucet with a sprinkler head, under which the hands can be held. The water is turned on by pressing a button in the floor. When the foot is removed from the button, the faucet is shut off.

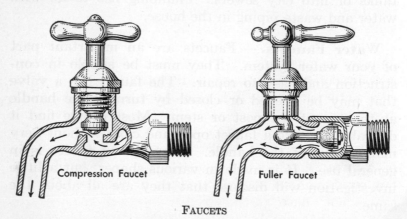

Compression Faucet   Fuller Faucet

FAUCETS

The faucet on the left must be opened and closed by hand. The Fuller faucet is self-closing. No spring is necessary in this faucet. The pressure of the water flowing in the pipe pushes the valve shut unless it is held open.

Faucets for Draining the Water Pipes. — In the cellar a valve or faucet is placed where the water pipe comes into the water meter from the street main. When this valve is closed, the water is prevented from entering the house. An outlet just beyond this valve is provided; it can be opened so that the water in the house pipes will flow out if the faucets in the rest of the house are open. Why must they be open? Can you give several reasons why one might wish to take all the water from the pipes?

General Problem 4. How Can Safe Water Be Provided to Safeguard Health?

Healthful Water in the House. — For home use the water must be clear, free from objectionable odor and taste, and free from dangerous germs. Water from wells or springs which may have been polluted with sewage or industrial wastes should be boiled for twenty minutes or more to kill all possible disease germs before it is used for drinking or food preparation. Likewise, city water should be boiled if there is any possibility of its containing disease germs. Boiling for less than twenty minutes may not destroy all disease germs. In the case of the city, the Board of Health will usually notify the people if there is need for any special care, but great caution should be taken in the use of water that is not known to be safe.

Water that has been boiled tastes flat when cooled, because the dissolved air has been driven out by the heat. Therefore it is a good plan to cool the water after boiling and then to shake it with air, some of which will dissolve and improve the taste.

Faucet *filters* are sometimes fastened on faucets to remove fine sediment but not, as some people think, "to remove bacteria." Most filters of this sort not only are useless but may become a source of danger, because sediment collecting in the filter may act as a breeding place for germs. The greatest objection to filters lies in the fact that they give a false sense of safety. If any kind of faucet filter is used, it should be cleaned and boiled frequently. You, as a student of science, should know that ordinary faucet filters do not offer any protection against germs.

SAFE AND UNSAFE WELLS

Which of these wells is unsafe? Why? What important factor should be considered before a well is located on a farm?

Vacation Dangers. — When a person is out hiking, motoring, or camping, great care should be taken with respect to drinking water. "The Old Oaken Bucket" may bring water from a well in which drainage collects from barns or outhouses. The water, though it may be clear, sparkling, and cold, may contain disease germs. The farmer says, "It's all right to drink; we drink it." True; it is possible that the bodies of the people who drink it may have built up a resistance which protects them against the disease. You may not have that resistance; so beware! When you are not certain of the safety of drinking water, boil it before using it.

Chemical preparations are available that may be carried on a trip to sterilize (kill germs) water if needed.

Iodine, compounds of chlorine, and potassium perman-
ganate are useful, but you need to know just what
amounts must be added to the water.

Community Health. — The health of a community
is very closely dependent upon the abundance and safety
of its water supply.   Lack of water or the use of water
containing disease germs may threaten the lives of great
numbers of the inhabitants.   Therefore, it is the foremost duty of a community to provide an adequate supply
of safe water.

Highly trained engineers, scientists, and health officers
must plan, install, and operate purifying equipment to
guarantee a satisfactory supply.   Before proceeding to
the next section, review the problems of providing an
adequate and healthful water supply to a community.

Sanitary Control of the Sources. — Let us study
a typical city to see how it safeguards its water supply,
how it brings the water from the source to the reservoir,
and how it purifies the supply.   This city secures most
of its water supply from two lakes (natural reservoirs),
one 395 feet in altitude above the city, and the other
586 feet in altitude above the city.   The two lakes
together have a surface area of about 2800 acres and a
drainage area, supplying the water, of about 45,000
acres of land much of which is forested.   (What is the
relation between forests and water supply?)

Most of the land bordering the lakes is owned by the
city and it is possible, therefore, to restrict people from
living on the shores.   Hence there is no danger of direct
contamination by sewage.   The lake shores are patrolled
and kept clean, free from decaying fish, garbage, and
campers' refuse.

Not only is the near-by land protected, but the entire
drainage area is inspected continually by health officers.

No outhouses or barns are allowed to be located in places where their sewage would drain into streams flowing into the lakes. Thus every precaution is taken to keep the lake waters free from any material that would endanger the health of the people drinking the water.

The same care should be exercised with respect to the drainage into springs and wells used as private sources of water supply. All cities and other thickly populated areas should see to it that similar protection is given their water sources. Science and the engineer leave room for no failure in such matters.

Acme

MAKING WATER SAFE TO DRINK

A safe water supply is always necessary for the United States Army. Here soldiers are treating water with a portable purifying outfit.

FIELD RESEARCH:

Appoint a committee from your class to investigate thoroughly your own water supply. Build a model to illustrate how it works.

From your local Board of Health you can get information about the number, if any, of cases of typhoid fever during a number of years.

Bringing the Water to the Reservoirs. — Since the lakes are above our typical city, the flow of water takes place by gravity through large conduits. Referring to the diagram on page 298, you can trace the course of the water. An intermediate reservoir provides a place where the fine sediment can settle. From this reservoir the water flows by gravity to the distribution reservoirs placed on hills near the city.

The water, after traveling long distances through closed conduits, loses much of its dissolved oxygen, and so it is sprayed into the air as it comes into the distribution reservoir. This process is called *aëration*. It causes the water to dissolve the oxygen of the air which improves the taste of the water, helps to oxidize organic matter, and, to some extent, kills certain kinds of germs that may be in the water.

The Purification of Water. — The purification of water to make it safe for drinking does not mean that the water will be chemically pure. Chemically pure water does not contain any dissolved minerals or air, and it is free from all kinds of sediment. The purification of water on a large scale consists of:

(1) *Getting rid of the insoluble material or sediment.*
(2) *Killing any disease germs that may be present.*
(3) *Aërating the water.*

The insoluble material is removed partly by settling. The water is passed slowly through large tanks. This gives time for most of the sediment to settle. You remember that water must be in motion to carry sediment along with it, and that when water stands still most of the sediment settles to the bottom. Some sediment may be so fine that it takes too long for it to settle. For this reason water from the settling tanks is passed through filters to remove the last traces of sediment.

Bacteria in water may be killed by dissolving a very small amount of chlorine in the water (0.1 to 0.5 parts chlorine to 1,000,000 parts water). The chlorine and the water form an acid which destroys bacteria. The chlorine treatment may be given both before the water has been allowed to stand for settling and after filtering, or only after filtering, depending upon the quality of the water in the beginning.   Occasionally water is *chlorinated* just before it goes into the distributing conduits.

Other methods of killing germs in large quantities of water are by the use of a gas called *ozone*, by treating the water with *rays of ultra-violet light*, and by treating

Courtesy John C. Taylor Company

WATER PURIFICATION

This water-purification plant at Milwaukee, Wisconsin, is one of the most modern in the world.   Water in the filter beds shown here is so clear that it reflects the lights and the ceiling with remarkable sharpness.   Is clear water always safe water to drink?

the water with small quantities of *silver nitrate*.   These latter methods, however, are not so easily controlled as is the chlorine method.   They are also more expensive and consequently less frequently used.

The methods of purification are about the same whether the water is transferred by gravity or by pumping and whether the water comes from a lake or a river.

Chemically Pure Water. — We have learned that by "chemically pure" water the scientist means water which contains no dissolved gases or solids and no suspended material. It is very difficult to obtain absolutely chemically pure water, but water sufficiently

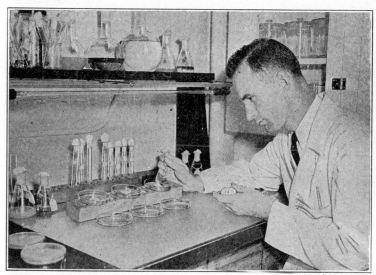

Columbia Newsphoto

TESTING WATER IN THE LABORATORY

pure for most chemical purposes may be obtained by simple *distillation*.

The separation of two or more substances by the process of distillation depends upon two factors:

(1) The mixture must contain a liquid which may be changed to a gas at a convenient temperature and changed back to the liquid state again by cooling.

(2) The material (or materials) dissolved in the liquid must not change to a gas easily, or, if it is another liquid, it must have a much higher boiling point than the first.

EXPERIMENT 29

How can pure water be obtained from a salt solution?

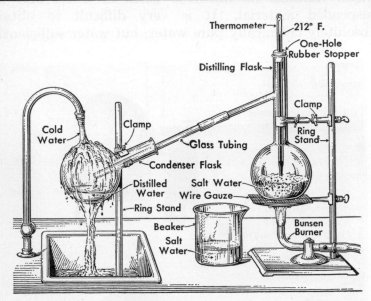

What process is taking place in the flask at the right? What kind of energy is causing this to happen? Where does that energy come from? How much difference would it make if the thermometer bulb were lowered so that it reached into the water? Try it.

What process is taking place in the flask at the right? What is being removed from the steam? Where does it go? Why does the salt not go over with the steam?

WHAT TO USE: — A distilling flask (250 cc.) with one-hole rubber stopper to fit; thermometer; a condenser flask; cold running water; a beaker; two ring stands and clamps to support the flasks in position; Bunsen burner; and a cupful of salt water made by dissolving two teaspoonfuls of salt in the water.

WHAT TO DO: — 1. Set up the apparatus as in the picture, with about a cupful of the salt water solution.

2. Start the cold water running outside the condensing

flask. If running water is not convenient, cold water can be poured on the condenser flask from a beaker.

3. Heat the solution slowly to boiling and keep it boiling quietly until about half gone.

4. Note the temperature of the steam as the water boils.

5. The condensed steam formed in the condenser flask is called the *distillate.* Pour out some of it and test it for color, taste, and odor.

6. Pour out what is left in the distilling flask and test it for color, taste, and odor.

WHAT HAPPENS: — 3. Did steam form and pass out of the distilling flask?

Could you see the steam change back to liquid in the condensing tube?

How fast did the distilled water drop from the end of the tube into the condenser?

5. Describe the distilled water.

6. What was left in the flask? Describe it.

CONCLUSION: — Explain how you prepared the pure water.

APPLICATION: — How does the making of maple sugar depend upon distillation? Why is ocean water salty?

When a sample of water containing substances in solution is boiled, the water portion changes to a gas (steam) and escapes, and the solid materials of the solution remain, since they will not change readily to the gaseous state. The gaseous water given off is condensed to a liquid again by passing it through a pipe surrounded by cold water.

Any two liquids may be separated by distillation, provided the boiling point of one is considerably lower than the boiling point of the other. For example, alcohol has a boiling point of 172.4° F. and water a boiling point of 212° F. Therefore, it is possible to separate these two liquids by keeping the temperature of the mixture only slightly above 172.4° F. At this temperature the alcohol will change to a gas and escape to the condensing tube, leaving most of the water as a residue. However, a very small amount of water will also be driven off with the alcohol since water evaporates to some extent at all temperatures.

In order to understand thoroughly the process of distillation you may need to try Experiment 29. The methods of distillation differ slightly with different substances, but the science principles are the same.

Commercial water *stills* (devices for distilling) are made of metal, usually tin, because tin does not dissolve in the water. Means are provided to operate the still continuously and to care for the distilled water automatically so that large quantities may be produced with the least possible amount of attention.

Distilled water is needed by chemists in their work, by people who make up medicines, and by scientists generally for testing purposes. Batteries for automobiles should be refilled with distilled water to prolong their life. Ordinarily distilled water is not necessary for drinking.

Applications of Distillation. — The process of distillation has many important applications. *Gasoline* used in automobile engines is a liquid obtained from *crude petroleum* by distillation. At different distilling temperatures different liquids are driven off from the petroleum, such as *gasoline, kerosene,* and various grades of *lubricating oils.*

Soft coal, although a solid, can also be distilled by heating it in an airtight container. This causes gases such as *coal gas* and *ammonia* to be given off. The solid material left is called *coke.* This kind of distillation is called *destructive distillation. Wood alcohol* is obtained by destructive distillation of wood.

Thinking Things Over. — Probably you have studied some things about water every year you have studied science. This is because water is such an important substance. At this time it might be well to try to recall from your earlier experiences what you have learned before, and then think over the new facts you have just been discovering. If you do that, you will find that many of the facts about water have been presented over and over again.

Many scientists have studied water for years and yet they are still learning new things about it. So you too must expect to meet problems of air and water over and over.

This topic had to do especially with the water supply and its relation to health and industry. Our next problems relate to the uses of water.

Key Words

aëration	drainage area	purify
chemically pure	faucet	reservoir
chlorine	filter	sediment
condenser	gravity	sewage
conduits	insoluble	source
contamination	lateral pressure	upward pressure
destructive	oxidize	water supply
distillation	plumbing	water table
downward pressure	pollute	

Key Statements

1. Well waters and spring waters contain minerals in solution.
2. Wells and springs are fed from ground water.
3. Water for a community should be abundant, safeguarded at the source, and purified for drinking before distribution.
4. Water may be safe for drinking and yet not be chemically pure.
5. Water may be crystal clear and cold and yet be unsafe to drink.

6. Lakes and rivers are common sources of water for com-munity uses.

7. Water may be brought by gravity to a community from sources higher than the community. From sources lower than the community, water must be pumped into storage tanks or reservoirs for distribution.

8. Water exerts a downward (gravity) pressure due to its weight.

9. Water pressure increases with its depth.

10. At any point in water, pressure is exerted equally in all directions — down, up, and sideways.

11. Water flows downhill, or seeks its level, because of gravity.

12. In small systems, compressed air in a tank in the basement can be used to force water through the pipes of a house.

13. Plumbing consists of devices for distributing and controlling water in the house and disposing of wastes.

14. A community must employ trained people to plan, con-struct, provide, and test an adequate water supply.

15. The water sources of a community water supply must be protected against contamination.

16. The purification of water for drinking purposes includes separation of insoluble sediment and killing of disease germs.

17. Chemically pure water may be prepared by distillation.

Thought Questions

1. What care should be taken in locating a well on a farm?

2. Why are wells a possible source of danger in villages that do not have a sewage system?

3. Why are dams constructed with thicker walls at the bottom than near the top?

4. Why will not faucet filters take germs from water if germs are present?

5. Why should drinking water of unknown source be boiled?

6. Why do some wells "dry up" during dry spells when others do not?

7. Why does not cistern water contain minerals in solution?

8. What are the desirable characteristics of a water-supply source for a large city?

9. What advantages has a gravity system over a pumping system of water supply?

10. What evidences can you give from observations of nature that water exerts a gravity pressure?

11. Why is a galvanized water pipe preferable to a plain iron pipe?   Why is copper or brass pipe preferable to either?

12. What happens when water is mixed with air?

13. How may large quantities of water be treated to kill any disease germs?

14. Why must liquids have different boiling points if they are to be separated by distillation?

Projects for Your Science Discovery Book

1. Investigate your home to discover how it is supplied with water and how the wastes are carried off. How many sizes of pipes are used?   Are the pipes galvanized (coated inside and out with zinc), or are they black iron, copper, or brass?   Are the hot-water pipes of the same material as the cold-water pipes?   Report your answers with explanations.

2. Make a diagram of the water pipes of your home.

3. Visit your community water supply and make a diagram which explains it clearly.

4. What special care is taken to safeguard your water supply?

5. Find out what water pressure is required for fire protection in your community.

6. Write an account of some famous water-supply system.

7. Would a spring be likely to have a greater force of flow if the opening were near the top of the water table or below it?   If a well is dug or drilled for some depth below the water table, how high do you think the water will stand in the well?   Explain your answers.

8. If you have a leaking faucet at home, place a pint jar or measuring glass under the drip. Note the time. Keep track of the jar and note the time when it becomes full. From your data calculate how much water (gallons) leaks from the faucet in 24 hours. How many gallons would this be in 3 months (the usual period for a water bill)?   What does the waste cost you?

9. Learn all you can about the dangers of getting typhoid fever from drinking polluted well or spring water. Find out the facts about vaccination against typhoid. Ask your doctor for information.

RUB-A-DUB

The first rule of health is cleanliness. And the greatest aid to cleanliness is soap and water.

Uses of Water in the Home

I will open rivers in high places, and foun-
tains in the midst of the valleys: I will make
the wilderness a pool of water, and the dry
land springs of water.

— Isaiah

Do you know:

1. What makes water hard?
2. How soap works?
3. When you should wash your hands?
4. How water helps to keep the home sanitary?
5. How water safeguards your eating and working?

General Problem 1. What Kind of Water Is Best for Cleaning?

Hard and Soft Water. — You have learned that water is a wonderful solvent. The minerals it dissolves from the rock and soil may be beneficial; on the other hand they may be very troublesome. That is the case with certain lime compounds. as we shall discover in our investigations of hard and soft water.

One of the important uses of water in the home, restaurants, factories, and public buildings is as a cleansing agent. Certain minerals in the local water supply have an important bearing on its usefulness for cleansing purposes. The terms "hard water" and "soft water" indicate that some water contains lime materials in solution while other water is not so affected. Perhaps the terms hard and soft came originally from the fact that it is hard (difficult) to make a good soap suds with water containing lime, and easy to make the suds with soft water such as rain water. Or perhaps the feel of the two kinds had something to do with their naming.

The minerals that cause hardness of water are *calcium bicarbonate* and *magnesium bicarbonate, calcium sulfate* and *magnesium sulfate.* Wells, springs, and lakes are fed with water that has passed through soil and rock layers. If the rocks and soil through which the water passes contain lime materials, the water will dissolve some of them and become hard.

Earlier in your study of science you learned that the air contains *carbon dioxide.* This carbon dioxide gas of the air is slightly soluble in water and forms *carbonic acid* with the water. (Carbon dioxide plus water gives carbonic acid.)

FIELD RESEARCH:

Your breath contains carbon dioxide. Using a soda-water straw, blow your breath through water containing a piece of blue litmus paper. After a few minutes does the paper turn pink? If so, it shows that you have formed an acid in the water. It is called carbonic acid. It is this acid that helps water to form limestone caves.

Water containing small amounts of carbonic acid dissolves limestone slowly, forming calcium bicarbonate, which causes the water to become hard.

Rain water is soft water for it has had no opportunity to dissolve minerals. If rain water containing carbonic acid soaks into the ground and comes to the surface as spring water at some point, it may pass through limestone and become hard water. If, however, the water travels through rock and soil that do not contain the lime materials, it will remain soft. (Distilled water is soft water. Does this help to explain why rain water is soft water? How is rain water like distilled water? Recall the facts about the water cycle.)

Temporary and Permanent Hardness. — Have you ever noticed whether there is a deposit in your tea kettle at home? If there is, your hot water pipes are probably being filled with a similar deposit. It is the same sort of material that is deposited by hot springs and geysers. The deposit is due to heating the *calcium bicarbonate* which is dissolved in the water. When heated, calcium bicarbonate gives off the gas carbon dioxide and leaves the insoluble calcium carbonate. Therefore, if a water is hard because it contains calcium bicarbonate (or magnesium bicarbonate), it can be softened by boiling. This sort of hardness is *temporary* hardness. Calcium bicarbonate (soluble) plus heat forms calcium carbonate (insoluble). The insoluble material cannot affect the hardness of water.

Dissolved lime substances like calcium sulfate and magnesium sulfate are not decomposed by heating; therefore, hardness caused by these minerals is not affected by boiling and is called *permanent* hardness. (Would teakettles used in some localities have more deposit than in other places? Why?)

FIELD RESEARCH:

Perhaps you know an engineer who will tell you some facts about "boiler scale" and how it hinders the heating of water in the boiler. It will make a good story to bring back to your class.

You will understand about temporary hardness of water better if you can try Experiment 30.

EXPERIMENT 30

Can temporary hard water be softened by boiling?

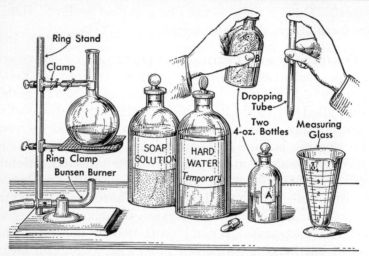

Straight thinking is needed in this experiment; so make sure you know just what your problem is and what you are to do. The size of the bottles is not important so long as they are not too large.

WHAT TO USE: — Water with calcium bicarbonate in solution. This is called "temporary hard" water; a dilute soap solution; two 4-oz. bottles with glass stoppers or corks; a dropping tube (made by melting a glass tube and drawing one end to a small opening; should be about 8" long); a flask; supports; a measuring glass; and a Bunsen burner to boil some of the "hard" water.

WHAT TO DO: — 1. Boil a portion of the diluted "hard" water for several minutes and then cool it to room temperature.

2. Put 2 oz. of boiled water into the bottle labeled *A* and 2 oz. of unboiled hard water into the bottle labeled *B*.

3. Now add the soap solution, drop by drop, counting each drop, to the water that has not been boiled (*B*), shaking the water between drops. Keep adding soap until a fine permanent suds results (a suds that will last for one minute).

4. Repeat the soap test using the boiled water (*A*).

WHAT HAPPENS: — 1. Did boiling the hard water cause any noticeable change in its appearance? Describe.

3. How many drops of soap did you use for the unboiled water?

4. How many drops of soap did you use for the boiled water? Which was the softer water; that is, which sample required the fewest drops of soap to make a good foam or suds?

CONCLUSION: — Did boiling the water soften it? How?

APPLICATION: — Why does some water leave more of a deposit in automobile radiators or teakettles than water from other sources?

Note: Temporary hard water can be made by passing CO_2 through limewater until the precipitate that forms redissolves. By this process you have made a solution of calcium bicarbonate. For use, dilute this solution with ten times its volume with distilled water or rain water.

Save a portion of the water with calcium bicarbonate in solution for Experiment 31.

Your experiment has proved that the temporary hardness of water can be softened (made less) by boiling. You have read that boiling does not, however, soften permanent hardness due to calcium and magnesium sulfates. In most cases of hard water the permanent hardness is much greater than the temporary hardness. It is important, therefore, to know how to soften the so-called permanent hard water. A method has been found of softening permanent hard water with washing soda. It is illustrated by Experiment 31.

Certain substances like washing soda, borax, trisodium phosphate, and others when dissolved in water unite chemically with the minerals which cause hardness. Insoluble forms of sulfates and carbonates are produced. United with the dissolved substance, the minerals no longer affect the water. Thus the water is soft.

KEY EXPERIMENT 31

Can hard water be softened by the use of washing soda?

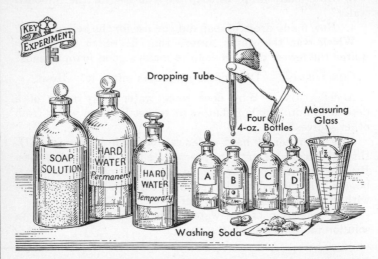

It will be a good additional problem for some of you to try to explain why a solution will not drop out of a dropping tube when the finger is kept tight against the top end.

WHAT TO USE: — A sample of temporary hard water (saved from Experiment 30); a sample of permanent hard water (made by shaking some distilled water or rain water with a small amount of calcium sulfate); a dilute soap solution as used in Experiment 30; four 4-oz. bottles with glass stoppers or corks; a dilute solution of washing soda (one teaspoonful to one pint of water); measuring glass; and a dropping tube.

WHAT TO DO: — 1. Label the bottles *A*, *B*, *C*, and *D*.

2. In *A* place two ounces of the temporary hard water; in *B* place two ounces of the temporary hard water and one half teaspoonful of the washing soda solution, and shake.

3. Using the soap solution as in Experiment 30, find the number of drops required to make a permanent suds in *A* and in *B*. Record your data.

4. Repeat as above, using permanent hard water in C and permanent hard water plus one half teaspoonful of the washing soda solution in D. Record the number of drops of soap solution used in C and in D.

WHAT HAPPENS: — 3. How many drops of soap solution did you use in A? In B?
4. How many drops of soap solution did you use in C? In D?

CONCLUSION: — Can temporary hard water be softened by the use of washing soda? Explain.
Can permanent hard water be softened by the use of washing soda? Explain.

Note: You may repeat the experiment using borax solution, trisodium phosphate, or any commercial water softener instead of the washing soda.

APPLICATION: — Do you think the use of water-softening substances would save soap? Why?

One thing the experiment teaches is that hard water requires more soap for proper suds than soft water. Soap costs money; so hard water is expensive to use for cleaning purposes.

In dishwashing machines, laundries, and heating plants where soft water is an advantage, special water-softening equipment is used that works continuously. Plan a trip to such a place to find how the softening is done, what substances are used, and the advantage of softening the water. Water-softening outfits work on the same principle as illustrated in your experiment. The hard water passes through a layer of a special water-softening chemicals. The bicarbonates and sulfates are changed to insoluble substances that do not use up soap.

The use of soap with the water is a very necessary aid in cleansing of fabrics, woodwork, dishes, the skin, or the hair. We have learned that the hardness of the water affects the amount of soap needed. Now we shall investigate soap to find out what it is, how it is made, and how it works.

General Problem 2. How Does Soap Aid Cleansing?

Varieties of Soap. — There are many varieties of soap. Some of them, according to advertisements, will do very special things. As a matter of fact soaps have one use in common, namely, they help to clean. The essential differences in soaps depend upon whether they are made from vegetable or animal oils and fats, whether they are made from potash or from soda ash, whether they float or sink in water, and whether they occur as a hard cake, a soft jelly, or as a water solution, called "liquid soap." All soaps have water in them and are used to aid water in its cleansing action.

A cake of soap, although it appears to be dry, contains a certain amount of water. A cake of soap that you buy may be from 15 per cent to 50 per cent water.

LABORATORY RESEARCH:

Cut a few thin slices of soap from the center of a cake. Weigh them and dry in an oven at 220° F. for one hour. Weigh the residue. Calculate the percentage of loss of weight as water. You can compare one soap with another by this method.

Soap Substitutes. — A soap substitute may or may not be superior to soap. It may be used because it has some properties not possessed by soap. Some soap substitutes are well suited to special purposes. There are a large number of soap powders or cleansing powders which contain small amounts of soap with varying amounts of *washing soda* or other water softeners. In some cases, scouring material is added.

Scouring powders have an important use, provided the scouring material is not hard enough to scratch the surfaces that are scoured. Once the polished surface of a utensil becomes covered with fine scratches, it is harder to clean. Therefore, we should use scouring powders which will not scratch.

Some soap substitutes contain no soap whatever. They are substances such

KEEPING THE BATHROOM SPOTLESS WITH A SCOURING POWDER

as washing soda, trisodium phosphate, and sodium metasilicate which when dissolved in water help to loosen dirt and grease.

Water for use in dishwashing machines frequently contains trisodium phosphate or sodium metasilicate. Dishes washed in correct hot solutions of these chemicals may be rinsed clean and will dry shiny and free from germs without being wiped with towels. This plan not only saves soap and labor, but the dishes are likely to be cleaner than when washed by older methods. The water used must be very hot.

Soaps are sometimes "loaded" with cheap substances that make the cake larger and heavier. Such substances are called *fillers* and may or may not have a value. For example, a soap for use with hard water may have some washing soda (sodium carbonate) or other softener added to help soften the water. It is probably cheaper to buy washing soda and pure soap separately and then add the washing soda or other softener to the water as needed.

Rosin is sometimes added to soap and is generally indicated by its yellow color. Rosin is a filler that has doubtful use in a soap. It may help in the formation of a suds or lather. Another chemical called *water glass* is sometimes added to soap. It is a filler that has no important use.

We cannot give all the details of the many soaps and soap substitutes. The thing to remember is that any claims as to why one soap is better than another should be considered carefully, and evidence should be required to prove the claims. Do not be swayed by unsupported claims.

Raw Materials for Making Soap. — The materials used in the manufacture of any product are called raw materials. These raw materials must be worked on or changed or combined with something else before a finished product is obtained.

Soaps are made by the action of an alkali on a fat or oil. Fat or oil and the alkali are the raw materials from which soap is made. Before investigating the manufacture of soap we shall study briefly the raw materials used in its manufacture.

Fats and Oils. — Oils and melted fats make a grease spot on paper or cloth. Therefore, a piece of white paper will serve as a ready test for fats and oils.

Animal fats are usually solid substances at ordinary temperatures, but they are easily melted. If heated to boiling, the fumes may catch fire. Butter fat has such a low melting temperature that it is melted by body heat. This makes it especially valuable as a food. The fats obtained from seeds or other parts of plants are usually liquid at ordinary temperatures; thus they are usually called oils.

FIELD RESEARCH:

Test small samples of fats and oils as follows: Drop or rub a little oil or fat (warmed, if necessary) on a piece of white paper. Hold the paper to the light. A "grease spot" will appear lighter than the paper. If held so that light is reflected from the paper, the spot will appear darker than the paper. This is because the greased or oiled paper is more transparent to light than the paper itself.

Cream, butter, lard, and suet are *animal* fats. Olive oil, peanut oil, cottonseed oil, and linseed oil are examples of *vegetable* fats. Both animal and vegetable fats or oils are used in making soaps.

Alkalies. — The chemist classifies many substances as *acid*, *alkaline*, or *neutral* substances. *Acids* have a sour taste. They turn blue *litmus* paper pink.

An *alkaline* substance, in solution, has a bitter taste. When rubbed upon the fingers, it has a slippery feeling. It changes the color of litmus paper from pink to blue. These are ways to test for alkaline substances. Many alkaline substances are known to the chemist. We are interested just now only in those that are commonly used in the manufacture of soap, such as *potassium carbonate* and *sodium hydroxide*. Household ammonia is also an alkaline substance used in the home for cleaning, but it is not used in making soap.

Neutral substances such as *pure water* and solutions of *salt*, *glycerine*, and *sugar* do not change the color of litmus.

Soap-Making on the Farm. — Years ago on the farm our great-great-grandmothers saved little bits of fat and grease from the table all winter long. And even our mothers in many places today save fat and make their own soap. The hardwood ashes from the stove were saved and placed in a barrel with layers of straw and lime. In the spring, water was poured on the wood ashes and lime to dissolve out the potassium hydroxide formed from them. The alkali from the hardwood ash is mostly potassium carbonate. Chemical action with lime mixed with the ashes changes it into *potassium hydroxide*. The fat was dumped into a large iron kettle and a small fire built underneath. The fat melted and separated from the bone and other materials connected with it. The latter were discarded. To the clear, hot fat was added the alkaline solution of potassium hydroxide. The fire was increased and kept under the kettle of fat and alkali for many hours, or until soap formed. The mixture was stirred with a pole of green wood or an iron rod. After a time all the oily, fatty substance disappeared. Also, if the mixture was a good one, practically all evidence of the alkali, such as taste and sting, was lost. The fat and alkali had united and formed soap and a substance called *glycerine*.

Courtesy Procter and Gamble Company

SOAP-MAKING ON THE FARM

What were the raw materials used in this method of making soap? From where were they obtained?

The soap and glycerine were then poured into a barrel where they remained as a soft, dark brown, jelly-like mass.   This kind of soap is called *soft soap* because it does not harden into cakes.   Soap made from a potassium alkali does not harden.

Courtesy Procter and Gamble Company

THE KETTLE ROOM

Into these huge kettles are placed the fat and alkali for the first step in soap-making.

What do you think is the purpose of the pipes and valves shown at the right?

Soap is not usually made at home these days, but people who do make their own soap no longer need to make their own alkali from wood ashes.   It can be bought in small, convenient-sized cans.

If you would like to try your hand at making soap in the laboratory, Experiment 32 will tell you a good way.   You must follow directions and measure carefully if you want to make a sample of good soap.

EXPERIMENT 32

How can soap be made?

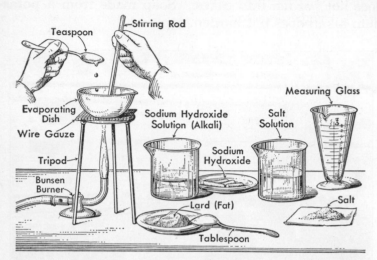

Instead of a porcelain evaporating dish you may use a small granite dish. Do not use an aluminum dish, because aluminum dissolves in an alkali solution.

WHAT TO USE: — Lard (fat); a 40% alkali solution (sodium hydroxide dissolved in water); a porcelain evaporating dish; a glass stirring rod; a tablespoon; a teaspoon; an iron tripod or other support; wire gauze; a beaker; a Bunsen burner; and a measuring glass.

WHAT TO DO: — 1. Set up the apparatus as in the drawing.

2. Put two level tablespoonfuls of lard (fat) into the evaporating dish.

3. Heat the lard gently until it melts and, while heating, add slowly one teaspoonful of the alkali solution, stirring constantly.

4. Heat gently, stirring constantly, until there is no evidence of oily particles and until a soap mass forms. Then add 3 ounces of water while heating and stirring.

5. Pour the mixture into the beaker and add one teaspoonful of salt solution (equal parts salt and water), heating gently and stirring.

6. Set the beaker and contents aside until the next day. Then take off the "cake" of soap formed at the top. Examine the liquid left in the beaker.

7. Test the soap to find if it will form a lather.

WHAT HAPPENS: — 3. Describe what happened when the alkali was added to the hot melted lard and stirred.

4. What happened when the water was added?

5. What happened when the salt solution was added?

6. Did a solid cake of soap form in the beaker?

7. Did it form a good lather? Was there evidence, in using the soap, of excess (extra) lard (fat) or excess alkali? If so, what was the trouble with your process?

Note: The liquid left in the beaker consisted of water, excess alkali, salt, and glycerine.

CONCLUSION: — State briefly a method of making soap. Do you think that other fats or oils could be used instead of lard? Try it.

APPLICATION: — Place a little oil in some water. Add a small amount of washing soda and shake. If suds appear, explain.

Modern Soaps. — The soaps used in our laundries today and those used for our hands and faces are purer and much better soaps than that made on the farm. There is practically no free (extra) alkali in a good soap to injure the skin or fabrics, and no free (extra) fat which would make the soap feel greasy. The alkali usually used — sodium hydroxide — makes a soap that hardens into a cake.

The manufacture of modern soap is a very complicated process, but the important steps are illustrated in the diagram on page 336. Several kinds of fats and oils are available, each having slightly different properties and requiring, therefore, somewhat different treatments.

MAKING SOAP

Follow the arrows in this diagram. What is the finished product? Does it make any difference which alkali is used in making soap? What is the important by-product made? What is it used for? How can the waste alkali be concentrated?

Boiled laundry soaps and boiled toilet soaps are made by placing the melted fat or oil into a huge kettle. The proper amount of the alkali solution is added and mixed with the melted fat or oil. Steam is then passed into the mixture. This heats the mixture and at the same time keeps it thoroughly mixed. The fat and the alkali gradually unite chemically to form soap and glycerine. Salt is now added which causes the soap to separate from the liquids which contain glycerine, excess alkali, and the added salt. The soap comes to the top of the kettle. The liquid is removed and pure glycerine is obtained from it by distillation.

The crude soap thus made is then treated with a more concentrated solution of the alkali. Water is added and the mixture boiled until it is fine-grained in appearance. The mixture is again "salted" and allowed to stand for several days. Once more the soap rises to the top and the liquid below is drawn off.

The next step in the process is the adding of perfume, borax, washing soda, or filler to the melted soap. The soap is then run into boxes and allowed to harden. After it has hardened sufficiently, the soap is cut into small cakes or bars, which are then pressed into special shapes with trade names stamped on. After drying they are wrapped and boxed ready for the consumer.

Not only is the manufacture of modern soap a complicated process, but also a process that requires great accuracy in measurement. Chemists constantly test the raw materials and the intermediate and final product to be sure it is up to standards set by the manufacturer.

Special Soaps. — Liquid soaps, floating soaps, mottled soaps, transparent soaps, and laundry soaps differ from one another principally in the final finishing processes. Liquid soaps are usually mixtures of potash and soda soaps dissolved in water and containing small amounts of glycerine. Liquid soaps used for toilet purposes are frequently made chiefly from coconut oil. Floating soaps are prepared by stirring melted soap in such a manner as to leave the soap full of very tiny air bubbles when it cools and hardens. The air bubbles act like little balloons which float the soap in the water.

Mottled soaps are made by adding coloring substances. Transparent soaps are made by dissolving hard soap in alcohol. Then, after removing any foreign material, the alcohol is distilled off, leaving a transparent, jelly-like mass which is allowed to dry in molds of the desired shape. Soaps for shaving, shampooing, use on the skin,

Courtesy Procter and Gamble Company.

Above — RIBBONS OF SOAP, SOON TO BE FLAKES

Below — A KEYBOARD OF SOAP

The soap is cut by piano wire, shaped, and then racked in rows to dry.

and in tooth powders are made with special care to avoid soapy odors, excess alkali or oil, and taste. They must lather freely.

Some soaps are called *medicated soaps* to indicate that they have some drugs in them. It is better to use drugs only on the advice of a physician, whether for use on the skin or in the body. Do not use medicated soaps unless advised to do so by a physician. They are expensive and probably of no more use than a good quality of toilet soap.

A By-Product in the Manufacture of Soap. — In a manufacturer's plant raw materials are used to make a desired product. Often other valuable substances than the main product are made at the same time. These are called by-products. An important by-product in the manufacture of soap is the *glycerine*. It is recovered from the waste liquid by distillation. The dilute glycerine thus obtained is concentrated and sold as dynamite glycerine. Dynamite glycerine may be still further purified for medical uses and other purposes.

An Emulsion. — Oil and water do not "mix" unless science is called to their aid. You know that if you shake a little olive oil or kerosene with water and let it stand, the oil will separate and rise to the top. The oil rises to the top because it is lighter than the water and will not mix with it. However, when the oil is broken into very small particles by shaking with substances such as soap or egg yolk, the water and oil no longer separate immediately. An *emulsion* is formed. An emulsion is a mixture of oil and water that will stay mixed for quite a while.

When your mother makes mayonnaise she probably mixes olive oil with a little egg yolk and then gradually adds vinegar or lemon juice for flavor. Thus mayonnaise is an emulsion.

Milk is a natural emulsion. You know, however, that after a while the cream (fat) of the milk will rise to the top. This proves also that cream is lighter than

---

FIELD RESEARCH:

Try the following experiment to make oil and water stay mixed. To a test tube two-thirds full of water add a few drops of oil. Shake thoroughly, and allow to stand for a few minutes. Does the oil become finely divided? Do the tiny drops gradually reunite into larger drops and rise to the top?

Now add a few drops of liquid soap and shake vigorously. Is the oil again divided? Do the drops reunite as before or do they appear to remain mixed throughout the water? If not, add more soap and repeat.

If you have succeeded in making the oil and water stay mixed for a time, you have made an emulsion. The soap sticks to the tiny oil drops and so prevents their uniting to form drops large enough to rise to the top.

the water in the milk, otherwise it would sink to the bottom when it separates. Have you seen milk that is called homogenized milk? In that milk the fat globules have been broken into such tiny particles that they do not separate from the rest of the milk and rise.

FIELD RESEARCH:

Take a small bottle of milk to school and examine a drop of it with a microscope. Try to see the tiny drops of fat.

Blowing Bubbles. — To blow big soap bubbles, a good soap solution is necessary. You know you cannot blow big bubbles with water alone, but when the soap is added, a strong elastic film appears to be formed.

FIELD RESEARCH:

To find out how much better bubbles you can make with soapy water than with water alone try making a soap solution and blowing bubbles with it. You can use a clay pipe if you have one or a glass tube or soda straw.

Another thing you can do is to bend a wire into a circle two inches in diameter. Tie a thread from one side of the ring to the other so that it will hang loose. Now "suds" the ring in your soap solution until you get a soap film to fill the ring. Is the thread held by the film? Does it extend in any special fashion across the ring? Now break the film on one side of the thread with a small piece of wood or other needle-like object. What happens to the thread? Does it look as if the film that was left contracted and pulled the string? Try it again.

If you have studied capillary action, you know that liquids rise into fine tubes such as those found in blotters, in soil, and in wicking. Do you think that water with soap in it would rise up (soak) into a wick or piece of cloth better than plain water? Try the following Field Research to find out.

FIELD RESEARCH:

Secure two clean glass tubes with very small bores. Stand one in plain water and the other in water with a little soap in it. Does the water rise higher with soap in it or without the soap?

You might also hang wicks in the water and in the soap solution to find out which rises faster and higher.

Soap added to water aids its ability to penetrate small spaces and so increases its capillary action. This effect enables water to soak into fabrics faster and farther than it could otherwise. The solution can also creep along the cloth surfaces and surround dirt particles better than plain water. Rinsing enables water to carry off the loosened dirt particles in the film which the water forms with the soap. The soap and water combination is an ideal team for cleansing purposes.

Soap as a Cleansing Agent. — By "dirt," as referred to on our clothes and bodies, is meant the daily accumulation of dust, dead skin tissue, and other particles held there by an oil. It is the purpose of soap to help remove such dirt. You have discovered that soap will *emulsify* fats and oil so that they will mix with water. You have also discovered that soap and water will soak into fabrics readily and loosen dirt particles. It is these two properties on which the cleansing action of soap depends.

You will be interested to try Experiment 33 which tells you some good tests to be made with soap.

Hot water is usually better for use with soap to clean greasy materials. In order that the soap can emulsify grease quickly, the grease or fat must be melted. Hot water will melt the common greases and fats such as occur on the skin, fabrics, or cooking dishes and table china.

EXPERIMENT 33

How does soap remove dirt?

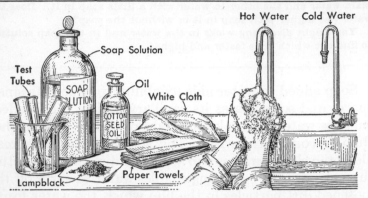

This experiment calls for you to do things with which you are very familiar. The difference is that in the experiment you have set up certain controls to help prove that the effects obtained are really due to soap.

WHAT TO USE: — Test tubes; oil or grease; lampblack (finely powdered charcoal); a liquid soap solution; a white cloth; and paper towels.

WHAT TO DO: — 1. Smear the inside of a dry test tube with oil. First try to rinse the oil out with water. Then try shaking soapy water in the tube and rinsing. Observe the appearance of the oil and soap after you have shaken the tube and contents.

2. Rub a little lampblack into the white cloth. Try to wash it out with plain water and then with water and soap, using a good lather. Examine the lather to find if it has taken up the carbon.

3. For three pupils: Let one wash his hands with plain warm water. Dry with a paper towel. Look for dirt on the towel.

Let the second pupil wash his hands with warm water and soap. Make a good lather and work it on the skin thoroughly. Now rinse the hands thoroughly with warm water. Dry with a paper towel. Compare the respective amounts of dirt on the two towels.

Let a third pupil use cold water and soap, and cold water for rinsing.

WHAT HAPPENS: — 1. By which method was the oil better removed from the tube?   What did the soap do to the oil?

2. By which method was the charcoal better removed? How did the soap help?

3. If the washing and rinsing removed the dirt satisfactorily, no dirt would be left on the hands to be rubbed off by the paper.

Which method removed the dirt from the hands the better? What do you think helped to hold the dirt on the hands?

CONCLUSION: — Explain the actions of soap in removing the dirt in each case.

APPLICATION: — Explain why mayonnaise (a mixture of oil, lemon juice and egg yolk) stays mixed better than the oil and lemon juice alone.   What is the use of the egg yolk?

Thoroughly emulsifying the fats and oils makes it possible for them to mix with water and be rinsed off. Soapy water soaks into the fabric or thoroughly wets the skin or other surface and loosens the dirt which may then be rinsed off.

Laundering Fabrics. — Proper laundering of fabrics not only keeps them clean and wholesome, but lengthens their life.   Good soap, water at the proper temperature, correct application, and thorough rinsing with warm water are the foundation of good cleansing methods. Clothing, especially that worn next to the body, absorbs perspiration.   The skin also gives off fatty or oily substances that lodge in the clothing.   Worn-out tissue from the skin becomes entangled in the fabric.   Such conditions make frequent laundering necessary.

When washing fabrics care must be taken not to cause them to shrink or to lose their color.   Woolen fabrics, especially, shrink very easily. They should be washed in lukewarm water with a mild soap.

Washing powders and bleaching agents should be used cautiously. If the water is hard, you can save soap by adding the correct amount of washing soda, borax, or other water softener. The water softener should be thoroughly dissolved before soap is added to the water.

White cottons should be washed and rinsed with water at a high temperature (approximately 160° F.). Rayons, wools, silks, and colored fabrics should be washed with water at a lower temperature. Good temperatures for colored cottons are about 130° F. and for silks, rayon, and wools 110° F. is about right. Frequently laundry thermometers are supplied with washing machines.

Sometimes when white fabrics are washed with soap they are slightly discolored after drying due probably to insufficient rinsing. In such a case they may be *blued* to make them look white. Too much bluing, of course, leaves a blue appearance. There are many brands of bluing substances on the market. Some are iron compounds and may leave rust spots on the fabric unless great care is taken to use the right amount. It is safer to use bluing compounds that do not contain iron. There is a good deal of science in laundering processes.

FIELD RESEARCH:

Arrange, if you can, to visit a modern laundry.

Laundry Machines. — Although soap and soft water are reliable agents in the laundry, they alone do not noticeably lighten the work of cleaning. Therefore, labor-saving devices are an important part of home equipment. Their development rests upon one or more scientific discoveries. The discovery by chemists of the action of soap and water in removing dirt is an example. In your study of the use of soap you proved that the removal of dirt depends upon the fact that the soap emulsifies the grease, and also soaks into the fabric to loosen the dirt. Hard mechanical rubbing is not necessary to this action. Hot or warm water with soap and sufficient agitation to form a suds are all that is needed.

Courtesy Westinghouse Electric & Manufacturing Company

A MODERN LAUNDRY MACHINE

After the laundry and soap are added, this machine automatically "does the wash." The dials are set, and the laundry is washed, rinsed, and dried. Even the water is turned on and off automatically.

The modern washing machine is designed to assist in the formation of an emulsion and to hasten the penetration of the soap and water into the fabric. It does this by various types of motions. It does not rub. Therefore the clothes are made cleaner with less destruction to the fabric. It is equally important to rinse the clothes thoroughly so the water may carry away the emulsified grease and loosened dirt. This also the modern machine does with a minimum amount of wear and tear on the cloth.

Then, too, the old method of wringing the clothes by hand to get rid of the excess water was laborious and destructive to the fabric. The hand wringer which squeezes the clothes between rubber rollers is an improvement over hand wringing. Even this method is hard on the buttons. Some machines depend for their action upon the same force that throws mud from a rapidly rotating wheel and prevents the earth and other planets from being drawn into the sun, — centrifugal force.

Machines are built that allow the water to drain out. The bowl is then whirled (rotated) very rapidly, causing a strong centrifugal force. The clothes become packed against the sides and the excess water is carried out by the centrifugal force, leaving the clothes only slightly damp.

FIELD RESEARCH:

Try this out of doors. Saturate a cloth with water. Roll it into a compact ball. Tie a short, strong string about two feet long to the ball and whirl it rapidly on the string. What happens to the water in the cloth?

Stain Removal and Dry Cleaning. — Accidents and carelessness are frequent causes of stains. Because so many modern fabrics contain synthetic materials and dyes, complete stain removal has become a very exacting procedure. Whenever there is any doubt about the fabric or the dye, do not attempt to remove the stain, but send the article to a good cleaner. If possible, tell the cleaner what caused the stain. If it is necessary to remove stains at home, a few simple rules will help.

Stains on clothing and linen are often due to contact with materials containing fats or oils. They may also be caused by contact with fruit juices, tea, coffee, chocolate, ink, or grass. Water, although it may help to remove spots, often needs assistance to be effective. Stains may be classified as follows:

A. Stains soluble in water, cold or hot.
B. Stains insoluble in water.
1. Stains soluble in denatured alcohol (inflammable), carbon tetrachloride (non-inflammable), or chloroform (non-inflammable), or some similar new materials, such as trichlorethylene. *CAUTION: On account of its inflammability, gasoline should never be used in the home for cleaning clothes or other materials.*
2. Stains emulsified by soap solution.
C. Stains insoluble in above liquids.
1. Stains on white cotton goods may be bleached with chlorine compounds and bleaching powder solution, such as Javelle water. (See directions for making and use as given on a can of chloride of lime.) Do not use Javelle water on colored goods, since it is likely to bleach out the color as well as the stain.
2. Stains on woolen, rayon, and silk fabrics may be bleached with an alkaline solution of hydrogen peroxide, with sulfur dioxide, or sodium bisulfite, or sodium perborate.

Chlorine compounds, such as Javelle water, *must not* be used with silk, rayon, or wool.

Coffee, chocolate, and tea stains can usually be removed by warm soap and water, followed with weak acetic acid.

It is particularly important to be careful in handling colored goods. If the stain is not removed by carbon tetrachloride or warm water and neutral soap, it is best to have a good dry cleaner do the job. Oil and grease stains are best removed by carbon tetrachloride. Grass stains are soluble in denatured alcohol. Iodine stains often may be steamed out or removed from the skin by rubbing with diluted household ammonia.

Dry cleaning is a process of cleaning fabrics without the use of water. In the early days of dry cleaning, both at home and in special establishments, gasoline was used. However, it is no longer used because it is not only dangerous, but leaves the fabric with an unpleasant odor. Modern cleaning liquids are non-inflammable and evaporate from the fabric quickly without leaving any odor. They are obtained from petroleum by distillation.

FIELD RESEARCH:

Make stains on pieces of cloth and practice their removal. This will help you if you have need to remove a stain on some garment or table linen.

General Problem 3.   Why Is Personal Hygiene Important?

A Clean Skin. — There is no doubt that a clean body and clean clothes are very important. We all agree to that. What we need to know is why they are so important. What science principles are there that we need to know in order to do the job most efficiently?

To understand clearly why the proper use of soap and water on the skin is necessary, we must study the *duties of the skin.* The skin is composed of two main layers. The *outer layer* consists of flat dead cells which have no feeling in themselves. They are continually worn off from the surface and are replaced by new cells of the same sort from underneath. The lack of sensitiveness of the outer layer, together with its toughness and elasticity, enables it to serve as a protecting layer of the body.

The *inner layer* of the skin is very much *alive* and very sensitive to touch, to warmth and cold, and to pain. You know this if you have ever scraped off the outer layer. The inner layer is also abundantly supplied with nerves, and tiny blood vessels called *capillaries*. This layer of skin also contains a great number of little coiled tubes or glands called *sweat glands*.

When you have a fire in your furnace, there is a certain amount of ash or waste material that has to be carried out. The same is true of your body. You eat food which is the fuel and inhale oxygen to burn it, and there is a considerable amount of waste matter that must be eliminated by the body. Some of this waste matter is eliminated through the skin. Each one of the little sweat glands has a *pore* (opening) through the outer layer of the skin. These pores are large enough so that you can see them in your skin if you examine it with a magnifier. If the pores become clogged, the sweat glands cannot get rid of the waste matter they contain. It is like stopping up the drain pipe. If the waste matter is held in the skin, it may cause *pimples, blackheads*, and a skin that is not clear. Also, if this waste matter is not eliminated it may produce a toxic (poisoned) condition in the body that makes one feel dull and have headaches.

A second important duty of the skin, is to act as a thermostat regulating the temperature of the body. You have learned that when liquids evaporate, they absorb heat and so cool the surface. When water from perspiration evaporates it takes heat from the skin. If a person tends to become overheated from violent exercise, the sweat glands acted on by nerves open up

and pour more sweat out onto the skin. This evaporates
and so removes heat from the skin and blood underneath.
Thus the body is protected from being overheated.
Anything that interferes with these actions may result
in overheating of the body; so you have another reason
for keeping the pores in condition to do their work.

Besides desiring a clean skin for the sake of our own
good feelings and good health, we have a duty towards
those about us. A person whose skin is clear and clean
is much more pleasing to us than one with a dirty skin.
Moreover, a skin which is allowed to become unclean
gives off a decidedly objectionable odor. While this
odor may not be noticeable in a well-ventilated room
containing few people, in a crowded room there is an
accumulation of such odors which becomes offensive.
Consequently, the use of soap and water to keep the skin
in a healthy working condition is a duty which we owe
not only to ourselves for health's sake, but to others for
social reasons.

A third use of the skin has to do with the sense of touch,
temperature, and pain. Most of you have studied about
the special senses, but it may be a good idea for you to
review them now. Some of the nerves in the skin have
endings (touch corpuscles) that are sensitive to changes
in temperature, or when touched. These special nerve
endings are closer together in some places than in others.
For example the tips of your fingers are more sensitive to
touch or feel than your back because there are more
touch corpuscles in the fingers.

The Use of Face Powders. — A brisk but gentle
rubbing or massage of the skin serves to draw to the
surface an increased blood supply. This causes a healthy
glow of the skin. Occasional treatment of this sort
will help to maintain the skin in a healthy condition.

Many people use powders (and rouge) to add to or suggest an appearance of cleanliness and freshness. These substances are not good substitutes for soap and water. People who carelessly or ignorantly cover up a dingy skin rather than take time for a thorough cleansing are risking skin trouble which may in time affect their health. Moreover, the continuous use of face powders is objectionable since they tend to fill the pores, unless the skin is frequently and thoroughly cleansed.

The use of powders to cover up skin defects is unfortunate not only because they do not cure the skin defect but because, on the contrary, they may possibly increase the skin trouble. Some face powders are objectionable because they actually contain harmful ingredients which, if the skin is broken, may produce sores.

An occasional use of simple powders, such as *talc*, may be of assistance in preventing the skin from chapping when exposed to severe weather. On the other hand, a healthy skin is not likely to be harmed by frequent exposure to the weather, provided it is kept clean and free from foreign substances.

Skin blemishes such as moles, pigment spots, birth marks, or warts should not be irritated in any way, since various kinds of sores may result which are difficult or impossible to heal. If they are such as to interfere seriously with one's appearance, a physician-specialist should be consulted. Quack skin and beauty doctors and unprescribed skin preparations should be avoided.

Your Teeth. — Your teeth are a most important asset to your appearance. You yourself probably notice nice teeth or poor teeth in another at first sight. And others notice your teeth, too. So, take good care of your teeth.

Ask your dentist about the best dentifrices (tooth preparations). Many have wintergreen or peppermint added for flavor, and very fine pumice or chalk for scouring.

When you clean your teeth, you are making the teeth, tongue, and mouth more healthy. You are safeguarding the entrance to your stomach, helping to prevent decay of the teeth and to make them more sightly; and you are keeping your breath pure and wholesome. Therefore, cleaning the teeth is of great importance. Once a day is not enough to preserve a good set of teeth, much less to preserve a poor set. They should be cleansed twice a day at the very least, and it is better if they are cleansed after each meal.

If little particles of food are allowed to remain in between the teeth where it is warm and moist, they rapidly decay and add a foul odor to the breath. You can easily prove this by drawing dental floss between the teeth and noticing the odor on the floss. Not only does such matter give a disagreeable odor to the breath, but every decayed particle of food serves as a breeding place for bacteria which may cause cavities.

Recent experiments indicate that the chemical *fluoride* helps prevent tooth decay by about 45 per cent. The fluoride treatment seems to be best if it is started when the child is about four years old, and followed at intervals by a series of brief, painless treatments until he is thirteen years of age.

Cleaning the teeth will also help prevent decay. Learn how you can thoroughly cleanse your teeth, and practice the method consistently. You will save yourself many an ache and many a dollar. Careful brushing is an essential part of the care of the teeth. Also use dental floss to clean between the teeth. Beware of poor tooth pastes and powders.

Visit Your Dentist. — Proper dentifrices are good friends to your teeth, but they, alone, will not assure healthy teeth. So important is it for us to have our teeth examined regularly that the authorities of many schools provide dental check-ups in the schools. In some high schools no pupil is allowed to graduate if he has not given proper care to his teeth. Why is this? It is because a person with go d teeth is less likely to be sick, and, therefore, of more economic value to the community.

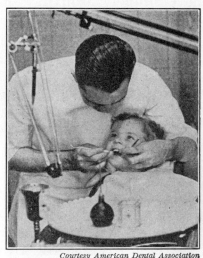

Courtesy American Dental Association

AT THE DENTIST'S

Have your teeth inspected and cleaned at least twice every year by your own dentist, unless this has been done in your school.

Cavities do occur. They are small at first, easy to fill, and cause little if any discomfort. However, the cavity if long neglected grows larger and larger and becomes painful and difficult to care for.

Without good teeth food cannot be properly chewed. Hence the food which is swallowed cannot be properly digested by the stomach without extra work on its part.

Digestive disorders may cause poor teeth and poor teeth undoubtedly set up digestive disorders. And so the trouble piles up. A good set of teeth helps you eat your way to good digestion and health. In a way food and teeth are partners. The proper food contains necessary minerals which help to build good teeth. Good teeth help prepare the food properly for digestion.

A Shapely Mouth. — Every person has two separate sets of teeth. The first set to appear is called the baby teeth or the *temporary* set. They "fall out," really are pushed out, at an early age to make place for the *permanent* set.

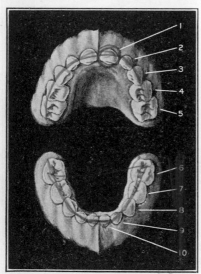

Courtesy American Dental Association

FIRST SET OF TEETH

1, 10. Central Incisors.
2, 9. Lateral Incisors.
3, 8. Cuspids.
4, 7. First Molars.
5, 6. Second Molars.

The first of the permanent molars, which appear when a child is about six years old, are frequently mistaken for baby, or deciduous, teeth. These four molars appear about the time the child loses his front baby teeth and replaces them with larger permanent ones. They are usually the first of the permanent teeth to show and frequently have flaws in their enamel covering. Therefore they should be given special attention by the dentist as soon as they push through the gums.

Sometimes the baby teeth are neglected because they are considered temporary. However, the child's baby teeth should be given just as good care as the permanent teeth.

There are only 20 teeth in the baby set, but 32 in the permanent set, including the third molars (wisdom teeth). They often do not appear until about age 24 or 25; sometimes they never emerge. When the permanent teeth appear, the roots of the first teeth are absorbed and the new teeth push through the gum causing the crowns of the baby teeth to fall out.

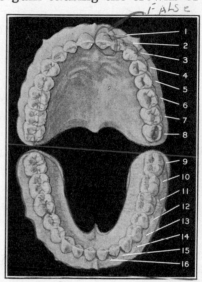

Proper food and clean teeth are the first step to healthy teeth. And healthy teeth promise a healthy mouth. But the dentist has taught us that there is another factor involved in the care of our teeth, — regard for their placement. It is a wise plan to have a young child's mouth examined by X-rays to determine whether permanent teeth are in their proper location and pointed in the right direction. While the jaws are in the formative stage, they are easily pushed out of shape by one or more of the permanent teeth coming in where there is too little room. Another cause

Courtesy American Dental Association

PERMANENT SET OF TEETH

1, 16.	Central Incisors.
2, 15.	Lateral Incisors.
3, 14.	Cuspids.
4, 13.	1st Bicuspids.
5, 12.	2d Bicuspids.
6, 11.	First Molars.
7, 10.	Second Molars.
8, 9.	Third Molars.

of misshapen mouths is mouthbreathing due to adenoids or other obstructions to normal breathing.

Parts of a Tooth. — It is a good thing to recall what you know about the *structure* of your teeth, for it will help you in your care of them. A tooth may be considered as divided into three parts — the *crown*, which rises above the gum; the *root* by which it is held in a bony socket of the jaw; and a short portion between the crown and the root called the *neck*.

Over the outer surface of the crown is found a layer of very hard mineral matter called *enamel*. The enamel layer is thickest on the biting end of each tooth and thinnest at the neck. The roots are covered with a bonelike substance called *cementum*. Covering the cementum of the root and attached to it is a layer of tissue which lines the wall of the socket in the bone and helps to hold the tooth in place.

Inside the tooth is an ivorylike substance called *dentine*, which is similar to bone. Inside the dentine is a hollow part called the *pulp chamber*, which holds the pulp of the tooth. The pulp is composed of connective tissue, nerve tissue, and blood vessels. Through the blood vessels food for the tooth is carried to it, and waste products are carried away. The nerves supply the tooth with sensation. These blood vessels and nerves communicate with the other blood vessels and nerves of the body through a small opening at the end of each of the tooth roots.

Tooth Decay. — Although it may not be strictly true that "a clean tooth never decays," you may be certain that uncared-for teeth decay much more quickly. The decay of a tooth is closely connected with the breaking, cracking, or disappearing of the enamel, and also with the eating of improper foods. However, scientists do not know exactly what causes the decay of teeth.

Particles of carbohydrate foods left between the teeth make good breeding places for bacteria. The bacteria give off an acid which may dissolve the enamel and cause the dentine to decay. This decaying process often continues inside the tooth for a long time before it is noticeable except to a dentist. See your dentist often!

Another possible cause of decay is a receding of the gums. The portion of the tooth not protected by enamel is thus exposed to the action of bacteria. Receding gums may be a symptom of a disease called *pyorrhea,* which if allowed to continue almost certainly results in early loss of the teeth. If this condition occurs, a specialist should be visited at once.

Foods containing calcium, phosphorus, and other minerals are necessary for proper growth of the teeth. These minerals are most abundant in fresh green vegetables. It is therefore important for you to include these foods in your diet. Scientists have also found that vitamin D is necessary for the proper use of these minerals within the body. An excellent source of vitamin D is sunshine. Vitamin C, found in certain fruits such as oranges, grapefruit, and tomatoes, is needed to keep gums healthy. Although proper diet is of great importance to the formation of good teeth in young children, it is also necessary in maintaining healthy teeth in older boys and girls.

Your teeth are constantly bathed in saliva. Saliva, you remember, is formed in the glands of the mouth. Some dental research workers believe that the saliva is important in the protection of teeth against decay. Just how the protection is afforded is not as yet fully understood. Drugs, dentifrices, and mouth washes sold to the public with claims that they will improve the ability of the saliva to help prevent tooth decay are useless.

The elimination of sweets from the diet will help to slow up the rate of tooth decay and may prevent it altogether in some individuals.

General Problem 4.   How Are Household Wastes Carried Away?

Sanitary Devices. — Just as water is a good cleansing agent, so the water itself will carry the dirt with it to the sewers if suitable equipment is provided. Sinks, bathtubs, and laundry tubs are all sanitation and labor-saving devices. Their value depends upon the force of flowing water that enables it to carry substances along with it just as water in the river can carry sand and stones.

Sinks should be placed so that the plumbing can be readily examined. Metal sinks (enamel or porcelain lined), sinks of special non-rusting metals, and porcelain sinks are most easily cleaned and kept sanitary. Sink waste pipes should be provided with *traps* to make a water seal between the sewer and the opening of the drain.

FIELD RESEARCH:

Investigate the water-using devices in your home to find out why they are located as they are. What material are they made of? How can they be kept clean and in repair? Make diagrams to illustrate what you find.

Traps. — You have examined the waste pipe running from your sinks, bathtubs, and laundry tubs, and have discovered that the water runs through a sieve in the bottom of the sink down through a pipe to the trap. A trap is so constructed that the water runs down one side and fills the other side to the overflow. This much of the trap is always filled. Then when more water runs into the first part, the second part overflows. Thus

Courtesy Crane

A MODERN BATHROOM

This room combines attractiveness and sanitary features. Note the walls, floor covering, and the fixtures. How do they aid in keeping the room clean?

there is always water standing in the trap. This water acts as a protective wall whose purpose is to prevent gases or foul odors from coming from the sewer pipes into the room. This is the main purpose of the trap.

Some traps are constructed so that they serve another purpose. These traps are arranged to catch debris such as matches, toothpicks, tea leaves, chunks of vegetables, and hair. The face or bottom of this type of trap may be removed easily in order to clean it out from time to time.

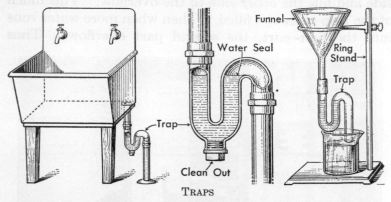

TRAPS

Traps differ in appearance, but are similar in one respect — all have a water seal. What is the purpose of the water seal? Make a trap like the one at the right. Explain why there is always water in this tube.

Toilets. — Toilets are designed to prevent backflow of gases and to provide a rush of water to carry the wastes away. In a *siphon-jet* toilet the water stands on both sides of the tongue and so prevents backflow of gases from soil pipes. This type of toilet is illustrated in the diagram. The water enters the basin and fills it to the rim. When the tank is flushed, some of

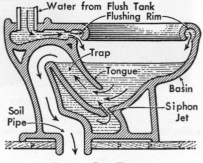

SIPHON-JET TOILET

This is a picture of a toilet split down the center. A "sectional" diagram like this shows inside parts. Refer to this diagram as you read how the toilet operates.

Why is it called a *siphon-jet* toilet?

this water flows down the side and some down through the jet, filling the outlet, which then acts as a siphon (a bent tube for drawing

liquids over the side of a container), and all the water is
carried out into the soil pipe.

FIELD RESEARCH:

Examine a waste trap provided by the teacher or obtained from a
plumber. Note how waste water enters and leaves. Is it so constructed that some water always stands in the trap? Why is that?
Make a drawing to show the construction of a trap and explain how
it works. Has the trap a "clean-out"? Why is that necessary?
Compare the trap with the one pictured in the diagram.

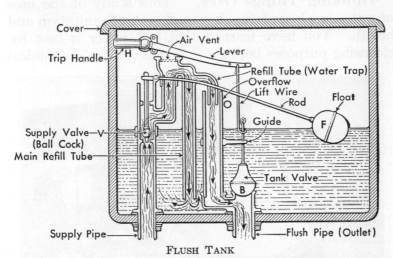

FLUSH TANK

Refer to this diagram as you read about the flush tank. Then test your
knowledge of its operation by explaining the purpose of each part labeled.

The construction of an ordinary *float valve flush tank*
is shown on this page. If the tank is emptied, the float F
sinks to the bottom and the supply valve opens, allowing
water to enter. At the same time the hollow rubber or
metal ball B closes the outlet. As the tank fills, the
float rises and finally shuts the supply valve at V. The
ball B is kept in place by water pressure above it. If
now the trip H is pulled, the lever arrangement raises

the ball, which, once raised and being lighter than water, floats, allowing the water to run out. When the tank is emptied, the ball drops down, closing the outlet again. The float drops and the tank refills. *O* is the overflow.

The proper disposal of human waste (sewage) is one of the most important municipal and rural problems, because the germs that produce typhoid fever, tuberculosis, cholera, dysentery, diarrhea, and other ailments may be carried in it.

Thinking Things Over. — Your study of the uses of water has been from the standpoint of sanitation and health. You have learned that soft water is best for cleansing purposes because it makes a more economical

H. Armstrong Roberts

FOLLOWING A GOOD RULE

To use water and soap freely and frequently is still one of our best
health measures.

use of soap and water softeners. The so-called hard water may be softened by use of certain chemicals called softeners. Water alone is not as good a cleanser as when used with soap. Body cleansing and good laundry practices are aids not only to health but to good personal appearance. The use of water and various aids to cleaning depends largely upon science principles and the properties of the materials.

Body wastes and their proper disposal present major health and sanitation problems. Our next unit will help us to know how wastes from the home and factory may be disposed of with the least annoyance and trouble.

Key Words

alkali	fat	plumbing
ammonia	glycerine	skin
baking soda	hard water	soap
by-product	lime	soft water
cavity	litmus paper	teeth
dentine	mineral	temporary hardness
deposit	molar	trap
emulsion	permanent hardness	washing soda
enamel	perspiration	

Key Statements

1. "Hardness" of water is caused by calcium and magnesium bicarbonates and sulfates dissolved in the water.

2. "Temporary hardness" can be decreased by boiling. It is caused by calcium bicarbonate and magnesium bicarbonate. These minerals decompose when heated.

3. "Permanent hardness" is not affected by boiling, but can be decreased by the use of water-softening agents. It is caused by sulfate of calcium and of magnesium.

4. Deposits in teakettles and boilers result from boiling water which has temporary hardness.

5. The principal function of soap is to act as a cleansing agent.

6. The cleansing action of soap depends upon its ability to emulsify fats and oils and to help water loosen dirt particles.

7. Soap substitutes usually contain some soap and other ingredients such as washing soda and grit.   Some substitutes, although they contain no soap, are valuable because they will soften water and loosen dirt.

8. Water-softening substances used with hard water before adding soap effect a worth-while saving of soap.

9. Soap is made by the action of an alkali on a fat or oil.

10. Glycerine is a valuable by-product of the manufacture of soap.

11. An oil emulsion occurs when the oil is so finely divided by an emulsifying agent that it will stay mixed with water.

12. Laundry machines are labor- and fabric-saving devices.

13. The treatment of a stain for its removal depends upon the character of the stain.

14. The skin regulates temperature, gives off wastes, receives sensations, and protects the body.

15. An unclean skin results in objectional body odors.

16. The evaporation of the moisture of perspiration from the skin acts as a cooling process to prevent overheating of the body.

17. Face powders should be used only with judgment.   Some are harmful, if used to excess.

18. Food allowed to decay in the mouth results in objectionable breath odors.

19. The three main parts of a tooth are: crown, root, neck.

20. Diseased teeth are responsible for many ills of the body.

21. Proper diet, including certain minerals and vitamins, is necessary to prevent tooth decay.

Thought Questions

1. Why does hard water require more soap to form a suds than rain water?

2. How can you soften water containing bicarbonates?

3. How can you soften water containing sulfates?

4. Why is water called "hard"?

5. What is an advantage of using water softeners with hard water in addition to soap?

6. Why are soap substitutes called soaps?

7. In what ways is an alkali different from an oil?

8. Why was farm-made soap of the early days a soft soap?

9. Why does a soap solution clean better than water alone?

10. Why does hot soapy water result in better washing than cold soapy water?

11. What is a bleaching agent?

12. Explain how whirling wet clothes dries them. How does this differ from what happens when clothes dry on a line?

13. How may powders used on the skin counteract the benefits of bathing the skin?

14. What conditions are likely to precede tooth decay?

15. What advantages are likely to result from frequent visits to a dentist?

16. What relation has a shapely mouth to the teeth?

17. How is modern plumbing a sanitary provision?

Projects for Your Science Discovery Book

1. Examine all the varieties of soap used in your home. Read on the wrapper what is said about each kind. Test each kind to find which one makes the best lather on your hands. Report your discoveries.

2. Make a collection of household substances and test with litmus paper. List them and indicate in each case whether it is an acid, alkaline, or a neutral substance.

3. Make a report on various laundry equipment machines and their advantages for laundry work.

4. Write a story about two boys looking for a job. One has a clean skin, fine, carefully kept teeth, and a bright, alert eye. The other boy is like the first except that his teeth show neglect.

5. Compare the shape, number, and functions of your teeth with those of a cat or dog. Explain the differences.

6. Make a collection of as many samples of tooth pastes and powders as you can. Read the labels and advertising material that comes with them. Criticize the statements in the light of your knowledge. Are all the claims just? Is each paste or powder safe to use?

7. Investigate the traps about school. Are they all of the same kind? Do they all work in essentially the same way? Compare them with the traps at home. Are they different? Illustrate each kind of trap.

8. Make a collection of all the brands of washing powders and water softeners available in your community.

Study the labels to determine what claims are made for each product, and then decide by experimenting and by your knowledge of the facts about such materials, whether or not the claims are valid.

Weigh the contents of each package and from the price of the package and its weight calculate the cost per ounce of each. Try to account for the differences in cost. Compare the cost per ounce with that of washing soda.

Nor love, nor honor, wealth nor power
Can give the heart a cheerful hour
When health is lost.
                                    Gay

≫‖COMMUNITY SANITATION‖≪

Recently a strike of garbage collectors in a large city threatened the city with disease. Why is it dangerous to allow garbage to collect and stand for days outside the houses in cities or in the country? You can give some answers right away.

Suppose an accident to the sewerage system where you live caused wastes from the human body and other household wastes to accumulate. Would that be a health menace?

What about your milk or water supply? Are they subject to contamination that might endanger your health?

One morning the people of a thriving city were warned by a modern Paul Revere that the drinking water was contaminated due to river water getting into the drinking water system. "Boil your water! Boil your water!" came the warning by radio every few minutes. When one telephoned, central said, "The water is contaminated. Boil it!" Cars with loud speakers went through streets calling, "Boil the water!" Friends called friends on the telephone: "Have you heard that the water is contaminated? Be sure to boil it!" In every school the warning went out. Thus did the modern Paul Revere of science warn the people.

Responsibility for a community's health and appearance is a responsibility shared by the government and the citizen. Do your share in keeping your community clean, healthful, and beautiful. Be a Paul Revere for health.

COME ON IN!

What sort of community do you think built this pool for its children? Swimming in the pool is fun for the children and it is also good for them. Do you know in what ways?

Does the picture tell you anything about the importance of sanitation?

A Healthful Community

*We are coming to recognize that priceless
as is the power to cure disease, power to
prevent it is of far more worth to the community.*

— Rush Rhees

Do you know:

1. Why the healthfulness of your city is a concern of yours?
2. Why garbage should be protected from flies?
3. What valuable substances are obtained from garbage?
4. Why sewage disposal is a health problem?
5. Why water and milk present special health problems?

General Problem 1. What are some Problems of Sanitation?

The Water Supply. — The maintenance of an adequate supply of water for industrial and personal uses
is a health problem of first importance. You are familiar
with and should recall at this time how your water supply is guarded at the source, protected, and purified for
the consumer.

Water is especially suited to the life and reproduction
of germs, because it is a liquid and is often warm. Another reason is that water nearly always contains good
food for germs. Hence the importance of preventing
typhoid and other disease germs from gaining access to
it cannot be overestimated.

369

Water in abundance is required not only for drinking, but also for proper sewage disposal, and for general city cleanliness. In addition to these health needs an enormous amount of water is required by industry. Usually all needs are met with one supply.

Many communities now support indoor or outdoor swimming pools where the water is kept sanitary by replacement and sterilization. These swimming pools are of great value not only from health and exercise standpoints, but also because they furnish many people with the opportunity of learning how to swim. Recreation Departments or Safety Departments of many cities hold swimming and life saving classes during the summer. Boy Scouts and Girl Scouts learn to swim and many earn the Life Saving Merit Badge.

Many schools have beautiful swimming pools where most of the students learn to swim. Can you swim? If not, make it your business to learn. It naturally follows that the more people there are who can swim, the less danger there will be of lives being lost in water accidents. Water for all kinds of water recreations is a most valuable asset to community good-fellowship and health.

FIELD RESEARCH:

Appoint a committee to study and report on the swimming pools or "old swimming holes" and how they are kept sanitary.

Another committee might find out how many children in your school can swim and how many would like to learn. Perhaps you can start a swim class if there is none.

The Milk Supply. — Water and milk are two most important liquids. Without water life could not exist. Milk is one of our most necessary foods. Both of these liquids are danger spots in community health unless

AN ADEQUATE SUPPLY

This picture shows a section of the spillway at the Grand Coulee dam on the Columbia River.

they are safeguarded from disease germs. Your studies have shown you how much care is taken to provide an abundant and safe supply of drinking water. An abundant and safe milk supply is equally important. How is this provided?

Courtesy Borden Company

A BOTTLING PLANT

At the left the bottles are washed. They then go by conveyor to the machine in the center, where they are filled and capped. Finally, at the right, they are inspected.

Unfortunately milk is just as good a food for bacteria as it is for you. Therefore, the problem is to produce milk and deliver it to your table with as few germs in it as possible and without any disease-causing germs.

The first requirement in the production of safe milk is to have cows that are free from disease. Stables must be kept clean and well ventilated. If cows are milked by hand, pails should have a small opening in the top rather than a large open top. This is to prevent dust from entering. The cows should be cleaned before milking

and the attendants should be clean and free from contagious (catching) diseases. The milk should be chilled
as quickly as possible to prevent the increase of any
germs that may be present.

For community use the milk is collected from the farms
and taken to the dairy where it is weighed and where
samples are tested.   It is then pasteurized and bottled.

Some milk is bottled raw, but even with the greatest
care disease germs may be found in raw milk.   Therefore, it seems best to pasteurize all milk and cream.
This is usually done by heating the milk from 142° F. to
145° F. for thirty minutes. Pasteurizing kills all the
possible disease germs, but not all harmless germs.
Pasteurization may destroy Vitamin C; however, that
is not too important because Vitamin C is available in
orange and tomato juices and in other foods.   Children
appear to grow just as well on pasteurized milk as on
raw milk.   We shall discuss pasteurization in more detail when we study the use of heat in food preservation.

FIELD RESEARCH:

Appoint a committee to find out from the Public Health Bureau
what diseases may be transmitted by milk. Learn also about any
recent milk-born epidemics.

Another committee might be appointed to inspect a dairy and
report to the class on how the milk is pasteurized and bottled. Perhaps arrangements can be made for the whole class to visit the dairy.

Most states, cities, and towns, in order to safeguard
your health, have laws governing the protection, care,
and sale of milk.   You will be interested to get a copy
of those laws and make sure that milk delivered to your
home or school meets the requirements.

Unused milk is made into various milk products such
as butter and cheese.   Some milk is "evaporated" and
canned.   Large quantities of milk are "powdered."

This is done by spraying very finely divided milk into a room where the air is warm and dry. The dry air quickly absorbs the water from the milk, leaving it in powdered form. Another interesting kind of milk is called "homogenized." This milk has had its fat globules broken into fine particles, and as result the cream (fat) does not rise to the top of the milk. Some milk is treated with ultraviolet light which appears to increase the amount of Vitamin D, the sunshine vitamin.

Another milk product is chocolate milk. Chocolate milk is supposed to be made by adding a little sugar and chocolate to whole milk. Therefore, it will have a good amount of fat, approximately 3.8 per cent. It is a wholesome drink. In many parts of the country, however, chocolate milk is made from skim milk. Often it is called "chocolate drink" or "chocolate chill." Its fat content may be as low as 2 per cent or 2.5 per cent.

Milk is most important in your diet because it contains easily digested fat and a good quality of protein in the best proportion for young people. Even more important are the calcium and other minerals which milk contains which are required for the development of good teeth and bones. Milk is especially rich in Vitamins A and B_2 (G). Vitamin A is especially important in preventing night blindness. Vitamin B is sometimes called the "pep" vitamin. Milk also contains most of the other vitamins although in smaller amounts.

Good milk is made up approximately as follows:

Fat	3.5–4%
Proteins	0.7–1.5%
Lactose (sugar)	6.0–7.0%
Minerals	0.15–0.3%
Water	87.5%
Vitamins	A and B_2 (G) and others

Be sure you get a quart or more of safe milk every day for your teeth and bones' sake. It is good — drink plenty of milk.

Sewage and Garbage and Rubbish Disposal. — Next in importance to the need for safe water and milk is the need for proper disposal of sewage, garbage, and rubbish. Human beings who are sick may contaminate sewage and rejected food with disease germs. Therefore, sewage and garbage become a possible source of contagious diseases through transmission by flies or through contamination of the water supply. Then, too, good sewage and garbage disposal means cleanliness and freedom from offensive sights and odors. Rubbish often contains cans with decaying food and dirt from many sources.

Clean Streets. — Much of the filth and débris of the streets is washed by rain or by street flushing into the storm sewers. Street dirt contains not only manure from horses, refuse spilled from wagons, and pieces of food material of all kinds, but it also contains expectorations of people who may have some form of contagious disease. Therefore, the streets should be cleaned of all refuse daily; they should be sprinkled regularly to keep down the germ-carrying dust; and they should have an occasional washing from the city water mains.

Tourists using the roads and parks and wooded groves around a town are often thoughtless about throwing out or leaving litter and refuse from their lunches. See that you join the group of thoughtful and considerate people who help to keep all highways and parks clean and sightly.

Most towns and cities have two sets of sewers. One set — the storm sewers — is large enough to carry off the water from rains. The other sewerage system is called the sanitary sewer. It carries wastes from the house. The sanitary sewer will be discussed in the next problem.

Harold M. Lambert

A MECHANICAL STREET-CLEANER

This strange machine is a modern street-cleaner. The brushes sweep the street and pick up the dirt. A little water is sprinkled on the street to settle the dust.

General Problem 2. How May Sewage Be Disposed of Properly?

What Is Sewage? — Waste matters from indoor or outdoor toilets, waste water from water basins, bathtubs, and sinks, and street flushings make up what we call sewage. Sewage contains dead organic matter and countless numbers of living organisms — bacteria and tiny one-celled animals. Some of these low forms of life are harmful, but many of them are useful. The useful ones act as tiny scavengers and help to break down the organic matter of sewage, making it harmless and inoffensive.

Under ordinary conditions the waste matter from an adult in one year is about 900 pounds, most of which is water. If to this is added the sewage of the streets and bits of food from the kitchen, and about 15,000 gallons (approximately 62.5 tons) of water a year used by each person in a city, you can get an idea of the enormous problem involved in sewage disposal.

Water and Sewage. — Because germs that produce human and animal diseases eventually find their way into sewage, it is important to prevent sewage contamination of all water courses, ponds, and lakes. It is possible that some person or some animal may need that water for drinking. Fish will not live in water that is badly contaminated with sewage. The results of sewage contamination include a decrease in the oxygen content of the water, an increase in the growth of water scums and molds, and the destruction of fish — all typical conditions of stagnant water.

Not only is the healthfulness of water related to the sewage disposal problem, but large quantities of water are required to carry the sewage materials to the disposal plants.

FIELD RESEARCH:

If you know of a stream that is polluted, examine it to find the kinds of plant life and animal life it contains and the kinds it does not contain. Try to have the pollution stopped.

Disposal in Rural Districts. — Objectionable methods of sewage disposal sometimes encountered in rural districts and small towns are indicated by the following rules issued by the Department of Agriculture (Farmers Bulletin No. 1227, Sewage and Sewage of Farm Homes).

1. Never allow the farm sewage or excrements even in the tiniest quantity to reach the food or water of man or livestock.

2. Never expose such wastes so that they can be visited by flies or other carriers of disease germs.

3. Never use such wastes to fertilize or irrigate vegetable gardens.

4. Never discharge or throw such wastes into a stream, pond, or abandoned well, nor into a gutter, ditch, or tile drainage system which naturally must have an outlet into some water course.

FIELD RESEARCH:

Examine a fly's wing, eye, and foot under a microscope. Can you discover how the fly carries filth? Catch some flies and place them under a wire screen with bread and water. Watch them for 15 days to observe their life history.

Disposal in Suburban Districts. — In country districts, villages, and new city and suburban districts where sewers have not yet been installed but where running water is available, sewage is frequently allowed to flow through tile into a covered tank or hole called a *cesspool.* As you study the diagram, you will see that the walls of the cesspool are built up of large loose boulders. This arrangement serves as a free place for the sewage to collect, and from which the liquid portion can seep or drain away slowly. Sometimes a second, or overflow, pool is dug at a lower level than the first. Cesspools need to be cleaned two or three times a year and the refuse burned or buried. At best the cesspool is not a desirable method of sewage disposal, since no provision is made for the destruction of dangerous germ life nor for the prevention of foul odors which sometimes accumulate.

Ultimately the liquid portion finds its way to some stream and so may pollute the water supply.

The Dilution Method. — The *dilution* method of sewage disposal depends upon the principle that if a harmful material is diluted enough, it is not to be feared. Some cities dump their sewage into rapidly flowing rivers or large canals. The sewage is thus greatly diluted, and

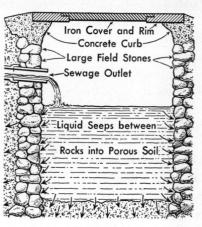

CESSPOOL

Compare the advantages and disadvantages of this cesspool with the septic tank pictured on page 380.

the oxygen dissolved in the water oxidizes some of the organic matter and makes it harmless.

If the stream is overloaded with sewage, complete decomposition of the organic matter does not take place, and the stream becomes a possible menace to health. The stream, at least near the sewage inlet, is rendered unfit for any use by man.

Another dilution method, much practiced, is to conduct the sewage by conduits far out into a lake or ocean. This plan has objectionable features because there is always potential danger of disease germs being distributed to drinking water intakes, in the case of lakes, and to bathers. To what extent fish may become infected is a problem not yet answered.

The Chemical Toilet. — In rural and suburban districts and in camps where running water is not available, the use of chemicals to decompose sewage is successfully practiced. An iron tank is arranged to hold several gallons of a concentrated solution of *caustic soda* (sodium hydroxide), to which is added a small amount of

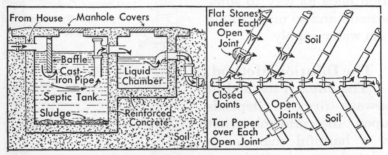

SEPTIC TANK AND FILTER BED

The septic tank is a good method of sewage disposal. When combined with a filter bed it is even better. Why?

How is the sewage made harmless in the septic tank?

What is the purpose of the baffles in the tank?

Why is there a separate liquid chamber?

blue vitriol (copper sulfate) or of *copper chloride*. The tank is provided with an outlet near the top so that as liquids collect, overflow takes place into a second tank at a lower level.

From the second tank the liquids flow through tiles under the ground to an area where it is safe to let the liquids soak into the ground. The solid organic matter of the sewage is acted upon by the caustic soda and liquefied into harmless substances. Odors are absorbed by the copper compounds. Occasionally the chemicals must be allowed to run off and a new charge must be added.

The Septic Tank. — The *septic tank* method depends for its action upon a kind of bacteria that lives on organic matter and does not need air. A watertight tank made of steel or concrete is divided into at least two compartments. The sewage flows into the first compartment in which most of the insoluble organic matter, called *sludge*, settles to the bottom. Excess liquid flows into the second compartment where more sludge is formed, and so on

PURIFYING SEWAGE WATER BY AERATION

through each succeeding compartment until only a clean and inoffensive liquid is left to flow from the final compartment. This clean and harmless liquid may be allowed to drain into the soil or into bodies of water sufficient to give considerable dilution.

The organic matter of the sewage is acted upon by the bacteria in the sludge and in a scum that forms at the surface. The bacteria help to break up the offensive material into harmless liquids and gases.

Study of the diagram on page 380 will help you to understand the general principle of a septic tank, and how it is constructed. Its value depends upon the helpful bacteria that decompose the organic wastes.

In general, the principle of the septic tank is used in modern sewage disposal plants for cities. Sometimes the liquid that flows out is sprayed into the air to enable it to dissolve oxygen of the air (aëration). This further purification must, of course, be made before the liquid is allowed to pass into a stream or lake.

General Problem 3. How May Garbage and Rubbish Be Disposed of Properly?

What Is Garbage? — Garbage is essentially vegetable matter with some meat, fat, and bones. A ton of garbage will contain approximately 1460 pounds of water, 80 pounds of grease, and 460 pounds of solids.

FIELD RESEARCH:

Watch the garbage pail for a few days to discover what goes into it. Does it contain only unavoidable waste? Or does it contain waste that is the result of carelessness?

Your investigation of garbage will no doubt disclose the fact that it consists of the waste parts of meat and vegetables, unfinished servings, moldy foods, and decayed fruits. Perhaps you will identify fats, oils, and grease, protein in pieces of lean meat, and carbohydrates in vegetables. All of these materials will decompose (decay) if allowed to stand too long. Offensive odors are then given off and flies attracted.

Four problems relating to garbage are:

(1) to reduce the amount by being careful in the handling and preservation of foods.

(2) to provide a suitable garbage pail.

(3) to have the garbage collected before it decomposes.

(4) to dispose of the garbage without offense to the community and at a profit to the community.

Because decay proceeds faster when the weather is warm, garbage becomes offensive more quickly in summer than in winter. Therefore, it should be collected and disposed of more frequently in summer than in winter. In camps and on farms garbage should be disposed of daily.

Garbage Receptacles. — Garbage pails should be strong, water-tight, and non-rusting. The covers should be fastened so that they cannot be removed by dogs. Frequently the pails are placed in inclosed compartments or in holes in the ground and suitably covered.

FIELD RESEARCH:

Make a trip to the store and study the different types of garbage pails on sale. Determine from the store clerk what he thinks are the advantages of each type. Decide in your own mind which is best and why. Report your findings and conclusions to your class. A drawing will help your description.

If garbage pails are left uncovered or are uncovered by dogs, the food material, which is likely to be scattered about, will attract flies and will present an unsightly and unsanitary appearance. The garbage pail should be cleansed thoroughly each time it is emptied. A good method to use in cleaning it is to sprinkle a little *chloride of lime* into the pail, then add hot water and stir with a cloth on the end of a stick or with a long-handled brush.

The chloride of lime is a disinfectant and deodorizer. It will destroy any bacteria, mold, or insect life present. Also, with hot water to melt the grease, the chloride of lime will react with the grease so that it can be easily rinsed out, leaving the pail "sweet" and clean. (The pail will not rust so rapidly if you will dry it and air it after cleaning. Why?)

Houseflies and Garbage. — If given the opportunity, flies lay their eggs wherever there is decaying organic matter. Garbage left in a pail, or lying about until the meat and fat begin to decay, forms food that flies like very much, and while there to eat, they lay their eggs. The eggs hatch into larvae called *maggots*. These change into *pupae* (a resting stage), from which emerge the new-born flies. A new generation of flies arrives every ten or twelve days from early spring to late fall and the female fly lays over 100 eggs at a time. Thus thousands and thousands of flies may be produced from a single pair in just a few weeks' time. Bright sunlight, heat, and exposure to air will usually destroy most fly eggs and larvae.

"Swat the Fly." — To combat this dangerous insect, the following rules should be observed:

1. Destroy all flies in the house, especially every fly that enters a sickroom.

2. Eliminate breeding places, — decaying matter of all kinds and manure. Most flies are born in unguarded manure piles on farms and in villages.

3. Prevent flies from getting at food in your home and in stores.

4. Screen all doors and windows.

5. Remove any possible breeding source at least every ten days to interrupt the generation.

6. *Remember*, when you see a fly in your house or on your food it probably came directly from a near-by place of filth and may carry disease germs on its feet and body.

The common housefly has so often been the carrier of typhoid fever germs that scientists have formed the practice of calling it the typhoid fly. A useful and cheap poison with which to attack this insect is a spoonful of formaldehyde in a pint of water, with a small amount of sugar to sweeten the solution. Pour it into small dishes and set the dishes wherever you find need for such measures. (*CAUTION: Put the dishes where children cannot reach them.*) There are also commercial preparations for spraying which are more effective and more convenient than the preceding method. The spray is harmless to individuals and to clothing.

American Museum of Natural History

A COMMON HOUSEFLY ON A PIECE OF BREAD

A recent material for destroying flies is the chemical, DDT, usually sold as a liquid mixed in a light oil, for sprayers. It is also available as "DDT bombs." In these "bombs" the DDT is mixed with a liquid which forms a fine mist when released from the "bomb."

Spring and summer are the best times for combating flies. Spray farm manure piles and stables to kill the larvae, and *avoid the conditions which breed flies.*

Private Disposal of Garbage. — The problem of getting rid of garbage from the farm home or in districts where there is no garbage collection is an important one that must be solved. You will agree that the garbage should not be thrown out where it can decompose and

become a menace to your health or that of your neigh-
bors.   It should be buried or burned.   The best method
of private disposal is burning.   Incinerators (ovens for
burning garbage and other refuse) are available for in-
stallation in homes or for outdoor use.   Recently home

A NEW GARBAGE TRUCK

These new dustless trucks are replacing the unsanitary "garbage wagons"
of old.   A truck such as this is expensive, but it probably saves its cost
many times in helping to prevent diseases.

garbage grinders have been devised.   All refuse from the
table is finely ground, after which it is flushed into the
sewer and so disposed of.

Community Garbage Disposal Problems. — The
safe and economical disposal of garbage for a community
has had the attention of scientists and engineers for many
years.

Feeding community garbage to hogs was unsatisfactory because the hogs sometimes contracted diseases. Burying large amounts of garbage required large areas of land which became a nuisance and health hazard.

Burning was found to be wasteful, and objectionable because of the odor. But in smaller communities, burning seems to be the only practical way of disposing of garbage, which is collected and brought to the *incinerator*. In larger cities various methods serve for removing the fats, used to make soap, from garbage. The other material is *reduced* to fertilizer. Experiment 34 illustrates how the fat may be dissolved from garbage.

A Modern Garbage Reduction Plant. — The garbage is collected regularly by a number of men using especially constructed trucks or wagons. It is collected early in the morning, generally before the city is awake, and frequently enough to reduce the nuisance of offensive odors during collection. The trucks go to the disposal plant in the center of the city, and here the garbage is taken into the receiving room for weighing.

It is then lowered through chutes into great kettles and covered with a solvent for grease. The kettles are then closed air-tight. Each kettle may hold five tons of garbage. The kettles have a jacket of double bottoms and sides and in this space steam is circulated to heat the garbage. Inside the kettle is a propeller-shaped arm that revolves slowly to keep the garbage and solvent thoroughly mixed. The steam is turned into the hollow wall or jacket and heats the mass to a temperature of about 208° F.

The heat causes water and some solvent to pass off as vapor through outlet pipes. Enough solvent is added so that at the end of about twelve hours of cooking practically all the water of the garbage has been driven off.

EXPERIMENT 34

How can fat be dissolved from garbage?

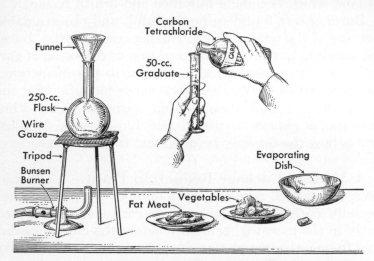

Do you remember what the word *solution* means? You have made solutions of salt and sugar, and now you will make a solution of fat. Instead of using water, you will use a liquid called carbon tetrachloride. Some carbon tetrachloride will evaporate when it is heated. Be sure you know what the funnel in the flask is for and what process, the opposite of evaporation, results from its use.

When evaporating the carbon tetrachloride from the evaporating dish, do not smell of it, because it may be irritating.

WHAT TO USE: — A small piece of fat meat (cooked) and pieces of vegetables to represent garbage; a 250 cc. pyrex flask; 50 cc. of carbon tetrachloride; an iron tripod; wire gauze; a Bunsen burner; an evaporating dish; and a funnel.

WHAT TO DO: — 1. Grind or chop the foods into small bits. Place two tablespoonfuls in the flask and add 50 cc. of the carbon tetrachloride.

2. Set the flask on wire gauze on the tripod or on the hot plate.

Place the funnel over the flask with its stem in the opening of the flask.   This is to prevent too great a loss of the carbon tetrachloride which is caused to evaporate by heat.

Heat the mixture gently for several minutes.

3. After a few minutes, pour off the clear liquid into the evaporating dish and place it on the wire gauze and tripod in place of the flask.   Heat carefully until the solvent appears to be gone.   *Do not heat the residue hot enough to burn it.*

Allow the contents to cool and examine them.

WHAT HAPPENS: — 1, 2. Did you observe solution of the fat taking place?

3. Was there a fatty residue left in the evaporating dish? Tell why you think it is fat.   Where did it come from?

CONCLUSION: — How can fat be dissolved from garbage?

APPLICATION: — How can a grease stain be removed from a fabric?

A quantity of solvent remains which contains the grease and fat in solution.   This continued heating also kills any germs or other life that may have existed in the garbage and renders the garbage inoffensive.

The steam is cut off from the jacket and the grease solution is drawn out through strainers at the bottom of the kettles.   More clear solvent is added to the mass in the kettle and stirred and drawn off.   The process is repeated until no fat or grease is left in the garbage. This "working" takes about one hour.   Any solvent remaining in the mass is driven out by heating for four hours.   The solvent vapor thus driven off is passed through cooling pipes to condense it to a liquid to be used again.

The material left in the kettle is dry and lifeless.   It consists of all material not soluble in the solvent, including bones, tin cans, and whatever non-garbage stuff was carelessly put into the garbage pails of the community. This dry material is taken out of the kettle and screened. The larger pieces of material are passed over a magnetic separator that holds on to all pieces of metal such as tin cans and nails.   What gets by the magnet is crushed and then screened again.   The final material that goes through the screen is sold as fertilizer.

The solution of fat is pumped into a still and heated. The solvent passes off as a vapor through condensing pipes, leaving the non-volatile grease and fat behind. The fat which is left is hot and in the liquid state.   It is pumped to fat-storage tanks and sold to glycerine and soap factories.

The above process has the advantages of being sanitary, inoffensive, and economical.   It is economical because the equipment can be placed near the center of the city, where the distance for the garbage to be hauled is short; the process recovers practically all of the fat; valuable fertilizer is obtained; and the solvent, after being condensed back into a liquid, can be used over and over again with but a small loss.

A Modern Rubbish Disposal Plant. — Rubbish consists of about everything a householder throws away other than garbage.

In our modern city nearly 400,000 pounds of rubbish is drawn to the disposal plant daily.   On delivery to the plant it is weighed and dumped into a receiving pit.   From the pit it is carried to the furnaces where it is burned.   The ash is then carted to the dump.

An interesting economical side of the problem is that the heat from the burning rubbish is used to generate a great quantity of steam which is used in the near-by garbage reduction plant.

General Problem 4. Who Is Responsible for Safeguarding Community Health?

Village and City. — Whether you live in the country, in a village, or in a city, you are responsible for any act or neglect that may endanger the health of others. As a student of science you have discovered natural laws which help you to understand the rules for sanitation. It is important, therefore, that you accept your responsibilities for promoting public health by cooperating with health officers chosen or appointed as your representatives.

County and city boards of health are charged with protecting your water supply and milk supply. They must provide inspectors of groceries and meats. They must also inspect places where meals are offered for sale, in order to maintain good sanitary conditions.

In some states and cities, dishes in restaurants and glasses in soda fountains are required by law to be treated so as to prevent spread of disease. This is done by using some disinfectant in the wash water or by using special lamps that kill disease germs. Barber shops, beauty parlors, and the like are subject to health and sanitation rules set up by proper authorities.

Working usually under the Board of Health are school and community doctors and nurses who help to promote sanitation and healthfulness in the school and home. With these officers you should coöperate fully and intelligently.

State and Nation. — While an individual village or city has certain responsibilities for sanitation and health protection, the state must have authority over matters that affect relationships among different villages or cities. So we find that milk and water supplies, foods for sale, housing conditions, and so on, are all under control of the State Board of Health. This is done to protect the health of the citizens of the state.

In like manner the nation has its health bureaus to regulate or control shipments of foods of all kinds from one state to another. Pure food and drug laws and laws for the control of foods, drugs, and cosmetics have been made to protect individuals everywhere.

FIELD RESEARCH:

Obtain copies of your local, state, and the national codes for sanitation and note wherein they overlap and wherein they are supplementary.

Thinking Things Over. — Now is the time to put on your scientific thinking cap. When you return from seeing a football or baseball game you probably talk it over with others. You try to recall the best plays and analyze them. You think about the poor plays and try to figure out how they might have been improved. So when you have completed the study of a topic in science you need to think it over and recall the important parts, how they are related to each other, how they affect you and your friends. Perhaps you will want to check some of the statements for accuracy or test the conclusions. You will need to know the Key Words and be able to use them accurately. The Key Statements may well serve to guide your discussions. The Thought Questions will test your mastery or knowledge of some problems of sanitation.

And now that you have gained some knowledge of the factors which govern the health of your community and the organizations set up for the protection of health, you are ready to turn to the study of the chief source of food supply — the farm and garden. Health and good food have a very close relationship.

Key Words

blue vitriol	disposal	oils
carbohydrates	fats	pupae
caustic soda	fertilizer	reduce
cesspool	garbage	septic tank
chemical toilet	grease	sewage
contamination	housefly	sludge
decomposition	incinerators	solvent
dilution	maggots	typhoid fever
disinfectant	magnet	unsanitary

Key Statements

1. The properties of water make it a satisfactory medium for sewage disposal.

2. Sewage consists of wastes from sinks, toilets, and streets, mixed with or dissolved in water.

3. Disease germs may be present in sewage; hence its proper disposal is an important factor in the health of a community.

4. Untreated sewage should not be allowed to pollute streams.

5. Flies should be prevented from access to farm and home wastes of all kinds.

6. The presence of flies often indicates the location of filth.

7. A cesspool is a drainage tank for sewage.

8. The chemical toilet depends for its efficiency upon the dissolving action of alkali.

9. The septic tank sewage disposal plant depends upon bacterial action to render the sewage harmless and inoffensive.

10. The application of scientific knowledge should result in the protection of inland and ocean water from pollution.

11. Garbage consists chiefly of food wastes. It should be protected from flies and should be disposed of before it decomposes.

12. Knowledge of the habits of flies is important in the campaign against disease.

13. Proper disposal of garbage involves frequent collections, inoffensive disposal plants, and the recovery of useful products.

14. The principle of the septic tank is the best to follow in the disposal of sewage.

15. Clean streets are found in healthful communities.

16. Dishes used in restaurants and soda fountains should be clean and free from disease germs.

17. The water supply in a healthful community is protected from pollution.

18. Communities, states, and the nation have health boards for the care and promotion of sanitation and health.

Thought Questions

1. What properties of water fit it for sewage disposal purposes?
2. Why will fish decrease in streams contaminated with sewage?
3. What principles are involved in garbage decomposition?
4. Why is garbage especially attractive to flies?
5. How is the knowledge of the life history of the fly applied to its control?
6. What is the relation of the fly to garbage and to health?
7. What property of fat is made use of in the disposal of garbage?

Projects for Your Science Discovery Book

1. Learn to open a clogged sink, using an air cup. Explain what makes the cup work.
2. Write a brief discussion of why cities install both sanitary and storm sewers.
3. Make a drawing of the waste pipes of your house.
4. Keep a record of the garbage collections in your community to determine whether or not they are frequent enough.
5. Make a study of flies. Watch where they go and what they eat. Report on what you discover.
6. Design a good garbage container and make one if you have access to a sheet metal shop.
7. Visit a community swimming pool and tell just what you think are its advantages to community life. Have you any criticisms of it?
8. Organize a trip to a near-by sewage disposal plant. As you inspect it and ask questions of the attendant, keep in mind the fundamental principles of sewage decomposition. Take notes and make a report of your trip.

The first farmer was the first man, and
all historic nobility rests on possession
and use of the land.

Emerson

UNIT V

▶‖ FARM AND GARDEN ‖◀

Before studying farm and garden problems, consider some experiences you have had with gardens of your own or some farm where you have lived or visited.

When you visit a garden what is your first impression? Is it that a particular flower or plant is beautiful or rare? Or do you see a picture? Do you feel that here is the result of someone's creative ability and knowledge of plants?

Probably every good garden, whether for flowers or vegetation, and every good farm represent not only imagination, but also knowledge of the principles of plant growth and skill and patience to carry out a plan.

Underneath the growing plants, do you see the soil which is the result of natural forces acting for ages and ages? If you do, you will understand the necessity for conserving that soil. Do you think it is important to cultivate and plant around the hill or across the slope rather than up and down? On a cornfield that sloped 8 feet in 100 feet the soil loss equaled one inch of good top soil in 2 years. In 16 years the top soil would be gone from that field. On a $16\frac{1}{2}$ per cent slope ($16\frac{1}{4}$ feet in a 100 feet) in 1936 planted to cotton there was a loss of 63 tons per acre from a single rainstorm in May, while a near-by field planted to grass showed no loss at all. Is your garden or farm losing its good soil because of improper use?

395

STARTING A PANSY BED

What work has gone before planting the pansies?   What work must now
be done if the bed is to be successful?

Garden Plants and Planting

I have in mind a garden old,
Close by a little-known highway,
Where aster, pink, and marigold
Keep their long summer holiday.
— Hutt

Do you know:

1. How to plant a seed?
2. Why garden soil is worked?
3. Why some seeds that are planted fail to grow?
4. How bacteria in the soil help plant life?
5. What a garden plan is?

General Problem 1.   How Is Soil Prepared for Planting?

What Soil Is. — Soil is weathered and ground-up rock, mixed with varying amounts of decaying organic matter (humus), water, air, and living organisms. You know that already if you think straight about erosion and its effects. However, it is an important statement to have in mind as we investigate soil in relation to the farm and garden. The soil in your garden may have been formed by the weathering and decay of local rock, or it may have been brought from distant places by glaciers or rivers. For perhaps a billion and a half years water has been at work preparing soil for plant growth. Rocks, ages old, have been broken up, ground into tiny particles, and mixed to form soils with a variety of minerals in them — minerals required as plant food. Wind, water, ice, changes in temperature, oxidation, and plants and animals are the agents that have transformed barren rock into priceless soil. Soil is more than a mixture of lifeless materials; it is teeming with life, and contains life-giving oxygen, nitrogen, and water.

Mildred Adams Fenton

SOIL MAKING

Year after year, for countless ages, running water has been wearing rock into soil. Can you explain why some rock remains after other has been worn away?

Soils vary widely on account of the rock substances which compose them. That is why we have clay, sandy, loam, and muck soils. Each is characterized by its name. Each requires special treatment and is best fitted for particular crops.

Soils differ, also, in size of particles, and so we have coarse gravel, fine gravel, and sand. The size of the particles is important in relation to drainage and air and water content. The finer the soil, the more air and water it can contain.

FIELD RESEARCH:
Investigate the soil of your neighborhood to determine how it was formed and where it came from.

Parts of the Soil and Their Uses to the Plant. —

Every part of the soil has its value to the plant; so a successful gardener or farmer must know the parts and their uses. Some of the bacteria in the soil help to decompose organic matter, releasing nitrogen to the air and making the rest suitable for plant use. Other bacteria take nitrogen from the air and combine it with oxygen and certain minerals in the soil to form an important substance — a nitrate — needed for plant growth. Without air (with its oxygen) in the soil this work would stop. Some of the soluble minerals are taken up by the root-hairs of plants with water from the soil and used by the plant for manufacturing its food.

ROCKS, SOIL, AND PLANTS

Minerals so necessary for plant growth are found in soil. In this photograph you can see how rocks broken into soil make plant life possible. How were these rocks formed?

The humus (organic matter) feeds bacteria and holds moisture in the soil. A mixture of sandy soil containing a little clay and humus (a sandy loam) in suitable proportions is desirable for gardening. Sandy soil, alone, drains too freely and dries out. Clay soil absorbs a larger amount of water than sandy soil. It gets sticky and soggy and does not allow the water to circulate freely. When it dries, it cakes and cracks. Water escapes rapidly through the cracks, leaving the dried clay chunks that are difficult to work properly. The mixture, sand and loam, retains moisture well and is easy to work.

Most soils are slightly alkaline to litmus paper, although some soils are acid. Most plants grow best in a slightly alkaline soil, but some do best in an acid soil. It is important, therefore, to test the soil to determine if it is acid or alkaline. You will be interested to learn how to test your soil. Or you may have your Farm Bureau test it for you.

Preparing the Soil for the Seeds. — Any soil that is gardened intensively must be fertilized and supplied with humus for each succeeding crop. Sometimes on large gardens and farms the humus is supplied by planting rye, or other leafy crops, the previous fall and plowing or spading under the green blades in the spring. Crops sown in the fall for plowing under in spring are called *green cover crops*. The green material dies and so adds organic matter to the soil. Plant food materials are supplied sometimes by changing the crops from season to season, called *crop rotation*, and by adding farm manure and other fertilizers. The farm manure also adds to the humus supply.

After proper fertilization, including the addition of lime if the soil is too acid, the soil is plowed or spaded and harrowed about two weeks before the planting time.

For many years farmers have plowed the soil deeply. Recent experiments by soil scientists show that in some

PREPARING THE SOIL

What is this operation called? Is it done before or after the seeds
are planted? Why is it done?

cases it may be better not to plow so deeply. In much of the wheat belt, for example, the plowing consists of stirring only the upper few inches of soil.

Just before planting, the garden plot is again harrowed thoroughly to produce a finely divided soil at the surface. The time between the plowing and final harrowing allows the weeds to start from seeds left over from fall. The final harrowing destroys these weeds and is a large factor in the prevention of weeds later on. Thus harrowing is of great importance to the gardener.

The smaller the seed the finer the soil it needs for early growth. Small seeds are barely covered with fine soil. Moreover soil must fit snugly about the seed and tiny new root that forms so that the rootlet can obtain the water and minerals it needs. If the soil is too coarse, the seeds may dry out and fail to grow. Seeds to grow must become soaked with water so that the outside skin is broken. Try Experiment 35 to find out for yourself how the character of the soil affects the growth of seeds.

General Problem 2.   Why Have a Planting Plan?

A Plan for Your Garden. — The most successful garden is the one planned long ahead. This is true whether you plan for a vegetable garden, a flower garden, or a landscaping project which includes the house, shrubs, flowers, and vegetables. The successful farmer must plan his crops several years in advance. He who waits until planting time to plan his garden is likely to be disappointed. In fact, a garden is a year-round affair and not just a spring and summer interest.

EXPERIMENT 35

Will seeds grow better in soil that is finely grained than in unbroken soil?

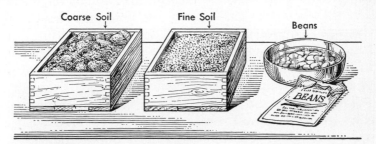

Coarse Soil   Fine Soil   Beans

In working this experiment, remember that it is on such a small scale as compared with a real garden that results are easy to obtain. If you can carry out this experiment in your garden, so much the better.

WHAT TO USE: — Two boxes of equal size; two samples of the same soil, one finely mixed and the other left in coarse lumps; and a package of seeds — peas or beans — that have been soaked overnight.

WHAT TO DO: — Fill the boxes, one with lump soil and the other with fine soil. Plant the seeds according to directions on the package, but do not break up the lumps. Water both boxes alike when you have planted the seeds.

Set the boxes in a warm place and observe and record the growth results from day to day.

Examine the soil each day to see which appears to dry out faster.

WHAT HAPPENS: — Do the seeds grow alike in both boxes? Does the soil dry out faster in one box than in the other? Why?

CONCLUSION: — Which method of preparing the soil promotes the better growth? Explain.

APPLICATION: — The smaller the seeds the finer the soil should be. Why?

If your plans for landscaping your grounds are not complete, you should at least select your garden plot in the fall. See that the weeds are removed before the season closes and that green cover crops are sown if needed.

J. Horace McFarland Company

CAREFUL PLANNING

Perennial phlox are nestled against the wall. At their feet is a row of annuals — alyssum. Notice that even the wall is used in this garden.

For the spring planting, January is not too early to begin your plans. (Refer to your Observers' Club Calendar for suggestions.) Is it to be a flower garden, a vegetable garden, or both? Are there shrubs to be placed for decorative effect about the home? If it is to be a flower garden, are the flowers to be *annuals* or *perennials?* Annuals are plants that grow flowers and seeds the first year, after which the parent plant dies. Perennials are plants that bear flowers and seeds each year for a number of years.

FIELD RESEARCH:

Send for seed and plant catalogs from reliable seed houses to help you decide what varieties of seed and plants you wish.

In selecting your seed, plants, and shrubs you must have in mind how long a time it takes the plant to reach its full growth. Some small vegetables mature quickly, and their place in the garden may be replanted with second sowings of the same or some other seed.

If flowers are in your plan, you should consider a color scheme so as to have a succession of blooms from early spring to late fall. Your perennials and shrubs must be given a permanent place in your scheme, and other planting must be made accordingly, keeping in mind color, time of flowering, and height.

FIELD RESEARCH:

Study some of the books listed in the bibliography to learn how other people have planned their gardens, and what they have planted. Visit commercial garden shows for suggestions of arrangement and varieties of shrubs and flowering plants.

In deciding what seeds, plants, and shrubs to plant it is necessary to consider at the same time the size of your garden plot and where each plant is to be placed. Therefore, you should measure your plot and draw a plan of it to scale.

From your catalogs and garden books you can determine how far apart rows of vegetables should be and how much room must be given for each of the plants or shrubs

you select.　You can then draw the rows on your paper
plan and can mark locations for individual plants.　Do
not forget to keep in mind the succession of vegetables
and flowers.

J. Horace McFarland Company

TRANSPLANTING

Some plants grow more satisfactorily if started in hotbeds or cold frames
early in the spring.　Later on when the outdoor soil is warmer, the young
plants are transplanted into the garden.

Your plans should include a planting calendar.　Some
of your seeds may start in *flats*, in *hotbeds*, or in *cold frames*
for transplanting later.　These must be carefully timed,
taking into consideration the date of late spring frosts
and the average temperature of the growing season.
The date for outdoor planting should also be placed on
your planting calendar.

Perhaps your garden is to be a "soil-less" garden.
If so, plan your tanks early, get the necessary materials,
and be ready to start it promptly.

FIELD RESEARCH:

Study the frost maps on page 118 to get an idea of the latest killing frost in the spring and the earliest killing frost in the fall. The number of days between them is your safe growing season for plants that are killed by frosts. The average temperature for your locality in spring and fall is also useful data.

The successful farmer plans his crops as carefully as the flower or vegetable grower. The farmer must plan to raise feed for his stock as well as crops to sell. The soil in one part of the farm may be better suited to one crop than another. It should be tested for acidity or alkalinity. The fields should be plowed and cultivated so as to conserve the soil. On hilly ground different crops need to be planted in strips following the contours of the hills, rather than up and down. This is called *contour* planting and prevents erosion.

Seeds. — The following clipping from a newspaper tells its own story:

'Taking the gamble out of agriculture' is a proposition that works for everyone's welfare. And the fundamental gamble in farming is the seed sown, whether you are working under glass or on a thousand-acre ranch. Think of the nurseryman who buys 20,000 dollars' worth of seed from abroad, plants them, waits and works a year, and finds out that most of the seed had no life. This has really happened.[1]

Here is one other illustration to show the importance seed plays in gardening and farming. A certain variety of cabbage seeds was obtained from two sources. Both quantities *germinated* (started to grow) satisfactorily, but the plants of one sample produced cabbages that weighed an average of 3200 pounds to the load while cabbages from the other seed, grown side by side with

---

[1] *Democrat and Chronicle*, Rochester, N. Y.

A HEALTHY GROWTH

There are no sick plants here, where rich soil, ample water, and
sufficient sunshine make growing conditions ideal.

the first plants, produced cabbages that weighed an average of 4100 pounds to the load.

Plants are liable to disease the same as people; and so the scientific grower tries to prevent his plants from getting sick. One way to do this is to use only healthy seeds. In some cases seeds are treated with certain chemicals that destroy disease germs or molds that may be on the seed. In the case of plants, fumigation is often used.

Such examples as these indicate that you should select your seed with great care. Seeds that will not germinate properly or are diseased waste time, land, and money for you. Seeds that germinate but grow inferior products are also to be avoided. You can test your seeds for germinating quality if you will follow the directions of Experiment 36.

Your investigation of the germination of seeds raises the question as to the parts of a seed and their function.

FIELD RESEARCH:

Soak a few seeds of beans and peas overnight. With a needle remove the outer skin, if the seed has one. (Refer to the diagram below for names of parts.) Carefully separate the parts and, using the hand lens, look for the little plant.

The outer skin protects the seed during its resting period, keeping it from drying out. The two bulky parts (some seeds have only one such part), the *cotyledons*, supply food to the little plant until it develops roots and leaves. Then it is able to manufacture its own food.

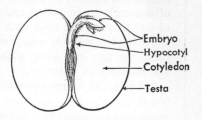

PARTS OF A SEED

The testa is the outer covering.

The embryo consists of a tiny stem and tiny leaflets.

What happens to the cotyledons after the seed germinates?

EXPERIMENT 36

What per cent of my garden seeds will germinate?

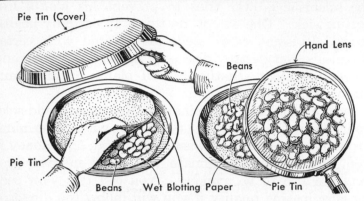

You have already discovered that a seed must have water and warmth to germinate, that is, to begin to grow. This experiment will help you discover whether cheap seeds are really inexpensive.

WHAT TO USE: — Seeds to be tested (if possible, secure cheap packages of seeds and expensive seeds for comparison); wet blotting paper; pie tins (two for each sample of seeds to be tested); and a hand lens.

WHAT TO DO: — 1. Thoroughly wet a piece of blotting paper and place it in one of the pie tins. Count out 50 seeds of a sample to be tested and cover them with a second piece of wet blotter, and then with a pie tin, but not air-tight.

2. Repeat with as many samples as you wish to test, and place the tins in a warm place. Keep the blotters moist but not standing in water.

3. After 48 hours examine the seeds of each sample, and count the number that have started to grow. Re-cover the seeds and examine them again after another 24 hours. Again count and record the number that have germinated.

4. Examine some of the seeds that did not germinate to observe whether they appear to have been well-formed seeds.

In each sample calculate the per cent of seeds that germinate.

WHAT HAPPENS: — 3. How many seeds of each sample germinated?

4. Describe the appearance of the seeds that did not germinate.

CONCLUSION: — In each sample of seeds what per cent germinated?

Is the per cent of germination high enough to warrant planting the other seeds of the sample?

Is it worth while to test seeds before planting them?

APPLICATION: — Does it pay to buy cheap seeds?

When a seed is planted it absorbs water from the soil, causing the cotyledons to swell and break open the outer covering. More moisture enters and the little plant, called the *embryo*, begins to grow.

The embryo has one or more leaflets and a little stem. The little stem grows, the leaves grow, and soon a tiny root appears. All this time the new little plant gets its food from the cotyledons which begin to shrink. After a while the cotyledons are, in the case of beans and some other seeds, raised out of the soil. Perhaps you will plant some seeds and see their changes for yourself. Soon two green leaves appear and then two more, and more and more as the stem gets longer and the root grows bigger. As soon as green leaves appear the little plant becomes self-supporting. Its green leaves, with water from the roots, carbon dioxide from the air, and energy from the sun make its own food. It is a miracle of nature.

Hotbeds and Cold Frames. — If you wish to raise early vegetables and flowers, you will have to learn to use hotbeds and cold frames. Both of these devices are boxes, with sides 12 inches to 24 inches high, set part way down in the soil and covered with frames with glass in them. The frames are adjustable to permit proper ventilation of the bed. The glass allows the radiant energy of the sun to go through and warm the soil underneath. At night the glass largely prevents the loss of heat from the soil. For these reasons, the soil under glass will be warm enough to cause seeds to sprout and plants to grow long before the soil outside would permit the growth.

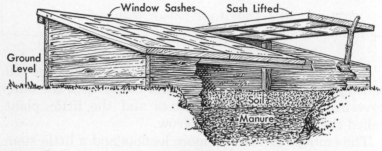

A HOTBED

An important part of the hotbed is the layer of manure.
Explain how the manure helps keep the soil inside warm.   Does the glass above help?   Why must the hotbed be ventilated?
What is the difference between a hotbed and a cold frame?

The hotbed is heated not only by the sun, but also by gradual decay (oxidation) of farm manure. Now it is possible to heat the bed with electricity. Of course with the use of electricity the temperatures can be controlled much more accurately.

To make an ordinary hotbed, soil is removed from within the box and a thick layer, one to two feet deep, of unrotted manure is put in. This is then covered with four to five inches of rich garden soil. This much is better done late in the fall. In the spring, the manure rots and gives off considerable heat to the soil. Therefore, with the top covered with glass, the soil warms very early. When the soil begins to heat, it will heat rapidly, and seeds should not be planted until the temperature has dropped to below 100° F.

A cold frame is like a hotbed, except that it has no manure or artificial heat.

J. Horace McFarland Company

A COLD FRAME

Study this picture and the drawing on page 412. Explain the difference between a cold frame and a hotbed. Why are these used for some plants rather than planting the seeds directly in the outdoor garden?

As the spring advances, care must be taken not to let the plants burn from overheating. With cold frames and hotbeds the glass must be opened for a short time each warm day and, finally, at night as well. Cold frames and hotbeds must be ventilated because plants must have fresh air. The bed, too, must be kept properly watered. (Refer to your Observers' Club Calendar for dates of starting seeds and for transplanting. And, of course, allowance must be made depending upon what part of the country you live in.) For detailed directions concerning the use of cold frames, hotbeds, and greenhouses you should refer to special books on those topics.

Part of the joy of gardening is to raise at least a portion of your own seed for the next year. You can thus study the whole life history of a generation of vegetables and flowers. Let some especially fine flowers go to seed. When they are ripe, gather the seed, and place in carefully labeled packages for storage until next spring or planting time.

LIBRARY RESEARCH:

Read about the work of Burbank, and perhaps you may do a little experimenting with plant breeding and improvement.

Rotation of Farm and Garden Crops. — Every plant takes certain minerals from the soil, such as phosphorus, calcium, and nitrogen compounds. Some plants require larger amounts of nitrogen compounds than others, and so take excessive amounts of these from the soil. Plants like clover, alfalfa, peanuts, and others, contain bacteria in *nodules* on their roots. These take nitrogen from the air and combine it with soil materials to make the nitrogen compounds, thus actually adding nitrogen to the soil. It is a good plan, therefore, to follow a nitrogen-using plant with a nitrogen-adding plant. This plan is called *crop rotation*.

With farm crops, a three-year or four-year rotation is common. In the south, a cotton crop may be followed by oats and then by corn. In the north, root crops, cabbages, and corn may be followed by oats, barley, or wheat. With the wheat may be sown timothy and clover for cropping the following season. Or the wheat may be followed by alfalfa. Clover and alfalfa are nitrogen-adding plants. They may be cropped for several years. The exact rotation depends on whether the farm is a dairy farm or grain farm. On both, the clover or alfalfa crop is always included.

J. C. Allen and Son

NITROGEN FOR THE SOIL

This is a fine field of alfalfa. Whenever possible, clover or alfalfa is included in a rotation of crops. Can you tell why?

Rotation of crops not only gives the soil a chance to recover minerals and compounds taken from it by the crops, but insects and diseases associated with one crop are likely to disappear while other crops are being sown. Of course with intensive farming as it is practiced in many parts of the United States, chemical analyses of the soil are made and the proper plant foods and minerals are added in correct amounts. Some crops require slightly acid soil, others neutral or alkaline soils. Certain plant diseases thrive in acid soils and not in neutral or alkaline soils. So farming becomes a science of soils and plants.

Garden crops also should be rotated to some extent, although soil deficiencies can be made up on small areas with special fertilizers. While you should consult special books on gardening for details on this problem, it will help you to keep in mind that, in general, *leafy* plants should follow *root* plants, and that *shallow root* plants should follow *deep root* growers.

J. Horace McFarland Company

A PLAN

In this picture the landscape gardeners are busy planning a rose garden.

The Ideal Garden. — The ideal garden is the one that expresses your own individuality. There are certain fundamental rules which are followed by good gardeners. But you must apply and adapt the rules to your own garden. Your own choice of variety and color will make your garden different from all others. The success of your garden will depend upon the seed you select, proper planting and thorough cultivation, and the thought you give to a plan in advance.

Making the Plan. — Before you lay out a paper plan for landscaping or a garden, visit well-planned landscaping projects in parks, private homes, and commercial gardens. Then consult books and current garden magazines for suggestions and instruction. If possible, talk with landscape architects, who know the value of planning.

J. Horace McFarland Company

A GARDEN

Here is the same garden in bloom. Does planning pay?

Then on a large sheet of paper mark in the shape, size, and location of your buildings, existing trees, shrubs, gardens, roads, and paths. With this as a basis, you can proceed to develop a complete garden plan.

Your plan should be laid out with a central line of development. If your grounds are not level, it may be necessary to include a profile plan to show where you must dig out or fill in to give the grades or slopes the best effect.

The following features are usually included in a landscaping plan and each should receive careful consideration:

(1) Drives and walks.

(2) Foundation planting about building. This consists of evergreens and shrubs to bring out architectural features of the building, hide walls, and give a tie-up between the building and ground.

(3) Border planting. This is planting along the drives and edges of the plot. Trees and shrubs are useful here in shutting off the garden from public view and forming backgrounds for border beds of flowers.

(4) Lawns and lawn planting. These are grass and special trees and shrubs.

(5) Hedges, fences, and walls to inclose formal or semi-formal gardens.

(6) Rock gardens and pool.

(7) Arbors, lawn furniture, and the like for decorative effects.

(8) Location, shape, and sizes of perennial and annual flower beds, rose garden, and vegetable garden.

(9) A planting list. Consider the hardiness of trees and shrubs required by your local climate; also height, foliage, colors in spring, summer, and autumn.

A careful study of the natural surroundings of the home, kinds of soil, drainage, and climate is desirable before you lay out your general plan. A complete plan, even though only small parts of it are planted each season, is better than to plan and plant each part without reference to a unifying scheme. Moreover, one derives pleasure in seeing a vision take form gradually. Above all, you should express your own individuality.

Garden Tools. — "A workman is known by his tools" holds just as true for a gardener as it does for any other workman. The good gardener buys good garden tools and then takes good care of them.   Each time when you have finished using your garden tools, clean off all dirt, and put the tools away in dry condition and thoroughly polished.   In addition to tools for working the soil, you will need a simple dusting or spraying equipment to aid in your fight against garden pests.

Why Cultivate the Soil? — Anyone who lives on a farm or just has a city garden knows that cultivation helps keep the soil from drying out.   What does cultivation do to preserve the soil water?

For years it was thought that the soil water rose to the surface through tiny tube-like spaces in the soil called *capillaries*.   Once at the surface of the soil, it evaporated.   The rise of the water through the spaces in the soil was explained as capillary action — a sort of pumping action that causes water to rise in fine hair-like tubes.   Thus it was believed that cultivation broke up the capillary tubes and prevented the soil water from rising.

This explanation may still be true for some kinds of soil, especially where the water table is within ten feet from the surface.   But soil water experiments now indicate that when the water table is below ten feet from the surface, very little if any water rises by capillary action.

How then does cultivation preserve soil water?   Scientists have found that plants evaporate great quantities of water — much more water than the surface of the soil evaporates.   Thus the best way of preserving soil water seems to be to remove all unnecessary plants.   *Cultivation is important in preventing loss of soil water because it removes weeds which take water from the soil.*

Sometimes a straw *mulch* is spread about a plant to help conserve the moisture in the soil.   A mulch is loose material placed on the soil. It preserves soil water by shading the soil from the sun's rays. In this way it reduces the amount of water evaporated directly from the soil. More important, the mulch covers the ground so thoroughly that weeds are unable to get started. Mulching papers or peat moss as well as straw may be used for a mulch.

Working the soil by spading, hoeing, and raking serves also to mix air with the soil. Bacteria at work in the soil need the oxygen of the air. The mixing of the top soil with air prevents the soil from becoming *sour* or *acid*. It also removes weeds, and this we know is most important in conserving the soil water.

Hoeing is necessary also to heap the soil about the roots of plants as in hilling potatoes and corn. This helps to hold the plants in place and to keep the light from the roots. If potatoes, which are really parts of the stem, are left uncovered in sunshine, they turn green and taste sweet.

In spite of efforts to conserve soil water, much of it is lost by evaporation from the soil and from the leaves of crops. Hence, unless the water table is near the surface of the soil, frequent rains or artificial watering are necessary. *Irrigation*, used to supply water in dry regions, has made the Central Valley of California one of the richest agricultural areas in the world.

In locations where irrigation is impossible, the only thing the farmer can do to combat a long drought is cultivate often to prevent weeds from using the little water remaining in the soil.

The home gardener, who can water during a drought, should do so infrequently but for long periods at a time, thus allowing the water to sink deep into the soil. He must also keep his plot free from weeds in order to save the moisture in the soil.

J. Horace McFarland

MULCHING

Straw placed on the ground around the plants is called straw mulch. One purpose of it is to prevent the loss of water from the soil. How? Can you think of another purpose for putting straw around these tomato plants?

Courtesy U. S. Bureau of Reclamation

IRRIGATION

The soil in this field of sugar beets in Oregon is soaking up gallons and gallons of water. The sugar beet plants will live from this stored water after the irrigation gates are shut off.

General Problem 3. How and When May Seeds Be Planted?

Starting Seeds in Flats. — In localities where the growing season is short due to long winters, seeds are often started in *flats*, shallow boxes 3 to 6 inches deep. Filled with moist sandy soil, they are used for starting seeds in the house several weeks before planting time outdoors. The exact time for starting seeds depends upon the plants and the locality. You may obtain accurate information from the local seed store, your school agriculture teacher, or the state College of Agriculture.

Especially in places where the growing season is short, better results follow if seeds are started indoors. Not only many flower seeds, but vegetable seeds such as cabbage, tomato, and melons are profitably started in this way.

FIELD RESEARCH:

Make a trip to a commercial greenhouse early in February to discover how the workmen are preparing for early vegetable and flower plants. Then prepare a flat for early seed planting. Consult your Observer's Club Calendar for suggestions. The seeds should be covered with firmly packed, sandy soil to a depth of about three times the length of the seed. Keep the flats in a fairly cool room. A temperature of about 60° F. is satisfactory. Moisten the soil a little each day, but do not soak it.

Transplanting. — The seeds may be planted too close together in the flat for proper growth after a few days. Therefore, when the seedlings have grown their second leaf, they should be transplanted either into cold frames or hotbeds, into other flats, or outdoors where they will be given more room.

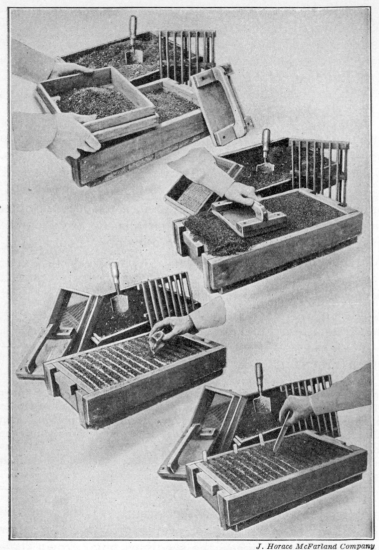

PREPARATION OF A SEED BOX

Sifting the soil; smoothing it; spreading the seeds; covering them.

The soil for transplanting should be a rich loam soil. Your investigations have shown you that the seed contains its own food for the first leaf development, but as soon as the second leaf appears the soil must furnish food-building materials to the plant.

FIELD RESEARCH:

For transplanting prepare a flat with moist, rich soil. Small pots may be used instead of flats. The night before you wish to transplant the seedlings, they should be well watered.

With a knife or trowel carefully take up a small number of seedlings. Select those that seem sturdiest and set each one in a small hole in the soil made with the finger or a small stick, and pack the soil firmly about the root. The seedlings should be set in the soil at about the same depth at which they have been growing. They should be set two inches or more apart to give room for proper development.

The plants should be watered daily and placed in sunshine, if this is practicable. If located near a window, turn the boxes about, to keep the plants growing straight. As the plants grow larger they should be gradually accustomed to outdoor air. They can be again transplanted to the outdoor garden as soon as danger of frosts is over. When ready for transplanting to the garden, they should be thoroughly watered the night before.

The soil about the roots should be taken up with the plant. When first set out, the plants should be protected against cold and against too-hot sunshine.

Transplanting Trees and Shrubs. — Deciduous trees (those that lose their leaves in the fall) are best transplanted before the new buds have started to grow in the spring, or after they have dropped their leaves in the fall. They are then in a resting condition and so are best able to stand the shock of a change. Roots and branches should be pruned, and the plant set in a hole and thoroughly watered and mulched. The soil must be packed very hard about the roots and, if necessary, the plant supported against the wind by guy strings.

Nursery stock obtained in the fall is usually fresh-dug stock. Spring stock is usually stock that was dug in the fall and held dormant in cold storage until spring.   Some spring stock is fresh-dug.

Evergreens also may be transplanted in the early fall or spring.   Fall transplantings must have time to make some root growth before freezing weather sets in; hence they should be kept well watered.

Courtesy Maryland Department of Forestry

READY FOR TRANSPLANTING

The small evergreens shown here are furnished by the State at a small cost to those who wish to plant them on their property.   Perhaps the little trees in this photograph will be doing important work in conserving soil ten years from now.

Outdoor Seed Planting. — Seeds are usually planted in rows or hills.   Rules for depth of planting are the same as for planting in flats.   When the seedlings planted out of doors have grown their second leaf, they should be thinned to give proper room for development. After thinning, the soil should be kept cultivated and weeded.

In your garden plan you have provided for successive plantings. You should follow your plan closely.

Growing New Plants without Seeds. — Many plants can be started by *cutting* or *slipping* off a branch and letting it take root in water or moist sand. In fact, this is a very valuable method of propagating various plants and shrubs. Geraniums and different types of ivies are often started by this method.

Some plants, like tulips, grow from *bulbs*. These plants form new growths or separate bulbs on the old ones each year. After the blossoms have wilted and their leaves have turned yellow, they may be taken up, separated, and new plants grown from each of the new bulbs. The food stored in the bulb enables it to grow the next season, although it may not blossom until the following year.

J. Horace McFarland Company

PLANTING TULIPS

The gardener is placing the tulip bulbs on the surface of the ground to obtain a pleasing arrangement. Later each bulb will be buried about six inches in the soil.

Some bulbs are often forced for house-flowering in the winter. For this purpose they should be placed in soil in pots and kept in a dark basement for a few weeks (to enable the roots to start) before they are brought into the warm air for forcing. Refer to your Observers' Club Calendar.

FIELD RESEARCH:

If you want to try your hand at this method of propagating plants, you must know what plant to use (see the Observers' Club Calendar) and where to make the cut.   At the point where buds grow on the stem — called a *node* — is the place from which roots can be made to grow. To make a cutting of a geranium, begonia, or any non-woody plant, use a sharp knife and cut off the end of a stem just below a node. There should be only one or two leaves above the node.

Place the node end rather deep in the moist sand — not too fine, for the little stem needs air as well as moisture.   After the new plant is well rooted it should be transplanted to a small pot.   The dirt in this pot should be good soil, with plant food in it.   The clean sand used in the first place does not contain appreciable amounts of plant foods. Moisture, air, and warmth are what is needed to start root growth. There are substances called *hormones* which scientists have discovered will aid or promote root growth which you may wish to investigate and use.   Later the cutting may be transplanted to a larger pot for the indoor garden or out of doors.

Grafting and *budding* are methods used to propagate many trees and shrubs. By this method a small branch or bud of the variety desired is planted in another tree by opening the bark and inserting the branch or bud into contact with the growing layer (*cambium*) of the plant being grafted. If you want to do this kind of plant propagation, you will need to go to some greenhouse or nursery for help.   Many roses and fruit trees are budded plants. Even shade trees are often budded to secure certain characteristics of growth. By such special methods of propagation, it is possible to obtain growing and bearing plants faster than from seeds.

Thinking Things Over. — The whole problem of growing plants involves a great deal of science.   Therefore it is to be expected that the scientific farmer or gardener will probably be more successful than one who does not understand and apply scientific principles. Moreover, since food growing is one of our most important industries, there are many colleges of agriculture where young men and women may go for training.

As we think back over this topic we realize the importance of the soil and its conservation. Then there is the need for good seed free from disease. Methods of planting and cultivating are necessary for proper plant growth. Later we shall study about protecting and storing the crops. When we think of crops we should have in mind not only things to eat, but timber and beauty.

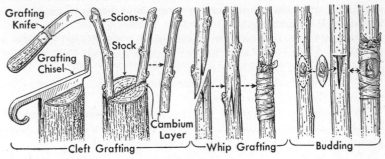

GRAFTING

These are methods of making part of one plant grow on the root part of another.

Many fruit trees and shade trees are grafted. The young stems are grafted onto a hardy root stock.

Did you know that orange trees are often grafted onto lemon roots? Can you think of any reason why this is done?

Key Words

annuals	cutting	mulching
budding	evaporation	node
bulbs	fertilizer	organic matter
cambium	flats	perennials
capillary action	germinate	propagation
cold frame	grafting	seeds
cotyledon	hotbed	soil
crop rotation	humus	transplanting
	irrigation	

Key Statements

1. Soil for successful gardening must be fertilized, supplied with humus, and tilled.

2. A garden, to be successful, must be well planned before it is planted.

3. Annuals produce seed the first year, after which they die; perennials produce seeds each year for a succession of years before dying.

4. Only seeds proven to be good by testing are worth planting.

5. A seed contains food material to support the growth of a new plant until the plant possesses roots and leaves to enable it to become self-supporting.

6. Hotbeds are heated by decomposing (oxidizing) manure or by electric coils. The glass helps to retain the heat both from decomposition and from the sun.

7. A cold frame is kept warmer than outside air by the glass retaining the heat from the sun.

8. Plants of the family of clover, alfalfa, peas, and peanuts maintain colonies of nitrogen-fixing bacteria on their roots. When plowed under, these plants add nitrates to the soil.

9. Rotation of crops is necessary to help eliminate plant diseases, conserve fertility of the soil, and conserve humus.

10. The ideal garden is one that not only produces excellent crops but also expresses the individuality of its gardener.

11. Garden tools will last longer and be more efficient in use if they are always put away clean.

12. Water is conserved in the soil by breaking up capillary tubes, by cultivation, and by destroying weeds.

13. Irrigation (artificial watering) is practiced where rain is infrequent during the growing season.

14. For early planting, seeds may be started in boxes in the house or in hotbeds or cold frames.

15. Seeds should be planted out of doors only when the soil has become warm enough to insure germination.

16. Certain plants may be propagated by cuttings, others by budding or grafting, and those with bulbous roots by separating the bulbs.

17. Trees and shrubs may be transplanted successfully in spring or fall.

Thought Questions

1. What is the reason for allowing weeds to start after the first cultivating in the spring, before final cultivating and planting?
2. Why will seeds grow better in finely worked soil?
3. Why is a garden plan and a planting calendar desirable?
4. Why are tested seeds preferable to ordinary seeds?
5. Account for the heat formed by the manure in a hotbed.
6. Why must hotbeds and cold frames be ventilated?
7. In rotation of crops, why is it not desirable to follow one crop with plants of the same family?
8. Why will a potato in a hill turn green if exposed to sunlight?
9. Why is it possible to start seeds indoors before it is safe to plant them outdoors?
10. What conditions are required for successful transplanting?

Projects for Your Science Discovery Book

1. Write a story about the local soil in your community, telling how it was formed and from where it came.
2. Make labeled drawings of a seed of a bean or pea.
3. Make a trip to a near-by truck or flower garden and report the facts you discover about its garden plans and crops.
4. Record the planting date, date of appearance of seedlings, and other information of interest in connection with the seeds planted in the flats in your schoolroom.
5. Keep a record of your outdoor planting experiments.
6. Learn to recognize "stands" of wheat, oats, rye, barley, and buckwheat.
7. Find out what is meant by certified seed.
8. In your garden, keep a part of one row well worked, and neglect a similar part for two weeks. Compare the two rows as to moisture retained, growth of plants, and growth of weeds.
9. Try placing black building paper between some of the rows of your garden. What happens?
10. Start corn, wheat, and bean seedlings in the laboratory, and then transfer them to water solutions (see Appendix) containing in one case all needed minerals, and in the other case no nitrogen, phosphorus, or calcium.
11. Organize a garden club and plan for landscaping a yard belonging to some one of your homes.
12. Try making green wood-cuttings.

Lynwood M. Chase

GARDEN BEAUTIES

This Cecropia moth is resting on a daffodil blossom. Some moths are garden friends, others are garden enemies. A careful gardener learns to tell the difference between them.

Farm and Garden Friends and Enemies

And so it criticized each flower,
This supercilious seed;
Until it woke one summer hour
And found itself a weed.
— Mildred Howells

Do you know:

1. Why weeds may crowd out other plants?
2. How many lives an insect has?
3. How to tell the difference between a beetle and a fly?
4. How to protect your plants against insects?
5. How birds help you with your garden?

General Problem 1. How Can Weeds Be Controlled?

Ways of Weeds. — How early in the spring does the dandelion blossom where you live? Do you not look for that first golden flower as a sign of spring? Why is the dandelion called a weed? Why do people try to keep it from their lawns and gardens? Everything that grows has its share of beauty. It is not surprising, therefore, that some weeds in bloom are beautiful to look at, and that others have interesting foliage. But weeds rob the soil of water, minerals, and space needed by your garden plants. Weeds are unwelcome and so we try to get rid of them.

Weed Control. — In order to help plants grow we must know what they need in the way of soil, water,

DANDELION YELLOW

Sending its flowering stalks up above neighboring plants, this weed is certain to have its seeds scattered by the lightest breeze.

minerals, and warmth. Some plants are more easily killed by cold than others. Some have shallow roots and are damaged by dry weather. The undesirable plants have needs also, and they have ways of reproducing that result in many new plants even under unfavorable conditions. This makes them difficult to control. It seems that some plants like *toadflax*, *burdock*, *pigweed*, *ragweed*, *mustard*, and *dandelion* are so hardy that they can actually crowd out other plants. Let us try to discover why they can outgrow so many more useful plants.

The *dandelion* has a very tough root that is difficult to kill. The stem can be broken off again and again and still new stems will grow. The root can be broken and still it will survive. The juice of the dandelion is bitter; therefore, animals will not eat the leaves. The flower head of the dandelion is really many single flowers bunched together; hence there are many seeds from each flower head. When each seed ripens, it is equipped with a parachute so that it is carried about by the wind. The seeds are hardy and if given a chance will begin to grow.

FIELD RESEARCH:

Collect some dandelion seeds and examine them to discover how the seed can be carried by the wind. You will be interested to examine them with a magnifying glass, if you have one, to discover their shape and structure.

The common *mustard plant* with its small, yellow flower produces a large number of tiny seeds that will survive the hardships of cold, wet, and dry spells that would harm other seeds. The weed is best controlled by cutting down the plants before the seeds ripen.

Pigweed and *ragweed* also develop many hardy seeds and must be controlled by keeping them cut down before the seeds develop.

FIELD RESEARCH:

Collect specimens of two or more common weeds that have seeds nearly ripe. Take them to school and count the number of seeds contained in each plant.

Toadflax, burdock, milkweed, wild carrot, and *mullein* (or mullen) are weeds that cause much damage. The crop losses from weeds alone are estimated to total many millions of dollars every year. The large number of seeds per weed, their vitality, the ease with which they are distributed, and their adaptability to many conditions of soil are reasons why the weed is a real problem for the gardener and the farmer. Some weeds, like *ragweed,* distribute pollen that cause some people trouble in breathing. Other weeds, like *poison ivy* and *poison oak*, are poisonous to the skin. These weeds should be completely destroyed by chemical sprays now available.

J. Horace McFarland Company

GOLDENROD

One of the most common weeds is goldenrod. Like many other weeds, it grows so rapidly it robs moisture and minerals from the more desirable plants.

Annuals among the weeds may be practically exterminated in a locality in one season, if none are allowed to go to seed. *Biennials* (plants which produce seeds the second year and die) and perennials are more difficult to get rid of. To control them, they must be dug out by the roots or killed by the application of certain chemicals.

Sometimes weeds appear where they are not wanted because the soil does not contain enough plant food for the less hardy plants. In such cases the useful plants must be fed so they can compete with the weeds.

FIELD RESEARCH:

Learn to identify the poisonous kinds of weeds that occur in your locality and know what to do if you or someone else is accidentally poisoned by any one of them. If you accidentally touch a poisonous plant like poison ivy, wash the hands or parts that may be poisoned as soon as possible with plenty of soapsuds and water, and see your doctor. If you walk through poison ivy, the poison may get on your shoes and stockings, and from them on to your hands. Watch out for poison ivy whenever you walk in the woods or wooded places. Look for the *sign of three leaves.* See that such weeds are destroyed in your community. Commercial sprays are now available which kill the plants.

General Problem 2.   How Do Insects Harm the Garden?

Insect Pests of the Garden. — If insects could talk, it is likely that their slogan would be "War to the bitter

Courtesy Bureau of Plant Industry, U.S.D.A.

SPRAYING A POTATO FIELD

This machine forces a fine spray of poison onto the leaves and stems of the potato plants.   The poison protects the plants from the potato blight disease.

end!"   It is true that man's task of conquering and controlling the vast hordes of destructive insects is gigantic. Some scientists wonder what the outcome will be.   Certain it is that to win the battle with the insects will require your coöperation and that of everyone else. With the aid of science and the natural enemies of harmful insects, there is hope.   Many years ago it was said that the "damage wrought by insects every year nullifies the labor of a million men." [1]   That statement is just as true today.

You have learned something of the rapid increase of flies, if they are not controlled.   With many insects the rate of increase is much greater than that of the fly. While there are many different kinds and varieties of insects, your problem as a gardener will have to do with only a small number, some of them harmful and some useful.   Certain classes of garden insects attack the roots of young plants; others suck the juice from the plant; still others eat the leaves.   You must know how insects live if you expect to combat them effectively.

Root, Stem, and Leaf Eaters. — One variety of insects is known as *root maggots*.   They attack the roots of young turnips, radishes, cabbages, and onions.

The winged female (fly stage) lives through the winter and deposits her eggs in the soil very early in the spring. In a few days the eggs hatch and the larvae that are formed begin at once to eat any tender roots that are available.   At the age of three to four weeks, a larva changes into the pupa stage, that is, it forms a case about itself in which it rests (or is dormant) for two weeks. During its resting period it changes into the winged stage and breaks from its case.   The winged female deposits her eggs, and so a generation is completed.   Each new batch of larvae feeds largely on roots of plants.   Several generations of root maggots are produced each season and they are able, therefore, to do much damage.

The *cutworm* attacks plant stems, cutting off the stems of young tomato plants near the ground.   A paper collar

---

[1] "The Greatest War of All Time: Man Against the Insect," by M. K. Wisenhart, in *The American Magazine*, March, 1928.

on each stem keeps the cutworms away from the plants. The life history of the cutworm is similar to that of the root maggot. The cutworm in the winged stage has two pairs of wings, is a moth, and flies usually at twilight

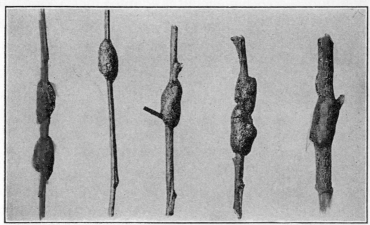

Courtesy Bureau of Entomology, U.S.D.A.

EGG MASSES

Insects often deposit their eggs in gluey masses on twigs. Hundreds of larvae hatch out of each mass.

or night.   For control, collect and destroy the larvae or use poisoned bait in the soil before planting seeds.

Some common leaf-eating insects are the *codling moth* (appleworm), *leaf rollers, gipsy moth, browntail moth*, and the *white-marked tussock moth*.   Various *tent caterpillars* are destructive larvae that change into moths.

Insects which eat stems and leaves may be controlled by poisons sprayed or dusted on the plants.   Rotenone and arsenic of lead are often used.   Rotenone is not harmful to people;   arsenic of lead is deadly poisonous.

FIELD RESEARCH:

Select a moth and study its life history, damage it does, methods of control.   (See Observer's Club Calendar for suggestions.)

Juice Suckers. — When you say a mosquito "bites" you really mean that it punches a little hole in your skin and sucks blood through a tube-like mouth. Many other insects feed upon plants much in the same way. These *juice suckers* have mouths adapted for sticking into the leaves and tender stems of plants and sucking the

Courtesy U. S. Department of Agriculture

MODERN WAR AGAINST GRASSHOPPERS

Grasshoppers are a continual enemy in the west. The spraying of poison by airplane is the latest step in our western farmer's constant struggle against them.

Let your imagination tell you the number of acres that a plane like this can cover in a day.

juices. They are like the mosquito except that they may kill a plant by taking so much juice.

Plant lice or *aphids* are a familiar example of sucking insects. The common *squash bug* and the apple *red bug* are other examples. They are true bugs. Their life history is similar to that of a *butterfly* and *moth*.

There are many species of plant lice. Their eggs, laid in the fall, last over winter and hatch out into lice in the early spring. They mature in a week or ten days. Many of the lice from the winter eggs are females which lay more eggs. There are as many as three or four generations in a season. The eggs laid in the fall carry the race over the winter months.

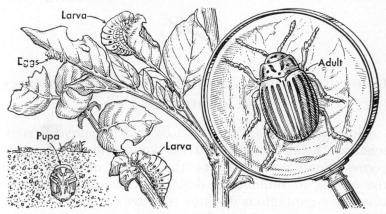

THE POTATO BEETLE FROM EGG TO ADULT

Find the four stages of the beetle pictured here. At which stage does this insect do most damage to the plant? How does this harm the potatoes? How does the farmer protect his potato plants from the beetles?

Juice suckers must be controlled by "contact" poisons, which must touch the insect to kill it. Nicotine, pyrethrum, and DDT are common garden contact poisons.

Beetles. — There are many varieties of beetles. Their life history is much like that of other insects. The egg hatches into a larva which is usually called a *grub*. Then comes the pupa or resting stage and finally the adult insect with its hardened, armor-like wing covers.

Some beetles, like the potato beetle, feed on plant tissues and some feed on other insects. You can protect your potato patch from the potato beetle by hand-picking the beetles or by spraying the leaves with poison.[1] Study the diagram of the life history of the potato beetle (page 441).

Study pictures of beetles in your reference books to make sure you can distinguish those that do harm from those which are helpful, like the *lady-bird beetles*.

General Problem 3. How Can Plant Diseases Be Controlled?

Sickness among Plants. —*Pasteur*, the great French scientist, little thought that his wonderful discovery of germs would contribute to the health of plants and the saving of millions of dollars. Like people, plants may have contagious diseases that are caused by germs. Therefore, it is important to recognize some of the most common diseases so that you may know whether to treat a diseased plant by spraying or dipping, whether to quarantine it, or perhaps destroy it by burning.

With plants as with ourselves it is important to know the symptoms of sickness, and what to do to prevent other plants from catching the same disease if it is contagious. Certain kinds of bacteria cause a *blight* of the leaves and young stems of fruit trees such as quince, pear, and apple. Blight may often be recognized by leaves turning yellow when they should stay green. Germs or spores which cause the blight may enter a plant through the pores, or through a branch which has been broken or cut. That is why tree surgeons always paint the fresh cut end of a limb of a tree. The disease germs may

---

[1] Directions for spraying or dusting are given in garden bulletins issued by the Department of Agriculture, Washington, D. C.

infect other trees by contact or they may be carried by insects.

Cabbage black rot is a bacterial disease which destroys cabbages and turnips.

Another class of plants, called *fungi*, cause even more plant diseases than do bacteria. One fungus with which you are familiar is the ordinary *bread mold*. Molds grow on the surface of fruits and on the leaves of many plants. Other examples of fungi are toadstools, puff-balls, and mushrooms. Experiment 37 shows under what conditions molds develop.

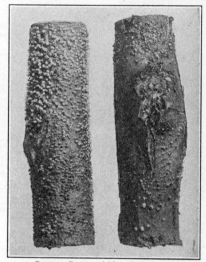

Courtesy Bureau of Plant Industry, U.S.D.A.

THE CHESTNUT KILLER

This is the chestnut blight which killed almost every chestnut tree in the United States. Some chestnut trees are now growing which appear to be able to withstand this fungus disease.

FIELD RESEARCH:

Place a piece of damp bread on a plate and cover it with a glass. Observe the formation of mold for three or four days. Examine some of the mold with a microscope.

Mold fungi occur in different colors. However, they do not contain any of the green coloring matter, called *chlorophyll*, of ordinary plants, and so fungi cannot manufacture starch as do the green plants. Since fungi cannot make their own food, many of them live on other plants to get their food. The plant on which they live is called the *host*, which is a good name for it, even though the guest, which does so much harm, is unwelcome.

KEY EXPERIMENT 37

Will germs and molds grow best when cold (40°–50° F.), warm (90°–96° F.), or hot (212° F.)?

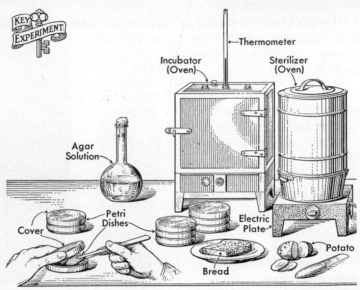

The oven and sterilizer shown in the drawing are like those usually found in science laboratories. However, if you do not have them, you can do the experiment pretty well without them. The sterilizer is really a steam oven. Instead of it you can use a regular oven that can be kept at a temperature of about 220°, which is necessary to kill all the germs in the agar solution to start with. This same kitchen oven can be regulated to about 212° F. for the experiment. A covered pan placed on a hot radiator will serve for the 90°–100° F. temperature.

WHAT TO USE: — Samples of stale moist bread; clean raw potatoes; 9 petri dishes and covers; agar solution; a refrigerator; an incubator (oven that can be kept at a temperature of 90°–100° F.); and a sterilizer oven that can be kept at a temperature of 212° F.

WHAT TO DO: — 1. Place a sample of the moist bread in each of three petri dishes. Expose each one to dust and cover with a beaker. Label them "cold," "warm," and "hot," and place in ovens or refrigerator accordingly.

2. Cut three thin slices from the center of the potato and place one piece in each of three petri dishes. Cover each and place the covered dishes in the sterilizer and sterilize them for 20 minutes (heat them at 220° F. for 20 minutes).

Moisten your fingers and lightly rub a spot on each piece of potato, using a different finger for each slice.

Label the dishes respectively "cold," "warm," and "hot," and place along with the bread samples.

3. Place melted, sterile, nutrient agar in each of three sterile petri dishes with covers. Allow to cool and expose to the air in a dusty room, or allow a fly to track across the agar in each dish.

Label "cold," "warm," and "hot," and place the dishes with the others.

WHAT HAPPENS: — After 24 hours examine each material (by looking through the glass cover which should not be removed). Record your observations and continue the experiment another 24 hours.

Examine and compare your observations with those of the previous day.

The experiment with the bread may have to be carried on for several days.

CONCLUSION: — Under what temperature conditions do molds and bacteria grow best?

APPLICATION: — What may cause moist clothes to mold if they are rolled up and put away where it is warm?

Some plant diseases due to fungi are *rust* on grains; *mildew*, which occurs on many plants, especially on fruits like the grape; *potato scale; club root* on cabbage; and *corn smut*. Blights that cause leaves of plants to curl or dry up and drop off are diseases caused by fungi.

Control of Plant Diseases. — Bacterial and fungus diseases of plants are controlled by spraying or by *fumigation* to destroy the germs, by *proper tilling* and *aëration* of soil that has become infected, and by *crop rotation*.

Various sulfur and copper preparations are used to combat bacterial and fungus diseases. Gardeners should use sprays and dusts regularly before diseases appear, for once one is started, it can seldom be cured, only checked. Diseased tops (and often diseased plants) should be burned.

General Problem 4. What Is the Garden Army of Defense?

Organization of the Gardener's Army. — With the hordes of insects, bacteria, and mold enemies constantly preying upon the plants of the land, is it any wonder the farmer and gardener need to muster an army to fight these pests? The gardener, of course, is the commanding general of the Garden Army; nature is his chief of staff; the insects are his infantry; the toads are his tanks, the snakes his artillery; and, overhead, are his aërial scouts, the birds. These divisions are the first line of defense, but they are ably helped by many special units which the commanding general calls to their aid. An army must be fed, trained, and directed, and a general must know his army well, if he is to be an efficient commander. Because you are the chief of your garden army, you must know the needs and abilities, the habits, and strength of your helpers.

The Insect Division. — The life history of useful insects is similar to that of the enemy insects. Only their habits or customs differ. Many of the enemy insects are *vegetarians*, as, for example, the potato beetle. Members of the insect infantry that help you in your war upon the harmful insects are *carnivorous*, that is, they prey upon other insects at one stage or another of their life history.

Usually they make their attack on the vegetarians. The *ladybird beetle,* our familiar friend the ladybug, eats countless numbers of plant lice. There are more than 2000 species of these beetles, all but a few of which feed on small insects or on the eggs of insects. They are usually of a bright color with dark spots on the wing covers, or dark-colored with bright spots. The mouth parts are adapted for biting.

Courtesy U. S. Department of Agriculture

A GOOD FRIEND

The praying mantis is so named because it often takes a praying position. Why do you think the two thick front legs are held in this position?

The *praying mantis* is another important member of the insect division. His long-jointed front legs have claws on the end with which he captures unwary insects.

FIELD RESEARCH:

Fix the appearance of a praying mantis in your mind by looking at the picture, then try to find one in your yard. It is colored green or brown for protection; so you will need to look carefully. You are most likely to find it in the early fall. If you find one, capture it and place it with grass and twigs in a glass with a cloth cover. Catch a fly and put it alive with the mantis. Watch the actions of the mantis to find out how it moves, catches its prey, and how it eats.

The *ichneumon* (ĭc-nū′mon) fly is among the most important fighters of the garden infantry division. There are many kinds of ichneumon flies. One way some attack the enemy is to lay their eggs beneath the skin of their victims. When the eggs hatch, each larva bores its way into the body of its *host* (the living thing upon whose tissue the larva will live), feeding upon the fat and blood of the host until it completes its growth. Some ichneumon flies lay their eggs on the skin of the insects they attack, and others lay theirs near the host insect so that the larvae after hatching may find their way to their prey.   Plants and animals that live upon the living tissue of other living plants and animals are called *parasites*. Of course, parasites sap the life of the host.

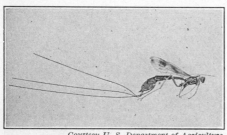

Courtesy U. S. Department of Agriculture

ANOTHER FRIEND

You may not like the appearance of this insect, but it is a good friend of the gardeners. Its name is the ichneumon fly. Read about it in the text and then tell why it is a friend.

Protection for the Infantry.—If we are able to recognize our friends among the insects, we can leave them unmolested. They are able, for the most part, to take care of themselves. Places, however, are provided for the scientific breeding of certain much-needed insects, such as the ladybird beetle, which can be distributed to localities requiring help in the insect war.

Toads of the Tank Division. — Science has shown us the way to secure facts and to use the facts to form judgments. Do you believe that toads cause warts? The toad has a warty-looking skin, but no one ever "caught" warts by handling toads. If you can find a toad in your garden, and you are fortunate indeed if one lives there, capture him and examine him closely. He will neither bite you nor give you warts. In fact he will rather enjoy the warmth of your hand.

The toad has a lightning-quick tongue with which he

catches flies and other insects. He is especially fond of large larvae or grubs that try to destroy the roots and leaves of your garden plants. He eats ants, spiders, potato bugs, aphids, beetles, and worms. In a year a toad in your garden may eat 10,000 garden enemies. Toads sleep during the day and do most of their hunting at night.

Toads and frogs are cousins and have much the same manners and customs, except that the adult frog prefers to live in and near the water, while the toad is more adventurous. He travels long distances from the pond where he was once a little tadpole, living in the water, and breathing by means of gills much as a fish breathes. As a grown-up toad he gulps in air and forces it into his lungs to get the oxygen. The adult toad is a land animal.

Brownell Photo

FOWLER'S TOAD

This toad is common in many parts of the country. Armed with a quick tongue the toad captures many insects which otherwise would destroy our plants.

Very early in the spring the toads travel to a pond to lay and fertilize their eggs. The female toad lays from 4000 to 15,000 eggs in the water and the male toad deposits *sperm* (fertilizing) cells over them. These find their way into the eggs, one sperm cell for each egg. Once inside the egg, the *nucleus* (center of development) of the sperm cell unites with the nucleus of the egg. The union of the two nuclei is called *fertilization*, and unless this takes place the eggs will not develop. By the end of about 12 days the eggs have developed into tadpoles. The tadpoles grow and gradually develop legs.

Their tails disappear and they crawl out on land as toads. They have changed from water animals to land animals. The adult toad passes the winter in a hole in the ground or lake mud where it hibernates.

FIELD RESEARCH:

Collect some toads' eggs in the early summer, and put them into an aquarium where you can watch them change out into tadpoles.

Since toads help to protect your garden by eating large numbers of insects, you should protect the toads. Leave their resting places undisturbed, and do not destroy their breeding places. Tell others what you have learned about toads, and enlist their coöperation in protecting them.

Snakes of the Heavy Artillery. — Why is it that so many people are either afraid of snakes or at least dislike them so much? It is true that there are a few harmful snakes, but by far the most snakes are real helpers.

The rattlesnake is the most-talked-of poisonous snake. Even so, only a small proportion of people bitten by rattlers die if the bite is properly cared for. Rattlers usually do not attack people unless they are surprised or cornered. Of the many kinds of rattlers the diamond-backed is about the worst. These grow to an average length of about seven feet. Rattlers feed by day except when it is very hot. They eat great numbers of rats and mice. In this way they are a real help to farmers.

Have you ever wondered about a rattlesnake's rattles? Like some insects, snakes shed their skin when it becomes too small on account of their growth. The first skin the rattler sheds leaves a sort of knob on the end of its tail. As more skins are shed, little rings or segments are left and held on by the knob. When the tail wiggles, these rings make a noise that warns one a rattler is near. The age of a rattler cannot be told by the number of rings because a snake may shed its skin several times a year.

Some common non-poisonous snakes are the garter snake, king snake, ribbon snake, gopher snake, and green snake. If you have any of these where you live, you will be interested in studying them at first hand. You need not be afraid of them.

Perhaps the most common snake in the United States is the garter snake. That is a good thing because the garter snake is very useful. It eats grasshoppers and many other insects. It also eats tadpoles and small fish if it can get them. Larger snakes, hawks, and bitterns are the worst enemies of the garter snake.

National Audubon Society, by Cruickshank

GARTER SNAKE

This is the snake you will see most commonly in your garden. It will not harm you. Most of the time it is searching for insects to eat.

If you can catch a garter snake, put it in a glass box with gravel in the bottom and a dish of water. Find it a few earthworms every 5 or 6 days and you will soon have an interesting pet. You can handle it without any danger. Sometimes it may give off a disagreeable odor if frightened, but this does no harm.

The garter snake mates in early spring and in the fall gives birth usually to 20 to 40 young snakes. Sometimes there may be 50 to 75 young.

You can recognize the garter snake by the colored stripes that run along its back. These are green and yellow or orange, and make a beautiful pattern against the darker green of the body.

Another very common little snake is the green snake. He is very hard to see against the leafy plants where he rests. This little snake eats many spiders, grasshoppers, crickets, and smooth caterpillars. He does not appear to like the woolly ones. As an insect eater the green snake is most helpful.

As a science student you should not let superstition or misbelief determine your thinking toward snakes. Learn the facts about them and then you will enjoy seeing them and want to protect them.

Birds, the Air Scouts. — No doubt you like birds better than snakes. That is to be expected, because most people like birds and say nice things about them. Then, too, they are probably more helpful to us. Let us see how the birds help us in our war on the insects.

Two common birds of the garden and field, the *phoebe* and *kingbird*, make a specialty of darting after flying insects. Phoebe will tell you her name, if you listen. The kingbird shows a white band across the end of his tail as he darts from the top of a tree to capture his prey in the air. Unfortunately, these birds do not always confine their attacks to the enemy insects. They may devour some useful insects. However, on the whole they are efficient assistants to the gardener.

FIELD RESEARCH:

Some day when insects are flying about, sit quietly in a convenient spot (take your Field Research Notebook with you to record your observations at the moment) and watch for flycatchers. Field glasses will help you to observe markings on the birds.

Note the ways of flying of the different birds, where they perch, their size and special markings, and the shape and size of their beaks. Listen for their calls.

Record your observations and later try to identify each bird you see by reference to your notebook.

Birds that catch insects as they fly about are called *flycatchers*. Other flycatchers besides the phoebe and kingbird are the *pewee* and *crested flycatcher*. The fly-catchers sit quietly as if asleep, suddenly dart out into the air to catch an unsuspecting insect, and then return to their perch.

Seed Eaters. — Have you planted your garden seeds or sown some grass seed only to have the birds come along and help themselves to a free banquet? Or have they eaten the ripened seed before harvesting? It is true that birds cannot tell the difference between your garden seeds and weed seeds. However, without the feathered seed eaters it would be very difficult to keep weeds under control. Birds consume hundreds of tons of weed seeds.

© *H. H. Pittman*

SONG SPARROW

Known from coast to coast for his "teakettle song," farmers also know the song sparrow as a friend who eats many harmful weed seeds.

The *chipping sparrow, song sparrow, white-throated sparrow*, and the sprightly little *goldfinch* are members in high standing in the Weed Seed Eaters Bird Club. Do you know "chippy" by his cheery song? Or the white-throated sparrow by his high-pitched call saying "Poor Sam Pea-body, pea-body, pea-body"? And do you know the goldfinch which sings as he flies through the air? Wild lettuce, mullein, dandelion, ragweed, and thistle seeds are among his favorite food. How many other seed eaters do you know?

FIELD RESEARCH:

With your field glass, your Field Research Notebook, an alert ear, and quick eye, go out to discover the seed eaters. Note their size, markings, where they hide when frightened, and the shape and size of their beaks. Is there any connection between these characteristics and what the birds eat?

The goldfinch is one of the few birds that sings as it flies. Listen for his song.

Courtesy U. S. Fish and Wildlife Service

ROBIN FEEDING ITS YOUNG

Worms and grubs are the chief food for robins, but they sometimes capture live insects, too. This robin is feeding a dragonfly to its young.

Grub and Worm Eaters.—Do you call anything that crawls a worm? Of course not! Snakes are not worms although there are some worms as large as small snakes. You have learned that the larvae of some insects are called *grubs*. They are worm-like but are not true worms. The grubs will change to the adult stage, if they live. True worms, of which the earthworm is a good example, reproduce new worms. But they do not go through the changes which mark the life history of insects.

FIELD RESEARCH:

While you are studying the seed eaters, you might like to start a collection of the seeds of all the weeds you can find. At the same time find out how each seed is scattered or distributed.

Many birds are very fond of both true worms and the worm-like grubs. Such birds are especially helpful to the gardener and farmer in eating tons of insect grubs. This is helpful because it is in the larva stage that most insects do the most harm. *Bluebirds, robins,* and

Allen Frost from Sawders

BLACK-CAPPED CHICKADEE

This little fellow has seized an insect larva from a decaying stump. Although very small in size, the chickadees do an important job in keeping down the numbers of insects.

orioles have great appetites for grubs and worms. The happy little chickadee, too, eats many larvae. In fact, in a day, one chickadee may eat several hundred grubs and hundreds of insect eggs. Watch the birds to find what they eat.

Eaters of Tiny Insects. — Have you seen the quiet, prim little *brown creeper* hopping along the trunk or branches of a tree hunting for insects? Frequently he starts at the base of a tree and hunts along up the trunk and limbs, then darts to the base of another tree. Another little bird, the *white-breasted nuthatch*, often works head downward as he travels from branch to trunk.

Both of these birds eat enormous numbers of tiny insects and eggs that are overlooked by less observing birds.

Again we mention the *chickadees* which flit from tree to shrub calling their own names as they alight to capture

National Audubon Society, by Cruickshank

A HELPFUL SONGSTER

A marvelous songster, the bluebird is also well known for its work in eating insects. The bluebird in this picture is entering its nest in a hole in a telegraph pole. What is in its bill?

their prey and protect your garden. They do their bit in the battle with the insects.

Except for the *hummingbirds*, the *kinglets* are among the smallest of our birds. They like the insects that are found on evergreen trees such as the hemlock and spruce.

The *warblers* are not really good singers although they do sing very high notes, so high that some people's ears cannot hear them. There are many kinds of warblers, all small, beautiful birds. They keep very busy eating little insects and eggs.

The *woodpeckers* are all helpers too, especially the *hairy woodpecker* and the smaller *downy woodpecker*. These birds stay in many northern localities all winter and work day after day protecting our fruit and shade trees.

The Army Musicians. — Nearly all birds are useful and nearly all eat insects, insect eggs, and seeds. You have become acquainted with some birds that have special likes for certain foods, but you should remember that they do eat a variety of foods, just as you should. Birds, of course, do not spend all their time eating. A few birds are good musicians and it will give you much pleasure to know these birds and their songs. Their songs cannot be described, you must hear them over and over again to appreciate them. Early in the morning is the best time to hear them.

The songs of the *robins* and *bluebirds* you must know. Then try to hear a concert by a *wood thrush* or a *hermit thrush*. The hermit thrush is considered by many to be the finest singer of them all. The *mockingbird* of the south is a wonderful singer. He sings not only his own songs but imitates songs of other birds. In the north the catbird imitates other birds. While his call is a meow like a cat, his song is sweet and varied.

FIELD RESEARCH:

Before and during nesting time the birds sing their best. It will pay you to sit quietly near a wooded lake or stream or retreat in your park at sundown and listen to them. At sunrise, too, the bird concerts are in full swing.

Learn the songs and calls of your most common birds and then try to hear the hermit thrush, the wood thrush, the catbird, or the mockingbird.

The saucy little house wren is a delight to hear. What are the best singers where you live? Listen to them until you know their songs and calls.

Four Bad Birds. — Probably all birds do some good, but a few have bad reputations because some, like the *English sparrow* and the *starling*, drive away other more useful birds. Practically every boy and girl in the United States can become acquainted with the English sparrow, also called the *house sparrow* because it stays around our houses. You have read how it was brought from Europe to help control some insects. But over here it didn't eat the insects as it did at home. It multiplied so rapidly that it became a nuisance. Even so the English sparrow does help in some parts of the country. Do not mistake the English sparrow as a relation of the fine American sparrows, all of which are very useful.

The *cooper's hawk*, the *sharp-shinned hawk*, the *duck hawk*, and the *goshawk* are four bad birds because they rob other birds' nests of eggs or young and attack many smaller birds. The goshawk is rare south of the Canadian border during spring and summer, and the duck hawk is common only near large bodies of water. Thus only two — the cooper's hawk and the sharp-shinned hawk — need worry us very much. Other hawks are most helpful because they eat large numbers of mice and similar animals, called *rodents*, and so prevent millions of dollars' damage to crops and fruit trees. Hunters on the farms often try to kill all hawks — referring to all of them as hen hawks. That should not be done. Most hawks are among the farmer's best bird friends. The beneficial hawks include the *Harris hawk*, the *red-tailed hawk*, the *marsh hawk*, the *sparrow hawk*, and the *red-shouldered hawk*.

The red-tailed hawk is sometimes called a chicken hawk because it may take a chicken once in a while. Its food consists mostly of mice, rats, squirrels, gophers, rabbits, shrews, grasshoppers, beetles, snakes, and frogs. Anyone who has had a fruit orchard badly damaged by mice and rabbits will welcome the red-tailed hawk.

The red-shouldered hawk is very beneficial because it eats many mice and insects. The best hawk of all is the marsh hawk and fortunately it is found in almost all parts of the United States and Canada. If you want still more facts about the hawks, it will pay you to read about them in some book on birds.

Bird Houses. — In many localities, the woods and forests have been cut away. Orchards and woodlots, if well kept, have no decaying branches and no holes in the trunks. In such places, birds that build nests in holes have few suitable choices. Stone walls and fences that formerly furnished nesting places for some birds are disappearing from towns and villages, so that there are few natural home sites for birds.

Some birds will nest in boxes put up for them, if the boxes are at the proper height from the ground and have the right-sized entrance. Bluebirds and wrens will be likely to nest in your yard, if you provide living accommodations for them.

A BIRD-HOUSE BUILDING CONTEST

With the help of your science teacher, your bird club chairman, and your woodworking instructor, start a contest for building bird homes, bird baths, and winter lunch counters. Make an exhibit of everything constructed, for the benefit of the judges and members of your school. In your Observers' Club Calendar you will find helpful suggestions.

Bird Baths and Lunch Counters. — Do you like to have the birds near you? Of course you do; not only for their songs, but because you know their value. In the summer, birds must have water for drinking and bathing. If you provide bird baths, many birds will visit your yard and help in its upkeep. A bird bath should not be very deep and should have sloping sides so that a bird may wade into deeper water gradually. It should be placed on a standard so that the house cat cannot sneak up and capture an unsuspecting bird.

In parts of the country where winters are rather severe, birds that stay the year round may have difficulty in securing enough food. To help these winter birds, you should build lunch counters and keep them supplied with food.   Suet fastened to a tree will coax the woodpeckers, tree sparrows, juncos, and nuthatches to visit your yard. Not only suet, but sunflower seeds, hemp seeds, squash and pumpkin seeds, corn, oats, and nut meats are appetizing to birds.   Seeds may be put into a little box from

National Audubon Society

WINTER FEEDING STATION

A feeding station like this is very easy to make.   Study it carefully and try to build one.   You can use wooden sides instead of glass if you wish. What is the purpose of the two large vanes?

which the birds may get them; or thrown on the ground kept free from snow. Finches, song sparrows, and vesper sparrows are some of the birds that are fond of hemp seed.   For more details and directions for making bird lunch counters you will need to consult your Observers' Club Calendar and other books on birds.   The Emergency Conservation Committee and the National Audubon Society will also give you information.   It is important to remember to get your food out early so the birds will know where to find it.

Bird Protection. — Cats are valuable, particularly on farms, because of the rats and mice they catch. But in cities, cats often become one of the chief enemies of birds. If you have a house cat, keep him well fed and he will not be so likely to want to hunt for birds. Keep him shut in during the early morning and evening, when birds are most apt to be about. Tie a bell about his neck to warn the birds if he tries to waylay them.

Stray cats should not be allowed to roam. Have all stray and homeless cats taken away by the Humane Society or other authorities. With your knowledge of the value of birds to your garden and how to attract and protect them, you should be able to do your share toward their conservation.

FIELD RESEARCH:

Get a copy of the bird and game laws and learn what birds are protected by law. Report violators to the proper authority in your locality.

National problems of bird and other wild life protection are now the work of the Fish and Wildlife Service of the Department of the Interior. Among others, two important acts or laws are of special importance in protecting our birds and other wild life.

Curiously enough, one of these acts, the Lacy Act, came about because of the English sparrow. You remember that this sparrow was brought to our country to help rid the country of certain insect pests. However, the English sparrow is very hardy and soon became adapted to our country. It increased in numbers so rapidly that in some places it crowded out our native songbirds. The Lacy Act now makes it illegal to bring to this country any undesirable bird or animal. The act also serves to stop the hunting of protected birds and animals for market or for their feathers.

The second important act is the Migratory Bird Treaty Act of this country and a similar one for Canada called the Migratory Birds Conservation Act. These acts help to protect all birds that migrate between Canada and the United States.

There are national and local organizations for the protection of wild life. Wouldn't you like to learn about them, about their work, and how you can help?

General Problem 5.   How Does Plant Life Continue?

Plant Reproduction. — The natural work of a plant is to reproduce more of its kind. The methods of reproduction vary in different kinds of plants. Some plants that have been mentioned are the algae and fungi. These plants have an interesting way of reproduction, but just now we shall consider the reproduction of the plants that have flowers and seeds. Such plants depend upon the flowers to produce the seeds from which new plants will grow, provided they receive the necessary care in planting, cultivation, and protection from disease and insects. Helping to provide proper conditions for flower and seed development is a matter of great importance in the garden.

The Flower. — The plant obtains food-building minerals and water through its roots from the soil, and carbon dioxide through its leaves from the air. As the plant matures, flower buds appear and finally the flower opens and discloses the wonderful parts from which the seeds develop. Many flowers have color through which they appear to attract helpful insects, and they may also attract by a fragrance. The words "appear to" and "may" are used because it is not really certain that insects are dependent upon color or fragrance to invite them to a particular flower.

PARTS OF A FLOWER

At the left is a Yucca flower; at the right, some Yucca moths; and in the center, the different parts of the flower. Can you name them?

The colored part of the flower is usually made up of *petals*. Outside the petals may be found the leaf-like parts called *sepals* (usually green). Each flower has a particular number of petals and sepals; so a knowledge of these is a help in identifying it. In a row inside the petals are little slender parts called *stamens*. At the end of each stamen is a little cup or box, the *anther*. In the center of the flower is the *pistil* with an *ovary* (seed case) at the bottom. A flower with all these parts is called a "perfect" flower. Some flowers lack one or more of these parts. They are called "imperfect."

FIELD RESEARCH:
Many flowers, for example, sweet peas and violets, have specially shaped parts. Collect as many different shaped flowers as possible, and try to identify each part. Flowers lacking either stamens or pistils are imperfect flowers. Some maples have imperfect flowers.

Have you ever dusted yellow powder from a lily or dandelion onto your hand? That powder consists of tiny grains, *pollen*. It forms in the anthers at the ends of the stamens. If the flower develops properly, some pollen grains will be dusted onto the head of the pistil and will send a slender hair-like shoot down through the pistil to unite with little seeds-to-be, *ovules*, in the seed case, the *ovary*.

FIELD RESEARCH:
The pod is the ovary of the pea blossom. The ovules, when fertilized, become the seeds, and when they ripen, they can be planted to produce a new plant.

With a magnifier, examine a cross section of ovaries of two or more different kinds of blossoms to see whether the ovules are of the same shape and number in different blossoms. Try to discover whether they are alike in shape, arrangement, and number in blossoms of the same kind. Cherry and apple blossoms are suggested for study. What use could be made of the facts you have discovered?

The process by which pollen travels from the stamens to the pistil is called *pollination*, and the process by which the nucleus of the pollen unites with the ovules is called *fertilization*. This is like the sperm from the male frog uniting with the frog's eggs to fertilize them. Unless the ovules are fertilized, they will not develop into seeds that can grow new plants. Pollination and fertilization, therefore, are two very important processes for the production of seeds, and anything that helps or hinders this process is of vital importance to the gardener.

FIELD RESEARCH:

If you have a microscope at home, or one at school which you are allowed to use, with the help of your teacher examine pollen from two or three different kinds of flowers to find out whether all pollen is alike in shape, size, and color.

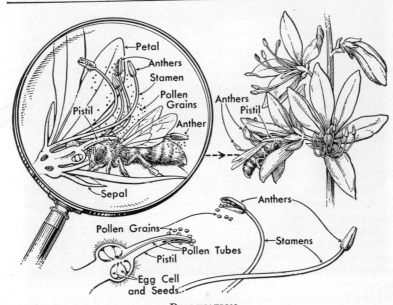

POLLINATION

Pollination is the transfer of pollen from the stamens to the pistil. Explain how the bee helps in this process.
With the help of this diagram name the parts of a cherry blossom.
What is the purpose of each part?

Flower Visitors. — Have you ever tasted clover-flavored or buckwheat-flavored honey? If you have, you must conclude that the bees that made the honey visited clover blossoms or buckwheat blossoms to obtain the *nectar*. Nectar is a sweet liquid which many flowers form and store near the base of the pistil and stamens, sometimes in special little cups. Its presence persuades insects and small birds like the hummingbird to pay the flower a visit.   Colors and odors, you have learned, seem to attract some insects.   There is a very good reason why nature has planned this to be so.

Courtesy Bureau of Entomology, U.S.D.A.

If you look carefully, you can see the long tube mouth of the bumblebee. Why does the bumblebee visit the flower?   How does the visit help the plant?

Insects Help Pollination. — A few flowers are so arranged that the pollen of their stamens is likely to fall onto their own pistils.   Such pollination is called *self-pollination*.   However, in some flowers the stamens may be missing, or the pistil may be missing; or the flower may be arranged in such a way that the pollen cannot fertilize the ovules in the ovary of the same flower. Sometimes the ovules and pollen in the same flower do not ripen at the same time; hence pollen from one flower is necessary to fertilize the ovules of the other. For these reasons the insects and birds are needed to help the process of pollination. The drawing on page 465 shows a bee helping to pollinate a flower. Notice the parts of the flower the bee touches.

An insect, the bumblebee for example, may light on a flower to drink its nectar. While doing so some of the pollen rubs off the stamens onto his coat. Perhaps the next flower (of the same kind) which he visits needs this pollen which may be rubbed from the bumblebee onto the pistil of the second flower. In this way the bumblebee aids in pollination. While the wind helps by blowing pollen from one flower to another, the work of insects is very necessary. Such a transfer of pollen from one flower to another is called *cross-pollination*.

In many cases cross-pollination produces improvements over self-pollination and, as you have read above, in some plants cross-pollination is absolutely necessary if seeds are to be formed. Cherry, plum, and peach blossoms require cross-pollination by means of insects. Better crops of apples result from cross-pollination. The honeybee is the most essential insect for this work, so fruit growers frequently raise honeybees in their orchards. Butterflies in the winged stage, moths, and flies are also helpful.

Thinking Things Over. — Curious isn't it what makes one plant a weed and another a useful plant? In fact, the dandelion has really a beautiful flower; if only it didn't spread so easily, people would like it. But even the dandelion is not always a weed. If you look in a seed catalog, you may find dandelion seeds for sale and at a rather high price, too. Why is that? The reason is that many people like dandelion leaves to eat as greens and so some gardeners raise certain kinds for that use.

When is a weed not a weed? When it serves some useful purpose. So it is with most plants. Some are more useful than others. The useful kind are protected and nourished. The less useful are eliminated from the garden to make room for the better ones.

We should always be careful not to call anything useless; rather we should say that it is not as useful as something else. As science pupils we must be careful always to qualify our statements when we do not have all the facts.

Once in a golden hour
I cast to earth a seed.
Up there came a flower —
The people said a weed.

J. Horace McFarland Company

Is the water lily a weed? Certainly it is not used for food, but its beauty adds to our enjoyment of many ponds. Perhaps its purpose is to help make the world more beautiful.

These lines are from "The Flower" by Tennyson. Perhaps you would like to read the rest of the poem. What did Tennyson mean?

Science has shown us ways to control plants that interfere with the proper growth of plants we wish to raise. Science, too, has discovered ways to combat sickness and disease among plants as it has among animals.

We have found that there are both useful and harmful insects although it is probable that all insects have some value. Here again we must consider relative values.

Our knowledge of the life history and habits of insects enables us to control them to some extent. Even so we need the help of toads, snakes, and birds in the war against the most harmful insects. Knowing the habits of toads, snakes, and birds, as well as helpful insects, we can supply their needs and try to protect them against their enemies. That is why laws have been made to prevent the slaughter of birds.

Of course the more we know about the way plants grow and reproduce, the better we can care for them. This knowledge also enables scientists to develop better varieties of plants, that is, hardier plants, plants with sweeter corn, and plants with more beautiful blossoms.

Your study of the insects and their relations to your garden has helped you to realize how important scientific knowledge is to the production

J. Horace McFarland Company

IRIS

From thick brown tubers grow these delicate blossoms. They spread with amazing rapidity, yet no one would call them weeds.

of food for the world. Without knowledge of the habits of insects and birds, and of characteristics of soil, of seeds, and plants, gardeners and farmers generally would have a pretty hard task to feed mankind. Thus thousands of scientists are experimenting continually to discover more about plants and animals. In the next chapter we shall investigate the harvesting and care of our crops.

J. Horace McFarland Company

ALONG A GARDEN PATH

How dreary our cities and towns would be if there were no flowers! A few bulbs and seeds and a gardener's careful work has produced this beauty spot.

Key Words

anther	ladybird beetle	pollination
beetles	life history	ragweed
bread mold	mildew	reproduction
chlorophyll	milkweed	root eaters
cocoon	mullein	seeds
codling moth	mustard	sepal
cross-pollination	nectar	sperm cell
cutworm	nucleus	squash bug
fertilization	ovary	stamen
flycatchers	ovules	tadpole
fungi	parasite	toadflax
grub	pigweed	warblers
hibernate	pistil	warts
host	plant lice	weeds
ichneumon fly	poison ivy	woodpeckers
insects	pollen	

Key Statements

1. Weeds are difficult to control because they produce many hardy seeds, or hardy roots.

2. A knowledge of the life history of weeds is fundamental to their successful control.

3. There are hordes of insect garden pests which must be controlled, but others are very useful to the gardener.

4. A knowledge of the life history of insects is necessary to their control.

5. Plants may contract contagious disease in much the same way that animals do.

6. A plant may be attacked by other plants called fungi, which eventually kill it unless the fungi are destroyed.

7. Some insects help in the control of other injurious insects by eating them, by eating their eggs, or by laying eggs in their bodies from which larvae hatch out and destroy the host.

8. Toads should be protected because they destroy great numbers of insects.

9. The toad lives the first part of his life as a water animal and the second part (adult stage) as a land animal.

10. Most kinds of snakes are useful as eaters of insects, mice, and rats.

11. Certain birds are especially active in eating seeds, and thus are very helpful in the control of weeds.

12. Many birds eat grubs and worms, others eat seeds (weeds), and still others eat flies. Such birds are helpers of the gardener.

13. All birds have calls and a few have beautiful songs by which you may know them.

14. There are a few varieties of birds classed as pests because they seem to do more harm than good.

15. Birds can be encouraged to stay in your neighborhood if you will provide them with nesting places, nesting material, water for bathing and drinking, and food.

16. Cats are among the greatest destroyers of song birds.

17. The natural purpose of a plant is to reproduce its kind.

18. Flowers contain the organs of reproduction in plants.

19. Pollination, one step in reproduction of plants, consists of the transfer of pollen from the stamens to the pistil.

20. Fertilization, the second step in plant reproduction, consists of the union of the nucleus of a pollen grain with the nucleus of an ovule (egg cell).

21. Birds and insects help transfer pollen and so aid the process of pollination.

22. When the pollen of one flower is transferred to the pistil of another flower, the process is called cross-pollination.

23. Cross-pollination of many fruit trees depends upon the honeybee.

Thought Questions

1. Account for the wide distribution of weeds.

2. How do control measures differ for weeds that are annuals, biennials, and perennials?

3. Why are weeds objectionable?

4. How does a ladybird beetle differ in customs and manners from a tomato worm?

5. Why are some insects called "biting" insects?

6. Why are some insects called "sucking" insects?

7. What difference in the use of insect poison is required for biting and for sucking insects?

8. Explain how it is possible for an animal to live first as a water animal and then as a land animal. Does a land animal ever change to a water animal?

9. What does hibernation mean?

10. What peculiarities of the phoebe cause it to be called a fly-catcher?

11. What sort of beak do most seed-eating birds have? How would it compare with a flycatcher's beak?

12. What characteristics, other than shape, size, color, and markings should help you to identify birds?

13. Why will bird baths help to keep birds in your yard?

14. How does a plant take in water and minerals through its roots?

15. Where do plants get the energy to enable them to make their food from the raw materials?

16. Why must pollination take place before fertilization?

17. How are new plant varieties produced? Consider cross-pollination.

18. In what way is the honeybee a most necessary insect?

Projects for Your Science Discovery Book

1. Make a collection of all the different kinds of weeds that grow about your house and tell how each one is reproduced. Suggest a plan for the control or extermination of each.

2. Draw a picture of a dandelion seed and suggest a plan for controlling it. How can you put your plan into operation?

3. Make a list of poisonous weeds.

4. Examine the soil about a plant that has been cut off by a cutworm to see if you can find the cutworm larva. Put the larva into a cage with some soil and plants and observe it in its various stages. Describe your discoveries.

5. Make some labeled drawings of mold from your own observations.

6. Study the actions of a toad; find out what he eats and how he catches his prey, and if he has a home spot, and if so, when he stays there.

7. Try to catch a garter or green snake and keep it for a while. Be sure to feed and water it properly.

8. Observe the habits of a robin, bluebird, oriole, or mocking bird to find out what it eats, and what it feeds its young at nesting time. What is its song?

9. Describe a woodpecker, what it does, how it flies, and how its color helps protect it.

10. Make a labeled drawing of the parts of an apple blossom, trillium, or other flower.

11. Report on how many kinds of flowers in your garden are visited by insects and what insects make the visits.

12. Learn to identify garden and lawn weeds. How can they be controlled?

13. Learn to identify ragweed, goldenrod, and poison ivy. How can they be destroyed?

14. Make a study of the life history of a sucking insect, a biting insect, and a root eater. How can each be controlled?

15. Find out how some aphids are cared for by certain ants and how the ants are paid for their care.

16. Learn to identify three helpful insects. How can they be protected?

17. Visit near-by farms and try to find examples of apple- or pear-tree blight, or black rot on the cabbage or turnip. Learn what the farmer does to control the diseases. If you find diseased material, go back again with your teacher, taking along several petri dishes with prepared culture medium. Dust materials of the diseased plant on to the petri dishes. Keep one dish closed for a control. Take the dishes back to school and incubate them for 24 hours at 37° C.

18. Learn how to use spraying and dusting materials for the control of insects, plant disease, and fungi.

19. Go to the library for information about the Australian ladybird beetle and how it helped to control the cottony-cushion scale of California. Try to find out about other beetles and their work. The squash ladybird beetle and the bean ladybird beetle are harmful. Find pictures of them so that you may know these two beetles when you see them.

20. Visit someone who keeps honeybees and study the bee's methods of work and living.

And nature does require
Her times of preservation.
Shakespeare

UNIT VI

⚞CONSERVATION⚟

What does it mean to conserve? Does it mean not to use? Certainly not. It means to use without waste and for desirable purpose only. War, pestilence, and disease are three great wasters. Conservation then means the elimination of these monsters. Conservation goes further than that. It means that individuals, families, communities, states, and nations must look upon natural resources, not as their's alone, but as belonging to other generations, too.

That hasn't always been understood, because without the knowledge of science it was not always known that the forests could be destroyed, that the soil could be washed into the sea, and that the vegetation could be lost from the earth. Science shows us the way to use and to conserve at the same time. Let us now consider well the meaning and truth of the inscription in the dome of the National Academy of Science at Washington:

TO SCIENCE

PILOT OF INDUSTRY, CONQUEROR OF DISEASE, MULTIPLIER OF THE HARVEST, EXPLORER OF THE UNIVERSE, REVEALER OF NATURE'S LAWS, ETERNAL GUIDE TO TRUTH

FOOD FOR WINTER

Food conservation is the best example of what "conservation" really means. Here we see that conservation means saving for the future, planning ahead, using wisely.

476

TOPIC XVI

Food Conservation

They's something kind o'harty-like about the atmosphere
When the heat of summer's over and the coolin' fall is here —
Of course we miss the flowers, and the blossoms on the trees,
And the mumble of the hummin'-bird and buzzin' of the bees;
But air's so appetizin'; and the landscape through the haze
Of a crisp and sunny morning of the airly autumn days
Is a picture that no painter has the colorin' to mock —
When the frost is on the punkin and the fodder's in the shock!

— Riley

Do you know:

1. What the word "conservation" means?
2. How to tell when potatoes are ready to dig?
3. The relation of temperature to the preservation of stored potatoes, cabbage, or carrots?
4. What is meant by "quick freezing"?
5. What causes foodstuffs to spoil?

General Problem 1. Why Grow Vegetables in Your Garden?

Fresh Vegetables. — How many times have you heard people envy gardeners or farmers for their vegetables fresh from the garden? Did you ever eat peas or corn that were fresh picked and cooked? If you have, you know what the word "fresh" means. It means more sugar, more vitamins, and more enjoyment. Vegetables gathered from your own garden give you the satisfaction of supplying your table with the product of your own work. If your garden plans for planting are right, your garden will supply you from early summer until late fall.

However, this topic has to do with conservation, and so we must not be satisfied with better-tasting vegetables. We must save what we do not eat. For example, the unedible leafy parts of your healthy vegetables should be placed in a *compost* pile and allowed to decompose. The compost, as the decomposed matter is called, can be used as fertilizer for your garden next spring and so will return to the soil some of the materials taken from it by

Raymond E. Hanson

COWS MUST EAT, TOO

In the tall silo is stored winter food for the cows. Corn stalks and leaves are chopped in small pieces and blown into the silo.

This picture and the one on page 476 are very different. Yet are they not also quite similar?

the plants. A compost pile is made up of vegetable tops and fallen leaves to which thin layers of lime may be added. Sometimes sand and fertilizer are added. The decomposed vegetable matter forms a valuable humus or water-holding material. Diseased tops should never be added to the compost, but should be burned. The compost heap is one step toward conservation.

The Harvest. — The time of harvest lasts from the pulling of the earliest onion or radish to the gathering of your latest crop. However, the time for gathering the supply for winter is the harvest time of poetry and song.

Fruits and vegetables must be gathered when they are at the proper stage of development. Otherwise they will not keep well. Fruits for canning or for winter storage should be picked before they ripen too much. Hard-root vegetables are ready for gathering when they stop growing. Parsnips are not injured by freezing and so may be left in the ground all winter if need be. Potatoes continue to grow until the tops dry down. They are injured by freezing and so should be harvested before killing frosts come. The successful harvesting of crops all over the country is a very important item in the amount and cost of our fruit and vegetable food supply.

General Problem 2. How Are Foods Conserved by Storing?

Air Conditions. — Foods spoil for one of several reasons. They may dry out and wilt, which makes them less useful. They may be kept so warm that molds and bacteria grow, causing changes in their composition and

Kabel Photo

AUTUMN HARVEST

When the frost is on the punkin and the fodder's in the shock.

Autumn harvest — this is a partial result of the farmer's work of spring and summer.

rotting them. The conservation of raw foods, then, depends upon maintaining proper conditions to prevent shrinking and rotting.

Bureau of Plant Industry, U. S. D. A.

POTATO STORAGE CELLAR

Potatoes should be stored in well-ventilated bins. The best temperature for storage is 40°–45° F.

The proper storage of fruits and vegetables is a problem of ventilation, air temperature, and air humidity. Storage space should be clean, dry, and dark. Most fruits and vegetables should be kept between 33° F. and 40° F. to prevent the growth of molds and bacteria. Fruits which contain considerable amounts of sugar can be kept with the temperature at or near freezing.

FIELD RESEARCH:

Secure a thermometer and determine the freezing temperature of samples of pure water, water with sugar dissolved in it (one pint of water to three tablespoonfuls of sugar), and apple juice. For a freezing mixture use two parts of crushed ice to one part of coarse salt, well mixed.

Ordinary Storage. — Potatoes and cabbages should be placed in bins arranged to allow for ventilation. Near the end of cold weather they will need to be sorted over to take out any that are decaying and to remove sprouts from the potatoes, if such have started. Root vegetables such as carrots, beets, and turnips should be stored in clean, dry sand. It is best to leave a small portion of the stem on the vegetable.

Fruits such as apples, pears, quinces, and grapes should be kept very cold and well ventilated. It is more difficult to keep fruits in good, fresh condition for several weeks or months than it is to keep vegetables satisfactorily. Therefore, artificially cooled storage places are needed.

FIELD RESEARCH:

Take samples of carrots, potatoes, apples, pears, and grapes to school and accurately weigh each and record the weights.

Set each one on a side bench and weigh each again at the end of two days, and still again at the end of a week.

From the first and second weight and first and last weight of each sample, calculate the per cent of weight lost.

Which food lost the largest per cent by weight? What relation has the loss of weight to the character of the skin in each case?

Cold Storage. — Ordinary storage plants are subject to temperature changes due to weather changes, unless special precautions are taken, such as in cold storage. A cold storage place is a building so constructed that the walls prevent, to a considerable extent, the passage of heat in or out. Heat always tends to travel from warm objects to cold objects. Anything that obstructs the passage of heat is called a *heat insulator*. Therefore such a building, once it is cooled to the correct temperature at the beginning of the winter, will not ordinarily become cold enough to allow freezing to take place inside.

Neither will it warm up rapidly during warm spells or as spring advances. Hence, some vegetables will keep very well in it.

COLD STORAGE WAREHOUSE

Here are stored eggs, lard, apples, onions, and a variety of other foodstuffs. Can you see how this room is cooled?

The modern cold storage plants are built with very efficient insulating walls, and the temperature inside is controlled by artificial means. In these places, low temperatures can be maintained at all times, even through the hottest weather. Furthermore, because different food materials require different air conditions, temperature, and humidity, they can be placed in rooms where the best conditions are maintained.

Application of scientific principles to the preservation of raw foods results in many savings; for example, bumper crops can be kept for long periods, or may be transported in cold storage cars to distant points.

Quick Freezing. — A modern and efficient method of conserving foods is the quick-freezing method.

Courtesy Tennessee Valley Authority

COLD STORAGE LOCKERS

These individual lockers are kept at a constant temperature of 0° Fahrenheit. A family may rent a locker in which to store foods until needed.

Ordinarily freezing a vegetable or a fruit destroys its taste and appearance. Scientists have developed a way to freeze foods very quickly. When this method is used the food is not damaged as when it is frozen slowly. Have you eaten peas or berries that have been frozen by the quick process? When thawed out they are like fresh-picked foods.

In parts of Alaska the ground below a few feet stays frozen the year around. So people have cellars dug deep enough to reach into the frozen earth. There they place fresh fruits to be frozen and conserved until needed.

Today there are small quick-freezing units for private use. Not only are fruits and vegetables preserved by this method but fish and meats as well.

FIELD RESEARCH:

If there is a quick-freezing plant or unit near where you live, arrange to visit it, or send a committee to visit it for you and make a report to the class.

General Problem 3. What Are Some Home Conservation Methods?

Scientific Principles. — You have learned that decay is usually caused by germs, by molds, and by mildews. You have learned also that these non-green plants thrive best at warm temperatures and in the presence of moisture. The preservation of food, therefore, depends upon (1) a temperature so low that the organisms become inactive (they are not killed as a rule by low temperatures); or (2) upon the removal of moisture; or (3) destruction of the decay-producing organisms contained in the food; or (4) the addition of substances that prevent or retard the growth of decay-producing organisms. Frequently a combination of these methods is used.

Preserving by Heat. — When watching your mother canning fruit or making jam, have you ever noticed how careful she was to make sure the jar was clean and hot, and how quickly she covered the hot fruit or jam after it was put into the jar? This was to prevent any dust from getting in. The dust might contain mold spores or germs that could cause the canned fruit to spoil. Sometimes the fruit may be put into the jar and the whole thing heated at the same time and then covered.

Not only fruits, but vegetables and meats may be preserved by placing them in a container and heating them to a temperature high enough to kill all the germs and spores of molds. The container is then closed airtight while still hot. If you recall what you learned in Experiment 37, you will know that heat kills the organisms, and the sealing prevents other organisms from entering.

Courtesy National Pressure Cooker Company

CANNING FOODS IN A PRESSURE COOKER

The required temperature, which is 212° F. or higher, is obtained by placing the can in boiling water, or in a pressure cooker, used for cooking at high temperatures.

The pressure cooker is used for ordinary cooking as well as canning. Many modern ones are no larger than sauce pans. Their users claim that they are more economical of fuel (why?), and prevent nutrients from boiling off in steam. They use a science principle which you should understand. You have already learned that the air pressure is less at the top of a mountain than at the bottom. Also the air pressure is greater at the bottom of a deep mine than at the surface. This you know is because the weight of the air is what causes the pressure — more air, more pressure; less air, less pressure. The temperature of boiling water and therefore of the steam formed is lower with low air pressure and higher with high air pressure. The pressure cooker is called that because the cover fits on so tightly that when the water boils the steam cannot escape. The pressure inside, therefore, becomes greater. As the pressure builds up, the boiling water and steam get hotter and hotter. If the steam could escape readily as in an ordinary kettle or boiler, the water temperature would rise to about 212° F. and no higher.

There is one important thing to know about a pressure cooker. If the steam could not escape, no matter how much the water inside was boiled, it would burst and cause damage. To safeguard against such an accident the pressure cooker has a steam outlet with a spring in it so that when the steam pressure rises to a certain point the steam valve opens and lets some steam escape. Since the boiling temperature depends upon the pressure, this outlet valve can be set to maintain a required temperature and no higher. This temperature is often 220° F., or eight degrees hotter than ordinary boiling water.

Whoever uses a pressure cooker must be very sure that the outlet valve is working properly. This may be determined by watching the steam gauge on the cooker which shows the pressure. If the gauge shows that the pressure is getting higher than the danger mark, the heat must be turned off at once.

The pasteurizing of milk, discussed on page 373, illustrates the effect of heat upon certain germs, although the temperature is not so high as that used for canning.

The pasteurizing temperature, 142° F. to 145° F., does not kill all the organisms in milk. It does, however,

EXPERIMENT 38

Will heated (pasteurized) milk keep longer without souring than unheated milk?

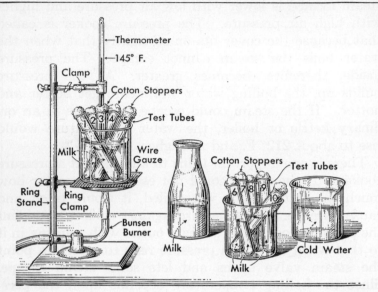

The cotton "plugs" are to keep out any dust particles that may be floating in the air, because they may contain germs or mold spores.

Be sure to label your ten tubes carefully, and keep in mind the different treatments the milk in each test tube receives. Tubes one to five are heated, while tubes six to ten are used for controls. Why are these controls needed?

WHAT TO USE: — Ten test tubes; a thermometer; cotton; a large beaker; wire gauze; a tripod or ring stand and ring; a Bunsen burner; fresh, raw milk.

WHAT TO DO: — 1. Half fill ten test tubes with milk and close the ends with tightly packed cotton stoppers. Label the test tubes 1 to 10.

2. Put tubes 1 to 5 in the beaker and add water until it reaches the top level of the milk in the tubes.

Place the beaker on a wire gauze on the tripod or ring stand and apply heat.

Put the thermometer in one of the test tubes of milk without removing the cotton stopper.

Heat the water in the beaker until the milk in the test tube is at 145° F. and maintain that temperature for 20 minutes. Is it fair to assume that the milk in all tubes is at the same temperature?

3. Remove the test tubes from the water and cool them rapidly. Set all ten tubes with the milk in them on a side bench or table in your science room.

After one day examine tubes 1 and 6, and on each succeeding day examine and record observations of tubes 2 and 7, 3 and 8, 4 and 9, and 5 and 10.

WHAT HAPPENS: — In which set of tubes did the milk keep sweet longest?

CONCLUSIONS: — State briefly how the souring of milk may be retarded.

APPLICATION: — Why must pasteurized milk be cooled quickly?

kill most of those which cause milk to sour, and it kills the germs that might cause diseases such as typhoid fever and tuberculosis. To find out for yourself what effect a pasteurizing temperature has on milk you will need to try Experiment 38. This experiment has a practical value because, if you are in the country or at camp and can buy only raw milk, you may want to pasteurize it before using it. In fact most doctors agree that it is much safer to use pasteurized milk and cream. Also all milk used for ice cream, chocolate milk, and other milk products should be pasteurized.

Cooking, too, is based upon good science principles. Not only does cooking meat, for example, make it more tender and improve its taste, but it kills germs that otherwise might cause disease. Pork especially must be thoroughly cooked to be safe for eating, since there is a rare possibility it may contain organisms that are very dangerous.

PASTEURIZING MILK

Courtesy The Borden Company

A pasteurizing room in a modern dairy. Try Experiment 38 and then explain the pasteurization process.

Preservation by Drying. — Bacteria and molds need warmth, food, and moisture to grow. These organisms cannot live without moisture, so one common method of keeping certain foods is to dry them.

FIELD RESEARCH:

Prepare two beaker-covered dishes as in Experiment 37, one with moist bread, and the other with dry bread. Set in a warm place for two to five days. In which case does mold grow better?

Secure some powdered whole milk. Dissolve one measure of powdered milk in the proper volume of water. Put it in a glass and set it where it will be warm for two or three days. Put a measure of the powdered milk by itself in another glass and set it with the first.

When the milk solution has turned sour, dissolve the dry milk in some water and find out whether it is also sour.

Apples are sometimes preserved by drying thin slices. Later, before using, the dried fruit is placed in water for a time, during which it absorbs water and swells. It can then be used as a substitute for fresh apples.

Ewing Galloway

SUN DRYING

Much of the fruit grown in the fertile valleys of California is preserved by drying. Here are acres of apricots being dried by the heat of the sun. Why is drying a good method of preserving some foods?

Fruits, vegetables, and meats are usually dried artificially so that the water is removed rapidly without overheating the foods. They thus retain practically all of their essential substances, and when water is added, they are very nearly like the fresh foods of the same variety. Sun-dried fruits are considered better than those artificially dried. Drying is the oldest method for the preservation of food. Sometimes the drying is supplemented by smoking or salting. In this case the salt or the smoke acids act as chemical preservers.

Preservation by the Use of Chemicals. — What is a chemical? That is a fair question. Any substance that will act on another and cause a change may be called a chemical. Salt and sugar are chemicals just as much as acids and alkalies. Vinegar contains acetic acid, which is a chemical. The baking soda your mother uses is a chemical. So when we talk about using chemicals to preserve foods we are using a word that includes several kinds of substances.

A strong salt solution is used to preserve such foods as pickles, peaches, fish, and meats. This is called pickling. Jams, preserves, and jellies are preserved with large amounts of sugar. Here the foods are placed in glass jars and covered with paraffin to keep out molds and bacteria. The use of salt and sugar as preservatives, in pickling or making jellies, depends upon the process of *osmosis* (the mixing of two liquids by passage through a thin membrane or porous wall).

Any organism that tried to live in concentrated salt or sugar solution would have its body liquids pass out by osmosis to dissolve the salt or sugar. In other words, individual cells of the organism would dry up and die. Of course some plants and some fish are adapted to the use of salt water, such as sea water. Moreover some molds can grow on the outside of substances like salt meats and sweet jellies.

There are several other chemicals used to preserve foods. Some of these are borax, sulfites, formaldehyde, salicylic acid, and sodium salicylate. Very small amounts of these substances dissolved in the food material will prevent the growth of germs and molds. Sodium sili-

Asahel Curtts

CANNED SALMON

Twenty-four hours before this picture was taken, the salmon were alive. Now they are packed in air-tight cans, ready for labeling and shipment.

cate, commonly called *water glass*, is a chemical often used to preserve eggs. It forms an airtight and water-tight covering around the eggs, but does not touch the material inside the shells.

While we know salt and sugar as preservatives are harmless, we are not sure about some more recently used chemicals. Therefore, their presence in a food, and their amount, must be stated on the label.

Preservation by Cold. — Most fresh meats, fruits, vegetables, and milk and cream are for immediate use in the home. Knowledge of the causes of decay enables us to care for such foods most efficiently. Not only do fresh foods need special attention, but opened canned goods need care to prevent waste. Even though the canned goods may have a special preservative in them, the food will spoil quickly if left in a warm place.

You have learned that the organisms that cause decay and spoiling of foods are inactive at low temperatures;

Courtesy Birds Eye Frosted Foods

A COLD PLACE TO WORK

It is always winter in this room.　When foods have been quick-frozen, they must remain frozen until ready to be eaten.

therefore the best method of caring for foods that are to be kept for a short time only is the cold method.　The foods may be kept in a cold cellar, in which case the cellar should also be dry and free from mold growths on the walls and floors.　Or they may be kept in refrigerators during warm weather, and in cold rooms during cold weather.　In any case, foods such as milk, cream, and butter should be kept covered to prevent them from absorbing dust and odors.

As already mentioned, small fruits and vegetables, and sometimes fish and meat, are preserved for long periods by freezing. The special quick-freezing methods result in very rapid freezing of the material without destroying the texture of the tissue. When thawed out, the food has retained its natural freshness. This method makes it possible to ship berries, cherries, peas, and other food products great distances without deterioration.

General Problem 4. What Keeps the Refrigerator Cold?

Heat Transfer. — To keep an object hot, it is necessary either to keep adding heat, or to prevent the object from losing what heat it has. To keep an object cold, it is necessary to prevent heat from being added to it. Keep these statements in mind in studying a refrigerator.

The refrigerator is a small-sized cold storage plant. It is used to keep perishable foods cold enough to prevent them from spoiling. The building of a good refrigerator depends upon knowledge and application of the principles of *heat transfer*.

You know from experience that if one end of a metal rod is heated for a few minutes, the other end becomes warm or hot. The heat travels, that is, is transferred from one end of the rod to the other. On the other hand, a stick of wood can be held in the hand by one end even though the other end is on fire. In this case, heat is not transferred from one end to the other. The metal is a

FIELD RESEARCH:

Test samples of copper, aluminum, glass, stone, brick, and porcelain to find whether they are conductors or non-conductors of heat.

Brown Brothers

FROM FARM TO CITY

Modern refrigerator cars are the result of understanding and applying the laws of the transfer of heat.

conductor of heat; the wood is a *non-conductor* of heat.

It has been found that heat may be transferred in any one of three different ways. Heat travels through solids by *conduction*. Gases and liquids transfer heat by *convection*. Heat may also travel through gases by means of *radiation*. Let us find out a little more about each of these methods of heat transfer.

Conduction. — The transfer of heat by *conduction* is from particle to particle (molecule to molecule). Ordinary matter is composed of very tiny particles called *molecules*. Most molecules are too small to be seen even with powerful microscopes. The molecules in matter are

all in rapid motion, something like little rubber particles
bouncing against each other.

When a substance is heated, the molecules bounce
faster and harder. When the substance is cooled, they
bounce slower and with less force.

When some solids are heated hot enough, they melt
and form liquids (example, ice to water). The molecules
in liquids bounce faster and harder than in solids. When
certain liquids are heated, they change to the gas state
(example, water to steam). In gases the molecules
bounce still faster and harder than in liquids.

Convection. — The transfer of heat from a hot object
to other objects by a circulation of gases or liquids is
called *convection*. The circulation results in currents
called convection currents.

Convection is the principal method by which heat is
transferred or distributed in liquids and gases. It is
possible because the molecules are free to move from one
place to another. *In convection, the heat is carried from
one place to another by the molecules, while in conduction
the heat is handed along from one molecule to the next.*

Radiation. — A third method by which heat is transferred is *radiation*. If you stand near a hot campfire,
your face and the front of your body quickly become too
hot, while your back continues to stay cold. The heat
seems to come straight from the fire until it strikes you
and there it stops. A wire screen placed between you
and the fire cuts off some of the heat. These facts are
well known to you by experience.

Outdoors on a bright sunny day, the heat seems to
come straight to you from the sun. While hot objects
seem to give out heat, actually they are sending out a
form of energy that does not heat up gases through which

the energy passes. The heat does not appear until the energy strikes a body. It then changes into heat energy, and we say the body has been warmed.

The *radiant energy* of hot bodies is given off in straight lines in all directions. The hotter the body, the more energy it radiates. The radiant energy is changed to heat energy only when it is stopped and absorbed by

Courtesy Santa Fe Refrigerator Department

INSIDE A REFRIGERATOR CAR

Study this picture carefully. How is heat prevented from entering the car? In what ways is this car similar to the household refrigerator shown on page 500? How does it differ?

another body. Radiant energy does not depend upon molecules to "carry" it along nor to "pass" it along; it can, therefore, pass through a vacuum. If this were not true, it is difficult to understand how we could derive heat from the sun.

Like all science principles, those concerning the trans-ference of heat have many practical applications in devices which add to our comfort in daily life.

FIELD RESEARCH:

Focus the rays from the sun through a hand lens or magnifier onto your hand. Do the focused rays burn your hand more than the un-focused rays? Draw a diagram in your Science Discovery Book to illustrate how the sun's rays may be focused.

Try focusing rays from a red-hot object in the same way.

Try reflecting the energy from a fireplace with a mirror or piece of polished tin.

Knowing how heat is transferred through solids and through gases, we should be able to construct a wall that will largely prevent the transfer of heat by conduction, convection, and radiation.

Refrigerator Construction. — Since the refrigerator is a device in which to keep things cold, the sides, top, and bottom must be built to prevent the transfer of heat into the box. Also there must be some plan to remove the heat already in the box or brought in by warm foods and warm air when the door is open.

The walls of a refrigerator are hollow and filled with air and *insulating* solids. *Insulating* materials are those that help prevent transfer of heat. Air is a poorer conductor of heat than wood, but heat is transferred by convection, if the air in the space is free to circulate. Therefore, the space in the walls is broken up into small air spaces by putting in packed, non-conducting porous material such as sawdust, broken-up charcoal, mineral wool, cork, or celotex. These substances are not only non-conductors, but are porous and therefore have the non-conducting property of air. Modern refrigerators have walls built of metals. This is practical because the air space in the walls can now be so thoroughly insulated.

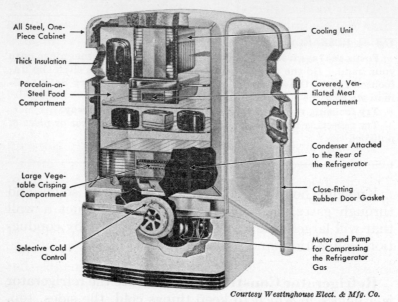

All Steel, One-Piece Cabinet

Thick Insulation

Porcelain-on-Steel Food Compartment

Large Vegetable Crisping Compartment

Selective Cold Control

Cooling Unit

Covered, Ventilated Meat Compartment

Condenser Attached to the Rear of the Refrigerator

Close-fitting Rubber Door Gasket

Motor and Pump for Compressing the Refrigerator Gas

Courtesy Westinghouse Elect. & Mfg. Co.

THE ELECTRIC REFRIGERATOR

Man learned, ages ago, that foods would keep for long periods if stored in cold places. Through the years scientists have steadily improved upon the methods used, until today the modern refrigerator is considered necessary in almost every household. Be sure you can explain the labeled parts in this illustration.

Moisture generally increases the ability of a substance to conduct heat; therefore the walls of the space are lined on the inside with moisture-proof paper or other material. Lining the walls with aluminum helps to prevent loss of heat by radiation. How?

Removing Heat from the Refrigerator. — Because the refrigerator is built with non-conducting walls, warm air inside will stay warm unless the heat is taken from the air and food inside. This is often done by placing ice in the box.   Ice must take in heat in order to melt.   The water from the melted ice flows out a drain pipe, carrying the absorbed heat with it.

When food is placed in the refrigerator, it is warmer than the air in the refrigerator; therefore, the food gives up heat to the air and becomes cold.   The ice absorbs this heat from the air, keeping it cold.   The ice melts and water runs out, carrying with it the heat brought in with the food.   Since ice melts at the surface only, the cooling of the air is more economical if the ice chamber is kept nearly full of ice.

Instead of ice for absorbing heat, modern gas and electric refrigerators make use of "freezing units." This method is better than ice since it is possible to keep the air at a more uniformly cold temperature. Moreover, these refrigerators are automatic and therefore require less attention.   There are several types of freezing units, and you may want to have a committee investigate them.   They all work upon the principle that when a gas expands it takes in heat, and when a gas is squeezed together it gives out heat.   In the cold unit a gas is caused to expand rapidly and as a result it absorbs heat from the air in the refrigerator.   This expanded and warmer gas is pumped out and compressed again. At the same time it is cooled by passing through some type of radiator.   It is then ready to be pumped back into the cold unit to expand and absorb more heat.

The ice, or the cooling unit, is placed at the top of the refrigerator.   Air in contact with the cold unit gives up some of its heat and becomes cooler and heavier than other air in the refrigerator.   Hence it sinks to the bottom and pushes up the less cool air.   As the cool air touches the food it absorbs heat from the food, leaving it cold.   This warm air then moves to the cold unit, gives up its heat, and sinks.   The heating of the air by the food and its cooling by the cold unit cause a continuous circulation of air in the refrigerator.

A good refrigerator must maintain a temperature of

Courtesy Westinghouse Elect. & Mfg. Co.

ELECTRIC REFRIGERATOR

The box-like compartment at the top of the refrigerator is the cooling unit. What kinds of foods are kept there? Under the cooling unit is the meat tray. Is it warmer or cooler than the rest of the refrigerator?

about 42° F. near the bottom, and not more than 50° F. at the top of the food chamber.

If the refrigerator is built so that good air circulation occurs, the air will deposit much of its moisture on the cold unit. Dry air results. You have learned that molds and bacteria grow best in warm, moist air; therefore, if your refrigerator maintains a low temperature and dry air, you have removed two of the conditions under which food spoils. On the other hand we wish to prevent some foods from drying; so modern refrigerators have several compartments — one where the air is cold and dry, another where the air is cold but moist, and a third compartment so designed that food or water placed in it may be frozen solid.

FIELD RESEARCH:

Visit a store that sells a standard make of refrigerators and have the clerk explain its good points. The store may have a model of the side wall that you can study to learn how it is insulated.

Keeping the Refrigerator Clean. — The refrigerator should be kept very clean at all times and so its lining should be smooth, waterproof, and not easily stained. Enamel or porcelain lining is best. The inside of the refrigerator may be kept clean and "sweet" by washing it frequently with a cloth, dampened by a solution of washing soda. The surface should then be wiped clean with clear water. Scouring powders should not be used because the tiny scratches fill with dirt and are difficult to clean.

FIELD RESEARCH:

Study the refrigerator in your own home to find out whether it is satisfactory; that is, if constructed to permit good air circulation. Does it keep a temperature below 50° F. in the warmest part? Is the lining such that it can be thoroughly cleansed? Are the foods placed in the proper location in the refrigerator? Are foods allowed to cool off before they are put in the refrigerator? How does this affect the ice or electric bill?

Care of Foods in the Home. — Your knowledge of the causes of the spoiling of fresh foods teaches you that the conservation of the food requires that it be given immediate attention. Milk bottles should be cleaned on the outside and placed in the refrigerator as soon as possible after delivery. At no time should milk be allowed to get warm unless you wish it to sour quickly. Nor should it be allowed to stand in the sun even on cold days because that may destroy some of the vitamins.

Meats also should be cleaned, if necessary, and placed in the refrigerator until needed for cooking. The meat should be kept covered to prevent drying unless you have a cold moist compartment. Green vegetables should be cleaned and wrapped in paper or placed in covered trays or jars in the refrigerator. They will then keep fresh and crisp.

General Problem 5. Why Is Food Protection Health Protection?

Pure Foods and Drugs. — Milk is one food that needs especial care because it is a very suitable substance for the growth of germs. Typhoid fever occurring in

the family of a careless milk producer has been transmitted to other families where milk from his dairy has been distributed.

While milk and water are especially suited to distribute contagious diseases, other foods such as vegetables and meats may do so, too. Therefore, all foods for human or animal use should be carefully guarded against germs. Meat markets, grocery stores, candy shops, and all other food stores should be required to observe sanitary regulations.

Black Star

THE DRUGSTORE

The containers of all drugs and medicines, except those prescribed by a physician, must be clearly and accurately labeled. It is up to you to read the label. If you are not sure whether the drug is safe, consult your doctor.

Not only are foods, including milk, required by law to be protected against flies and dirt and disease, but they must meet certain standards set by the United States Pure Food and Drug Acts. Canned foods must have labels which tell the weight of the contents and the names of any preservatives used.

Drugs and medicines must also meet standards established by the United States Pure Food and Drug Acts. All drugs are dangerous except as prescribed by a physician. Some drugs, such as narcotics, are so dangerous that druggists are not allowed to sell them without a doctor's prescription. All patent medicines must have a proper label stating the contents in case of dangerous drugs. Headache medicines, especially, are to be avoided because of the harmful drugs they are likely to contain.

Laws pertaining to foods and drugs are for the protection of the health of the people who cannot always be sure what a food or drug may contain, or what it may do. Alcohol and other narcotics are especially dangerous drugs, and their use is regulated by law. You are familiar with the effects of alcohol used in excess.

FIELD RESEARCH:

Pour a little medicinal alcohol on some white of egg. What happens?

Alcohol takes water out of delicate tissues and affects them somewhat as it affects the white of an egg.

Alcohol and other narcotics are habit-forming drugs and so should be used only on the advice of competent physicians.

The Health Department. — The health of the community is particularly the problem of its Department of Health and the chief health officer. This department is responsible for proper safeguards of the milk and water supply, the sewage and garbage disposal, sanitary stores and markets, and clean streets. It must be constantly on the alert to prevent the spread of disease from any source. The Health Department needs your coöperation in upholding its standards and enforcing the laws of the country, state, and town.

Thinking Things Over. — Food, along with shelter and clothing, is one of the three main necessities of life and comfort. Is it any wonder, then, that the conservation of food is a major problem? Conservation means the use of a substance efficiently and without waste. In the case of food you have discovered that it involves also the growing of food.

Courtesy *Westinghouse Electric Company*

ARE THEY FRESH?

The inspector is holding an ultraviolet lamp. If the egg is fresh, it will glow a scarlet color under the ultraviolet light. If the egg is old, it will be a purple color.

In the case of vegetable foods it is important to understand good methods of gardening and farming. Then having raised the vegetables we must apply scientific principles to their preservation and distribution. If not properly cared for, food not only may spoil, but may even be the means of distributing disease germs.

While we are thinking of vegetable foods, we must have in mind also meat products of all kinds. In fact meat products depend upon a suitable supply of vegetable food for animals.

Typical methods of preservation of foods depend upon heat treatment, cold treatment, and chemical treatment.

Each has special advantages; but after all is said and done, the preservation of food is also a safeguard for health.

Key Words

alcohol	freezing	pasteurize
annual	germs	preservative
bacteria	heat transfer	pressure
circulation	humidity	radiant energy
cold storage	insulate	radiation
compost	membrane	refrigerator
conduction	mildews	sanitary code
conductor	molds	typhoid fever
convection	molecule	ventilation
drugs	non-conductor	water glass
energy	osmosis	

Key Statements

1. The problem of food storage involves proper ventilation, proper temperature, proper humidity, and fresh quality of the product to be stored.

2. The preservation of fresh foods for long periods depends upon killing bacteria and molds, and upon sealing to prevent entrance of additional organisms, or by holding the food at such a low temperature that organisms are inactive.

3. Foods may also be preserved by drying, smoking, or by the addition of chemicals that will destroy germs and molds and prevent more from growing.

4. The construction of efficient refrigerators depends upon a knowledge and an application of the principles of heat transfer.

5. Conduction is the transfer of heat from molecule to molecule of a substance. Conduction occurs most commonly in solids.

6. Heat is transferred by conduction more readily by some solids than by others.

7. Convection is the transfer of heat from one point to another by the movement of the heat-bearing molecules. Convection currents are due to unequal heating and occur most commonly in liquids and gases.

8. Hot bodies (usually solids) give off heat by radiation.

9. Radiant energy travels in straight lines and is changed back to heat energy when it is stopped and absorbed by another body. It can be reflected the same as light.

10. Refrigerators are cool because the cold unit absorbs heat from the air.

11. In a healthful city, stores are sanitary and their foods are protected from dust, flies, and handling.

12. The laws pertaining to alcohol and other narcotics are observed in a healthful city.

13. Your health department is chiefly responsible for the health of your community, but you must do your part.

Thought Questions

1. How do the problems of conservation involve science and economics?

2. Why can fruits be kept without freezing at a temperature of 32° F. or slightly below, while potatoes will freeze at 32° F.?

3. Why is the humidity of the air a problem in the construction of cold storage rooms?

4. In canning fruit or vegetables, why is it important to seal the can?

5. What are the conditions favorable to the growth of bacteria and molds?

6. Explain why drying a food helps to preserve it.

7. Why will foods keep longer in cold air than in warm air?

8. Describe the construction of the walls of a good refrigerator. What determines the efficiency of the refrigerator?

9. Where should a food having an odor be placed in a refrigerator? Why?

10. Why is 50° F. the maximum air temperature of a good refrigerator?

11. You have seen refrigerating pipes in meat counters. What makes them become covered with ice?

12. How is the preservation of food related to your health?

13. Why are food and drug laws necessary?

14. Why must the production and distribution of milk be carefully regulated?

15. Why should foods in stores be protected against flies and from handling?

16. What can you do to coöperate in maintaining a healthful city?

Projects for Your Science Discovery Book

1. Visit a cold storage plant and write an account of your observations. Tell what foods you saw and how the temperatures were controlled.

2. Make a report on the relation of moisture to the spoiling of foods.

3. Make a collection of labels from canned foods to find which ones contain special preservatives. Note which substances are used and how much.

4. Make a diagram of a heater in a room and indicate by arrows the direction in which the air will circulate.

5. Make a study of refrigerators and sketch a diagram of an efficient refrigerator wall.

6. Discuss the various methods used in canning fruits at home.

7. Obtain samples of dried foods and experiment with them to learn how much water they will absorb.

8. By visiting a fruit store, determine good methods of packing fruit.

9. Study the cold pack method of preserving vegetables.

10. Study the effect of low temperatures on the keeping of apples by selecting two apples nearly alike and placing one in the refrigerator and one in the kitchen. Examine them from day to day for at least two weeks.

11. Build an ice box, insulating it properly. Test its efficiency.

12. Determine the temperatures and humidity of the air in a refrigerator.

13. Devise and work an experiment to illustrate the conduction of heat.

14. Devise and work an experiment to illustrate convection currents.

15. Make a trip to your city health department to learn about its activities.

"SMOKECHASERS"

Sharp eyes have detected a suspicious puff of smoke in the distance. The Ranger, or "smokechaser," on the right is about to investigate.

What does this picture tell you about conservation of natural resources?

TOPIC XVII

Conservation of Natural Resources

Two billion acres of land within the United States; the rain and snow that fall on this land; the rivers, waterfalls and lakes; the coal, oil, gold and silver, and other mineral deposits that lie on and beneath the land; the people that live here and their multitude of talents, skills, and activities — these are our natural resources. The wealth of the nation is measured in the way we conserve, use and develop these resources.

— National Resources Planning Board

Do you know:

1. What is a natural resource?
2. Why natural resources are not everlasting?
3. Whether life is a natural resource?
4. What is our most valuable natural resource?

General Problem 1. How Can You Conserve Land and Water?

Coöperation. — How can you conserve land and water? That is a sticker, isn't it? And yet if you will think back over your science studies and your experiences, you can find the answer. Of course, it is not for you to work alone but to do your part — shoulder to shoulder with everybody else. Perhaps you may have to help someone else, who does not understand as you do, because he has not studied science.

Conserving Soil and Water. — The conservation of soil and water has become one of the most important

511

problems of our nation. From the time the first settlers came to this land up to the present, millions of acres of fine farmland have been ruined by erosion — especially by water and wind. Millions and millions of acres of valuable top soil have been swept away by wind and water. It is estimated that every year enough soil is blown or washed from American fields to fill a train of freight cars 390,000 miles long — a distance from the earth to the moon and more than halfway back again.

Our government is working hard to stop soil erosion. Farm agencies show farmers new practices to hold soil. Great dams are being built to control flood waters and save land from floods. The stored water is later distributed to grow more crops. The Soil Conservation Service has planted strips of trees to break the force of winds sweeping across the plains. Experiments are being tried in which airplanes are used to scatter grass seeds over hundreds of acres. Farmers are being shown how to plant the slopes to prevent erosion; they are being shown how to conserve the fertility of that soil; they are being shown how to keep gullies from starting.

What You Can Do. — The problem of soil conservation does not belong to the government alone. It is your problem, too. Perhaps erosion is going on in fields or lots near your home. You can take steps to stop it. You can also do your share by helping to support the conservation plans of your own community and state.

Most of all you can help by being well informed about the problem. If you live on a hilly farm, it is your duty as a good citizen to know how to plant and cultivate a field — around the slope (contour planting), not up and down.

You can plant crops that help the soil absorb or soak

BEFORE AND AFTER

These two pictures give proof of the value of planting trees to stop soil erosion. The upper picture was taken before any trees were set out.

Three and one half years after planting black locust trees, the lower picture was taken. Wasteful soil erosion has been stopped.

up rain water instead of making it easy for the water to run off over the surface.

You should also know about strip planting — a prac- tice of planting strips of different crops around a slope. Some of the strips are planted to grass crops, especially valuable in holding the soil. With this method the soil is kept from being washed down the hill.

But even if you live in a city, soil erosion is your prob- lem. The most important thing for you to do is to be well informed as to causes and extent of erosion through- out the country. You can help the Soil Conservation Service by understanding the tremendous problem and by coöperating in every way.

General Problem 2. How Can You Conserve Wild Life and Vegetation?

Partners: Wild Life and Vegetation. — The cost of soil erosion in the United States has been estimated at 400 million dollars annually. This amount, however, does not include the loss of wild life that has resulted. If the soil is ruined, vegetation follows. With the loss of vegetation, muskrats, beavers, raccoons, and other wild life disappear.

It is curious how these things are all interdependent. It is what is called the balance of nature. When man upsets the balance by permitting overgrazing of the land by cattle or sheep, or by cutting or burning the forests, or by draining swamps, he is indirectly destroying helpful insects, birds, and animals.

Abundance. — When the first settlers came to this country 300 years ago, they found dense forests and fertile plains. Wild life seemed to exist in unlimited numbers. Have you read of the thundering herds of buffalo and the endless clouds of passenger pigeons? Ducks in migration stretched on for days and weeks. Where have these animals gone? The wild life only *seemed* to exist in unlimited numbers. Hunting killed off many. Draining swamps destroyed breeding grounds. Cutting forests took the homes of some. Lack of food killed others. Thus their numbers dwindled.

Science to the Rescue. — Now we understand that all wild life has natural enemies. And we must not reduce the numbers too much or the natural enemies will kill off the rest.

We know the kind of breeding places needed by various forms of wild life, and sanctuaries have been provided.

Modern sewage and garbage disposal plants and proper utilization of industrial wastes are protecting fish in many of our streams. All should be protected. Only then shall we have fish in abundance again.

Fires, largely the result of carelessness, have destroyed millions of acres of forests and left the wild life to starve and die. Now modern methods of spotting fires and controlling them are gradually mastering the demon fire.

What You Can Do. — Boys and girls, men and women — all of us — are learning the value of wild life and how it can be conserved. We must all do our part. You can help game wardens, fire wardens, and con-servation wardens do their work by observing the laws of conservation and urging others to do the same. As a science student you have the knowledge necessary to understand how it can be done. It is your opportunity to help protect and conserve our wild life and vegetation.

General Problem 3.   How Can You Conserve Minerals?

Our Use of Minerals. — This age is sometimes called the Industrial or Steel Age because of our great dependence upon iron and other minerals.   Think of the minerals you use every day.   Foremost perhaps is iron, which is made into steel.   How different our lives would be without steel!   No trains, automobiles, tractors;   no bicycles, radios, skates;   no watches, airplanes, ocean liners.   Our modern way of living would be impossible without iron and steel.

Other minerals, though not so common as iron, are also of great importance.   Some, added to iron, produce various steels — hard and brittle, or soft.   Aluminum is a metal that became vital with the development of aviation.   Why?   In recent years greater quantities of aluminum were needed than ever before.   This led to the development of a process which extracts aluminum ore from certain clay soils.   Another light, tough mineral, magnesium, has made its way into lightweight ladders, wheelbarrows, lawnmowers, etc.   Magnesium is now extracted from sea water.   Copper, silver, gold, gypsum, lead, salt, tungsten, zinc, chromium, nickel — the list of useful minerals is almost endless.

Our Mineral Resources. — We have huge deposits of iron, copper, gypsum, sulfur, salt, etc.   Our iron deposits in the Lake Superior region have produced endless tons of iron ore.   After the heavy drain on these deposits for the recent war, we realize that our resources of iron and other minerals have limits.   If they are wasted now, they will vanish like some of our wild life and forests.

Lead and zinc, necessary in paints, will not last forever — perhaps only a generation.   More deposits may be

Courtesy American Mutual Liability Insurance Company

AH-H-H-H!

Wandering streams like this one are vital sources of water for animals. We can help conserve our country's wild life by not allowing such life-giving brooks to become polluted.

discovered, but we cannot plan on that.   It is better to conserve what we have.   Gold, silver, asphalt, and borax are other minerals that need conservation.

What Can You Do? — You can prevent needless damage to metal objects and apply your knowledge of corrosion and rusting.   You know that moisture and air combine to attack metals, while the acids in air attack other metals.

Both rusting and corrosion can be prevented to a large extent by keeping the surface of the metal free from moisture. You should wipe off garden tools, skates, bicycles, and other metal equipment, before putting them

Courtesy American Mutual Liability Insurance Co.

WASTE

Too much salt used on icy winter streets caused this destruction. The salt speeded up rusting and corrosion of the metal parts. If it is necessary to use salt on streets, can such waste be prevented?

away. With other metal objects, paint or wax will help prevent rusting and corroding.

Engineers, too, can make use of science to discover better ways to mine and refine minerals and so prevent loss. Scientists can discover more substitutes for metals. Does this statement remind you of plastics? There are many kinds of plastics — man-made substances which are replacing metals for toys, steering wheels on cars, lamp stands, and a variety of other uses.

General Problem 4. How Can You Conserve Fuels?

Sifting the Ashes. — Do you know how to care for a stove or a furnace? If so, do you watch the ashes to see if you are wasting coal? Years ago, many people sifted the ashes to save the partly burned coal. Some people do this even now. It is a good idea, but it is a better idea to regulate the fire so that the coal is all burned the first time.

Four Fuels. — You know from your studies and from your observations that there are four common natural substances used for fuel: wood, coal, oil, and natural gas. Each fuel has its advantages and disadvantages depending upon where a person lives. But the problem of which fuel to use is not so important as learning how to burn or use that fuel in an efficient manner, such as learning how to tend the furnace properly.

If there were unlimited amounts of fuels, it wouldn't make much difference whether people saved or wasted them. But they are not unlimited.

Wood. — Once this country seemed to have an inexhaustible supply of timber for lumber, for fuel, and for all sorts of wood products. Now we know that is not the case. By careful planning and scientific forestry, we may have enough for our needs. But we certainly will not have any to waste.

Energy from the Sun. — Coal is a mineral that took millions of years to form in the earth. Every pound of coal represents stored energy from the sun — energy stored by plants that grew in the early days of our earth. Trees growing now are storing energy all the time, energy in the form of wood.

Keystone View

FIRING A FURNACE

The same amount of coal will give large or small amounts of heat, depending upon how efficiently the furnace is fired. Do you know the proper steps in taking care of a furnace fire?

There are many deposits of coal in the United States, and geologists think there is enough coal to last for many generations. But that does not give us the right to waste it.

Coal is often wasted at the mine; it is wasted at the factory and in the home. By building more efficient engines, furnaces, and stoves science is helping to save coal. Buildings are insulated so that less heat is required to heat them in the winter. In these ways fuels can be conserved.

Oil — Liquid Gold. — The story of oil is one of over-supply and misuse and waste.   No one knows exactly how great the oil reserves are in our country, but most

Courtesy Magnolia Petroleum Company

A MODERN SEARCH FOR BURIED TREASURE

This man-made island has been built in the Gulf of Mexico.   Deep under the water drills are biting into rock in search of oil.   What does this picture suggest about conservation of oil?

scientists believe the supply is limited.   If oil is wasted, we may exhaust our supply within a generation.   Scientists constantly search for ways to extend the use of oil. Geologists are discovering more and more deposits, some even under the ocean.   Other scientists are experimenting with extracting a type of oil, *shale oil*, from shale rocks.   Still other scientists are designing new and better equipment to use our oil more efficiently.

Crude oil supplies gasoline, lubricating oil, kerosene oil, other burning oils, asphalt, and vaseline.

Natural Gas. — Natural gas is another of nature's products that has taken millions of years to make. Gas like oil has been wasted in enormous amounts. Now,

Ewing Galloway

GAS TANKS

These are natural gas tanks, not gasoline tanks. Gas stored in huge tanks like these in Texas may be piped to cities hundreds of miles away for use as fuel.

however, it is being conserved. Natural gas from Louisiana is carried by pipes to Atlanta and St. Louis. Gas from Texas is piped to Chicago and Minneapolis, and even areas as far east as New York State are now receiving natural gas through pipe lines. Who knows, perhaps some day almost every town will have natural gas from the great sources in the south central part of our country. The more uses there are the less it must be wasted.

What You Can Do. — You can recall the science principles you have learned about the control of fire. By applying them you can prevent loss by fire and aid in more efficient burning of fuels in your home. You can become informed about the need for more careful mining and transporting methods. You can be scientific in making your judgments about conservation plans and laws.

Thinking Things Over. — This whole topic is intended to help you think things over; to urge you to look back in your book and your Science Discovery Book to discover the many details about conservation which you have studied. The time to think about conservation is not once a year but every day. Conservation in little things adds up to conservation in big things when on a nation-wide scale.

Everything you use needs to be conserved. Paper, pencils, ink, fabrics, leather, sugar, foods of all kinds, wheat, oats, and countless other articles must be conserved. Only with an abundance of these things can we have healthy, happy lives. And that leads us to our last topic — Conservation of Health — the most important of all.

Key Words

asphalt	insulated
balance of nature	low grade ore
borax	mineral
breeding season	polluted
contour planting	scientific forestry
corrosion	strip planting
environment	substitute
geologist	

Key Statements

1. Land is conserved by preventing erosion.
2. Contour and strip planting helps to prevent erosion of soil.
3. Water is conserved by preventing floods.
4. Shelter belts of trees help to prevent wind erosion and conserve water.

5. Loss of vegetation is followed by loss of wild life and then by loss of soil.

6. Man often upsets the balance of nature.

7. Scientific discoveries aid in conservation.

8. Corrosion of metals, a form of oxidation, is a cause of waste.

9. Man-made plastics may be substituted for some metal uses.

10. There are four common natural fuels — wood, coal, oil, and natural gas.

11. Energy from burning wood, coal, oil, and natural gas represents energy from the sun stored by plants millions of years ago.

Thought Questions

1. Why is coöperation necessary for the best conservation of soil?

2. How is vegetation, including forests, related to the conservation of our water supply?

3. How is erosion prevented by contour or strip planting?

4. How are wild life and vegetation partners in conservation?

5. How can corrosion be retarded or prevented?

6. Why are the hills not everlasting?

7. How is it that the heat from burning fuels represents stored energy from the sun?

Projects for Your Science Discovery Book

1. Write to the Soil Conservation Service, U. S. Department of Agriculture, for bulletins on soil conservation for your section of the country. Read the bulletins and then make plans to help save your soil.

2. Make a survey of the soil erosion problem in the yards of members of the class. Work out ways to improve the situation.

3. Look up data comparing amount of forested lands in the United States during Colonial days and now. Try to explain the causes of the differences.

4. Read about the days of the buffalo nerd and passenger pigeon and try to account for the near destruction of the buffalo and the complete destruction of the passenger pigeon.

5. Look up data regarding the pollution of streams and its effects. If streams in your neighborhood are being polluted, try to arrange plans to stop the pollution.

6. From your state department obtain data relative to the important minerals produced in your state. Study conservation methods in use.

7. Someone in the class might investigate plastics that are used as substitutes for metals. What metals?

8. Investigate and report on the conservation methods used in mining coal.

9. Investigate the geological formations in which oil occurs. Describe how oil and natural gas are wasted at the oil fields.

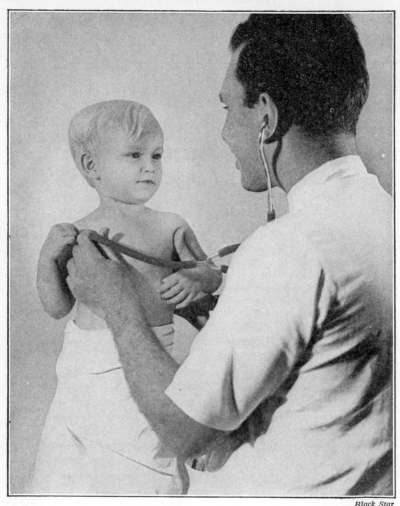

A HEAD START

The physician is our greatest helper in conserving our health. But he can only *help*. Real health conservation is up to us. Do you know what you should do to keep healthy?

Health Conservation

The health of the people is really the foundation upon which all their happiness and all their powers as a State depend.

—Benjamin Disraeli

Do you know:

1. How your health is related to the change of seasons?
2. Why some people get a cold more frequently than others during weather changes?
3. How water and its contents affect your health?
4. How your health is safeguarded through sanitation?
5. What to eat to keep well?
6. How to play safely?

General Problem 1. How Do You Adapt Yourself to Changing Natural Conditions?

Adaptations to Changing Seasons. — Have you seen a squirrel hiding nuts in the fall? Have you watched the birds on their southern journey as winter threatens? Or have you looked for their return? The bear fattens up on food and goes to sleep for the long winter.

Spring comes and up shoot the new plants. The buds open. In the fall leaves drop, and, through the long winter, plants die or rest.

Do these plants and animals know that spring or winter is on the way? Probably not, and yet many changes in their habits take place with the changing seasons.

You on the other hand know that winter or spring or summer or fall will surely come. How do you know these things if the birds do not? You can think, you can reason, and you can know, because men have found these changes always to take place.

L. W. Brownell

BEDTIME

With cold weather approaching, this bear is about to "hole up" for the winter. How do bears live during the winter months?

So all living things make adaptations to changing seasons. You plan ahead to provide for your health, your comfort, and your pleasure. Man must adapt his habits to such changes. He lays up food for the winter and adapts his home to withstand the cold of winter, the wind and rains of spring, or the heat of summer. By adaptations of his home, of clothing, and regulation of his diet, man protects and conserves his health. The careless, unthinking person who does not understand the need for adaptations, who does not plan ahead, does not provide for health conservation.

Adaptations to Changing Weather. — Your knowledge of weather factors enables you to forecast the weather ahead with some accuracy. And so you provide for rain, for wind, for snow, or for heat. You seek to protect your body against the weather changes that might otherwise affect your health.

In summer, light-colored clothing reflects more of the sun's energy than dark colors, and so helps to protect the body against overheating. Garments of cotton and silk permit the body to cool off better than do woolen garments.

H. Armstrong Roberts

WINTER WONDERLAND

Just as the trees are adapted to cold weather, so we must change our habits with the seasons.

What adaptations do you make to the winter season?

Rubbers protect the feet during wet weather. In these and many other ways you can adapt your customs and daily habits to changing weather. You do these things because it is good sense.

Even plants and animals take account of the weather for their well-being. Birds oil their feathers against rain and the pores in the leaves of plants are closed to conserve the water in dry weather.

Adaptation to Water Supply. — In desert countries, drinking water is more precious than food. Indeed life itself may depend upon it. The Indians made their trails to pass springs and streams of good drinking water. The pioneers traveled first along the water courses. Cities

Ewing Galloway

WATER FOR LIFE

Where there is water, there is life. Without water, there can be no life. Thus we have spent huge sums of money to construct reservoirs to bring water to our cities.

and industries have grown up near adequate water supplies. Man has always adapted his living to his need for water. He goes where water is, or spends millions of dollars to bring the water to his cities.

With increasing population, the crowding of people in cities, and the development of varied industries, nature's methods of providing water, safe for drinking, have proved inadequate. Therefore, man again must make adaptation to an impure, unsafe water supply by providing great water purification plants. Science has pointed out the dangers that may lurk even in bright, sparkling water, and science has found the means to purify the water and safeguard your health. The conquest of disease is in a very large measure dependent upon the scientific purification of water. Many, many lives have been saved by the purification of water.

General Problem 2.   What Adaptations Do You Make to Changing Man-Made Conditions?

Adaptations to the Need for Sanitation. — Neglect, filth, and disease follow one another with terrible certainty. With disease comes suffering and loss of life. What a glorious chapter in science it is that tells us how to prevent that suffering!

The great Pasteur first pointed out the way to avoid the dangers of contagious disease — every man, woman, and child owes him gratitude. Scientific men from the time of Pasteur on have added and are still adding to our knowledge of how to prevent disease.

FIELD RESEARCH:

Who in your town even now is working that you may have better health? Report on his activities.

Man builds his cities, his factories, schools, homes, and churches with careful provision for cleanliness. Clean streets, sewage and garbage disposal plants, smokeless chimneys, and parks are all signs of his adaptations to the need for sanitation.

You have the knowledge to enable you to understand the need for sanitation.   Apply that knowledge to your personal habits.   As a scientist in the making, you should have confidence in your scientific discoveries. If you have this confidence, you will observe the laws

Charles Phelps Cushing

FIGHTING DISEASE

With the aid of science, man has learned the need for sanitation.   Today clean streets, clean parks, and clean buildings help prevent diseases which were once common.

of health; you will keep your body clean, your teeth clean, your hair and nails clean, your clothes clean, and with it all you will keep your mind clean.

Adaptation to Food Supply. — If you eat to satisfy an uncontrolled appetite, you will suffer.   If you eat so as to produce growth, to maintain bodily vigor, and to develop mental strength, you will conserve your health. Through your science studies you have learned how food is produced and how it is safeguarded and preserved.

You have also learned something of the relation of food to health. You know that your diet must contain a proper balance of foods to furnish energy to your body and to furnish materials for the repair of worn-out cells and the building of new ones. It must contain the minerals needed for bones and teeth. It must contain the vitamins that are so necessary in regulating many body processes.

If you could compare your ordinary diet with that of boys and girls living near the Arctic Circle, or with those living near the sea in the region of the equator, you would find each group adapting its eating habits to the temperature of its environment. A man at hard, outdoor labor adapts his eating habits to the need of strenuous exercise, while an office worker must make adaptations to a life of moderate exercise.

We are daily faced with changes and, because we can think and reason, we can adapt our living to them.

General Problem 3. What Adaptations Can You Make to Safety and First Aid?

Accidents in the Home. — Did you ever fall down stairs or have a rug on a slippery floor slide out from under you? Do you know of anyone burned from hot grease catching fire on the stove, or from a gasoline explosion? If so, could these accidents have been prevented? Every day, everywhere, accidents of one kind or another are occurring in homes. It is said that there are more accidents in the home than anywhere else. Some are serious — resulting in broken bones, asphyxiation (ăs-fĭk'sĭ-ā'shŭn), blood poisoning, and even death. Others are minor accidents such as sprains, bruises, burns, or cuts. Accidents, whether big or little, are due to two causes: carelessness and misjudgment. Thoughtfulness will prevent those due to carelessness, and knowledge will help to prevent the others.

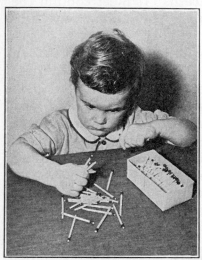

Acme Photo

WHAT IS WRONG WITH THIS PICTURE?

Industry for a number of years has conducted a successful campaign to lessen accidents due to the carelessness of its workers. It is just as true in the home as in industry that accidents do not prevent themselves. Something has to be done about them. So if we are to prevent the many accidents that occur in the home, we must know something about them, about what causes them, and then do something to prevent them.

Kinds of Accidents. — In the home, accidents fall into several groups:

1. Those caused by falls from chairs or steps; or on rugs that slip, or have worn places in them; or over tools and playthings left in unexpected places; or in slippery bathtubs; or in badly lighted places.

2. Those caused by burns or scalds from carelessness about stoves, heaters, worn-out electric cords, and inflammable cleaning fluids.

3. Those caused by asphyxiation from carelessness

about open gas jets, leaky gas pipes, defective furnaces, gas and oil stoves, and automobile engines running in closed garages.

4. Those caused by poisons and firearms from failure to label the poisons properly and failure to put both poisons and firearms out of reach of children.

5. Those caused by shock from handling electrical fixtures with wet hands.

6. Those caused by the careless use of sharp tools, broken glass, and so on.

7. Those caused by getting objects in the eye.

After you have read these seven ways in which accidents may happen in the home, have a class discussion of each one and try to plan how they may be prevented. Of over 30,000 *fatal* home accidents each year more than half are from falls, and about one sixth are from burns. Next are those from poisons, suffocation, and firearms. Perhaps you will think of other ways accidents may happen in your home. If so, add them to the list. The way to prevent accidents is to plan in advance so they cannot happen. It is better to be safe than sorry.

First Aid for Accidents. — Each of the accidents mentioned above may require special treatment and may need the services of a doctor. This book cannot tell you what to do in each case, and it does not take the place of a trained nurse or physician. All that can be done in a science book like this is to point out first things to do and things not to do in case of an accident. While these first aid suggestions refer to home accidents, they are equally applicable to similar accidents wherever they may happen.

The first rule in every accident is to "keep your head." Do not get excited, because if you do, you may cause additional harm. In case of accident act quickly, use good judgment and skill, and you may save a life.

Broken bones, dislocated joints, sprains, and bruises result from falls. *Bruises* should be treated with disinfectants to prevent infection of any kind. Even the slightest bruise is a danger spot, particularly if the skin is broken. A scratch in the skin is the open door for the entrance of germs that may cause inflammation or blood poisoning.

Ewing Galloway

FIRST AID

A First Aid kit is an important bit of equipment for every home and every automobile. But it is even more important to know how to use it. Study the First Aid rules on pages 536–538.

Broken bones and *dislocated joints* require the immediate attention of a physician. You should make the patient as comfortable as you can, where he fell. Moving him may make the fracture worse. Relieve the injured bone from strain by protecting it from being jarred. Do not try to treat the patient in any other way, except by giving him hot drinks in case of nervous shock.

Strains and sprains should be treated with cold, wet applications (not ice) until the doctor comes. Sprains are more serious than a strain, and are due to a tear in the ligaments of a joint. Sometimes it is difficult to tell a sprain from a fracture; so it is best to call a doctor. Strains and sprains may need to be bandaged.

Burns and scalds may be treated with oils, baking soda, or limewater. These relieve the pain and protect the spot from the air. Beware of infection. Blisters should not be broken. Severe burns require the attention of a physician.

Asphyxiation occurs from the shutting off of oxygen to the blood supply, or breathing air contaminated with poisonous gases such as carbon monoxide, coal gas, or smoke fumes. Fresh air and artificial respiration should be given until the doctor arrives.

Poisoning is treated in various ways, according to the kind of poison taken. Labels on the bottles usually give the "antidote" or directions for treatment. Bottles containing poisons should be odd shapes so they cannot be mistaken for other bottles even in the dark. Of course, poison bottles should be kept out of reach of children.

A *gunshot wound* needs a physician's care. Keep the patient quiet. Treat for shock if necessary. If there is much bleeding, it must be controlled as directed under cuts.

Shock from electricity or lightning may be treated with artificial respiration.

Cuts are of two kinds: small, surface cuts which can be safely treated with a disinfectant, and deep, ugly cuts where a vein or an artery is severed. *Call a doctor at once* if a vein or artery is cut. These cuts will bleed heavily. The blood from an artery is bright red in color, flowing in spurts. Blood from a vein is a dark, bluish red in color, and it flows in a slow, steady stream. The bleeding in both cases must be stopped. Pressure applied between the wound and the heart in the case of a cut artery, and on the side of the wound away from the heart in the case of a cut vein will stop the flow of blood.

In case of a very bad cut, a tourniquet is sometimes applied. Because of the danger of blood poisoning, it should not be used until all other measures fail. It is a tight bandage, with a lump in it to press on the cut vein or artery. The tourniquet should be loosened a little every few minutes to permit some circulation of the blood. A grave danger from cuts is possible infection.

If you get something in your eye, *don't rub it*. This only makes it harder to remove the object. Shut your eyes tightly for a minute. Tears will run and often wash out the speck. If someone is skillful, he may be able to turn up the eyelid and remove the object with a piece of tissue paper or the corner of a clean handkerchief or absorbent cotton. If it is not readily removed, put a cold cloth on the eye and go to or send for the doctor. Don't take any chances with your eyes.

Accidents Outside the Home. — Outside the home, accidents occur on the playgrounds, in the streets, in street cars, buses, automobiles, on bicycles, and other moving vehicles, and in burning buildings. Each year there are about 35,000 bicycle accidents which result in about 700 deaths. Whenever an accident occurs, do the sensible thing. Make the patient comfortable, send for a doctor, apply first aid if possible, and *keep your head*. In case of broken bones or other serious accidents, do not move the patient any more than absolutely necessary.

There are so many highway accidents involving automobiles and bicycles that every boy and girl should be aware as to how they happen. Your department of public safety will give you data about the number, cause, and time of day of most automobile accidents. Fast driving, driving by an intoxicated driver, driving with faulty brakes, driving with insufficient vision, taking curves too fast, passing on hills, and taking chances are a few of the causes of auto accidents. What can you do about it? You can refuse to ride with unsafe or unskilled drivers. It is not being sissy-like to object to recklessness in driving. It is just being sensible.

Often many pedestrians are injured or killed due to their own carelessness. You know how to be careful — so be careful.

Ewing Galloway

A MODERN HIGHWAY INTERSECTION

This is a fine example of the care engineers have taken to provide safe highways. But the best-designed highway is still as dangerous as the drivers who use it. Accidents don't happen; they are caused, and caused mostly by carelessness. It doesn't pay to be careless.

If you ride a bicycle, you can obey the traffic rules. Remember, if your bicycle and an automobile collide, your bike will get the worst of it.

There are thousands of swimming accidents every year resulting in nearly 5000 deaths. Can you swim? If you cannot, then learn to swim at the very first opportunity.

If you are to make successful adaptations to safety against accidents, you should remember two things: first, accidents do not *just happen*, and second, most of them can be prevented. Make up your mind that, beginning today, you will try to prevent accidents in your home by observing the following rules:

Remove all hazards which might result in falls.

Keep sharp knives in racks, scissors in sheaths.

Be sure to leave a door or window open where gas or oil stoves are burning or where an automobile engine is running.

Label all poison bottles, keep them tightly covered, and located in places where they cannot be reached by small children.

Never use gasoline in the house for cleaning.

Throw away defective electric cords.

Prevent accidents on the street and upon the highway by observing traffic lights and rules.   Be careful.

Thinking Things Over. — Our whole life is made up of adaptations to our environment. But our environment, you have discovered, is ever-changing. Therefore, if we are to progress, we must continually adjust our habits and customs to meet the changes in our environment. Most of these changes, the natural ones, have proceeded in an orderly manner. New changes will occur and science will help us to make our adjustments to them.

Your studies have helped you to discover, understand, and apply great laws of nature for the betterment of yourself, your family, and your community. With intelligent application of these laws, you will be able to control and use the factors of your environment for the continued progress of man. You will adapt your habits to your environment in such a way that your life will be as full of happiness, good health, and useful service as it is possible for a human life to be.

Key Words

accidents	contagious disease	sanitation
artery	disinfectant	shock
asphyxiation	eating habits	sprains
blood poisoning	exercise	tourniquet
burns	food balance	vein
	fracture	

Key Statements

1. Man adapts his living to changing seasons by changes in his shelter, clothing, and food.

2. In adapting his habits to changes in weather man seeks to conserve his health.

3. Increasing populations and crowded cities have made it necessary for man to make adaptation to impure and unsafe water supplies.

4. Scientists are constantly adding to our knowledge of the prevention of disease.

5. Science teaches the need for sanitation; thus community and personal hygiene become of great importance.

6. You must adapt your eating habits to the temperature of your environment and to the kind of life you lead.

7. Accidents in the home are often serious and are altogether too frequent.

8. Accidents are due to two causes, carelessness and misjudgment.

9. A knowledge of "first aid" is of value in the treatment of accidents until a doctor arrives.

10. Most accidents can be prevented.

11. Life is made up of adaptations to a constantly changing environment.

12. By intelligently applying the laws of nature you can control and use the factors of your environment for the continued progress of man.

13. Proper adaptation to your environment means a life of happiness, good health, and useful service.

Thought Questions

1. How have added comforts in the home brought about a change in man's adaptation to weather and climate?
2. What effect does air conditioning have upon adaptation to weather?
3. What branches of science have aided us in the purification of our water supply?
4. Where are epidemics of contagious diseases likely to start? Why?
5. Why are habits of personal cleanliness necessary to your well-being?
6. Why is variety in a diet necessary?
7. Do you think that accident insurance is a good kind of protection? Why?
8. Why should you know something about first aid?
9. What can you do to help prevent accidents in your home?
10. How is our environment constantly changing?

Projects for Your Science Discovery Book

1. Write an account of your own adaptations to the change of seasons and tell how your knowledge of nature's laws helps you to make these adjustments.
2. How can you use your knowledge of the cause and predictions of weather so as to adjust yourself to nature's ways and thus retain your health?
3. Draw up a list of items which would make a good Code of Safety for your household.
4. Draw up a Safety Code for street and highway traffic.
5. Make a list of simple remedies to be kept in the medicine closet and explain the use of each and why you included it.
6. Read about the great Roman aqueducts to find out why they were built. How do we know so much about them?
7. Find out what sort of tests for first aid girl and boy scouts have to pass.
8. Make a chart for a family safety drive, or for a "No Accident This Month" campaign. Perhaps your family will coöperate in actually keeping it for a month.

OBSERVERS' CLUB

Where you live can you see the same kind of plants and animals that a boy or girl can see who lives a few hundred miles north, east, south, or west of you? Can you see the same stars, moon, sun, and planets? When it rains or snows on your home, is it raining or snowing on all other homes?

These are questions you can easily answer. They are asked to call attention to the fact that people living in different parts of a large country like our United States may have very different experiences. Wherever you live, if you are a careful observer, you will see many interesting things that some other people miss. The Observers' Club is planned to help you become a better observer and so a better scientist.

Each month outdoors has its special charm and interest. To be sure, people who live in Alaska or California or Honolulu or Florida or North Dakota or Maine may see the same stars, the same planets, the same moon, and the same sun, but not the same plants, animals, and weather. Springtime on the calendar is the same for all, but how different the signs of spring are at that time. The lengths of day and night, the beginning of the seasons as shown by living things, differ in these far-apart places.

So it goes. The round of observations differs month by month and place by place. The following suggestions will help you learn what to watch for, but you must find for yourself the particular objects of interest and facts of nature for your community.

No matter where you live, you will find it interesting and helpful to organize an Observers' Club. Such clubs have officers whose duties are like those of officers in other clubs. Every member in an Observers' Club, however, contributes all he can to the club activities. Each member is on the alert for new things to observe, new facts to discover, new studies to make.

If your class wishes to organize an Observers' Club, arrange with your teacher for election of officers, and start as early as possible to prepare a program of the year's activities. Plan a schedule of meetings, arrange for a workshop, and prepare for as many different field trips as you can.

Above everything else, plan to make your club a conservation club.   Know exactly what conservation means and how it applies to your community.   Then do something worth while for conservation where you live.

ORGANIZATION

I. Chief of Staff, and Assistant Chief of Staff.
   A. Chief Health Officer, and Assistant.
   B. Chief Observer, and Assistants as follows:
      1. Weather Observer.
      2. Astronomical Observer.
      3. Bird Observer.
      4. Plant Observer.
      5. Geological Observer.
      6. Others as needed.
   C. Chief of Scientific Methods, and Assistant.
   D. Chief of Records, and Assistant.
II. Duties of these officers shall be those indicated by their titles.   Some suggestions follow, but please notice that duties suggested for one officer often suggest similar duties for another.
   A. Chief of Staff.
      This officer will announce and conduct meetings of the members of his staff as he and the staff may plan them.   At these staff meetings the general business of the club should be cared for.
   B. Chief Health Officers.
      1. This officer shall be responsible for adjusting the shades in the clubroom (classroom) for the proper control of light.
      2. He shall observe and record air temperature in the room when he enters and make adjustments if they are needed.
      3. Each day he shall make observations and records of the general properties of the air, such as dustiness, odors, and humidity.
      4. He shall have charge of such duties as the hygienic care of books and laboratory supplies.
      5. He shall be responsible for health charts and records.
   C. Chief Observer.
      1. This officer shall direct the meetings of his division.
      2. He shall see that reports of desirable observations are made and that charts and records of such observations are posted.
   D. Weather Observer.
      1. This officer shall record the club weather observations and make charts for them, including temperature, wind direction, wind velocity, condition of the sky, whether it rains or snows, and all such special observations (*e.g.*, a ring round the moon) which may be reported by different members of the club.

E. Astronomical Observer.
   1. This officer shall make charts for recording star observations.
   2. He shall watch for newspaper and magazine reports of astronomical events and keep the club informed in advance of such events.

F. Bird Observer.
   1. This officer shall prepare charts for recording reports of birds seen and identified by any and all club members.
   2. The charts shall record the name of the bird, date when seen, where seen, what it was doing when seen, and the name of the observer.
   3. No bird should be recorded as having been seen unless the observer supplies good evidence that the bird reported was actually seen.

G. Plant Observer.
   1. This officer shall provide charts, sketches, snapshots, specimens, and similar records relating to small plants, shrubs, trees, and greenhouse exhibits in the park or school greenhouse.
   2. He shall investigate interesting opportunities for observations of plants in the community and report them to the club.

H. Geologic Observer.
   1. This officer shall arrange exhibits of rocks and minerals.
   2. He shall search out and report interesting geological formations which may be visited by the club.
   3. He shall arrange exhibits of fossils and assist in the identification of fossils and other geological specimens.

I. Chief of Scientific Methods, and Assistant.
   1. This officer must be a straight thinker, accustomed to thinking things through. It shall be his special duty to see that statements made by the club members are accurate and that opinions are based on sound evidence.
   2. At the request of the staff, he shall be ready to assist in the examination of notebooks to check for thought and method.

J. Chief of Records, and Assistant.
   1. This officer shall serve as recording and corresponding secretary.
   2. At the request of the staff, he shall assist in keeping records of club members in their science work.

III. All meetings shall be conducted according to standard rules of order.
IV. Any member or officer who fails to live up to the duties of membership or office shall be subject to a hearing and removal by majority vote.

OBSERVERS' CLUB CALENDAR

September Observations

Stars. Star observations are best started by reference to the North Star, Big Dipper, and other constellations of the northern sky. These are the guides by which we may locate other stars. They are convenient because they are always above the horizon.

When does the September Equinox occur? Is it the same all over the world? What conditions cause the equinox? This is a job for your chief astronomer.

Planets. Are there any planets to be seen among the stars around the pole? Why?

Where should one look for the planets? Near the paths of what two celestial bodies?

What planets are visible in September? The planets that are visible to the naked eye are Mercury (with difficulty), Venus, Mars, Jupiter, and Saturn.

Note each planet's course among the stars and the times of its rising and setting.

An almanac, the newspaper, or some magazine like the following is a good place to look in order to learn what planets are visible each month and where to see them:

Sky and Telescope. Sky Publishing Corp., 91 Huguenot St., New Rochelle, N. Y.

Science News Letter. Science Service, Inc., Washington, D. C.

Nature Magazine. American Nature Association, Washington, D. C.

Weather. Observe your local weather conditions daily, and then check against the weather forecast as published in the newspaper.

To become a good weather observer you will need to observe and record the wind direction and velocity each morning or afternoon. Note the condition of the sky, the kinds of clouds, and the kind and amount of precipitation. Learn the different weather symbols found on the weather maps and use them to record your observations.

Of course, you will keep your ear open for weather sayings and signs, and check their accuracy.

Plants. Bring plants into the laboratory for fall and winter study. Geraniums, begonias, coleus, snapdragons, and ferns will be useful.

The Plant Observer will see that the plants are cared for properly.

Animals. Many birds migrate during the fall months. The Bird Observer should have charts ready to record arrivals and departures of birds. Other habits such as singing, feeding, flying, and perching may also be observed and recorded.

Gardeners will be interested in insects, toads, and snakes in their gardens.

How about a rat-extermination campaign, if one is necessary?

Special Item. Plan to collect and display farm and garden products on your Science Discovery Table. Each product should be correctly labeled.

Perhaps fruits and vegetables grown by class members can be displayed and prizes given as at a county fair.

The display might also include seeds of the various plants.

Plan a Science and Engineering Fair to be held in the spring. Write Science Service, Inc., 1719 N St., N.W., Washington, D.C., for help.

October Observations

Stars. As you continue your star studies, observe especially the Milky Way. Where is it? What is it? What importance has it?

Begin to look for "shooting stars" (meteors). Which star has to do with the times of sunrise and sunset? Since the equinox, the days are growing shorter and the nights longer. Why is this? Make a graph on the blackboard to show the sunrise and sunset times for this month. Are the days changing in length more in the morning or in the evening?

Try to locate The Swan (The Northern Cross) and Deneb its brightest star. Try also to locate other fall constellations such as the following:

The Scorpion is in the opposite part of the sky from Orion. The first magnitude star Antares is a bright red star.

The Archer is far to the south, lying in the Milky Way.

Aquarius, the Water-Carrier, contains four stars which form a Y and mark the water jug.

Boötes, The Bear Driver, contains the bright star Arcturus. The Northern Crown is a circlet of seven stars, one brighter than the rest.

Aquila, the Eagle, is the constellation with the very bright star Altair. There are bright stars on each side of Altair — three in a row — which will help you find Aquila. You will be interested to read the legend about Aquila.

Lyra, the Harp, with its bright star Vega, can be seen during the fall and also in May, June, and July.

Planets. Continue the observation of planets discovered last month if they are still visible. How have their positions among the stars changed?

Are any planets visible now that were not visible last month?

Is there an "evening star"? What is it?

Weather. What is your north latitude? When do you expect the first killing frost? Is that the end of your growing season? Why?

Continue making weather records and practicing weather forecasting.

Are the days gradually growing colder? How much on the average? Explain what is happening to cause the change.

Does the average wind direction change as the temperature changes? Why?

Plants. Do the leaves of the broad-leaf trees drop during the fall where you live? Or do they stay green for two years and then drop? What is an evergreen tree?

Do any of the following trees or shrubs grow in your vicinity? Which ones?

The Rose of Sharon	Fire Thorn (cotoneastu)
Red Oak	Beech
Poplar	Birch
Bittersweet	Rhododendron
Sumach	Red Maple
Cornelian Cherry	Iron Wood

Do their leaves show fall colors? They do in some parts of the country.

Bulbs for winter forcing may be brought in now. It is a good time also to make green wood cuttings from roses, hydrangeas, and forsythia. Such bulbs as hyacinth and narcissus should be kept cold for a few weeks after potting.

Animals. Try to find a toad in your garden. Where does the toad go during the cold months?

Which of the following animals live in your vicinity: prairie dog, gray squirrel, cottontail rabbit, prairie mole, spotted skunk, woodchuck? If some other variety lives near you, find out what variety it is. In any case, make a special study of the usefulness or harmfulness of at least one of the animals that makes its home near where you live.

Birds vary in different parts of the country, such as the robin of the north, and the southern robin. Of the following birds, find out which live mostly in one general locality, and which can be found almost everywhere in the United States: bobolink, bobwhite, prairie marsh (redwing blackbird), mockingbird, brown thrasher, flicker, red bellied woodpecker, blue jay, chickadee, crow, raven, cardinal. Select birds from different localities and make comparisons of their habits and environments.

"Swat-the-Fly" — Why? How many kinds of flies can you find? How do they differ?

Special Item. Plan now for Fire Prevention Week. If your town does not have a Fire Prevention Week, it will be a good idea for your science class to start one. Write to the National Board of Fire Underwriters and your State Department of Conservation for suggestions. Save property, labor, and lives by preventing fires.

Reference. If you are interested, write to the Department of Agriculture, Division of Publications, Washington, D. C., or to your congressman for one or more of the following publications if you can use them: [1] "F" stands for Farmer's Bulletins; "L" stands for leaflets; "C" stands for circulars.

No. 1495F. *Insect Enemies of the Flower Garden.*

No. 1828F. *Grasshoppers, and Their Control.* (10¢)

No. 1762F. *Home Canning of Fruits, Vegetables, and Meats.*

No. 1800F. *Homemade Jellies, Jams, and Preserves.*

No. 660F. *Weeds, How to Control Them.*

No. 1569F. *Earthworms as Pests and Otherwise.*

No. 1533F. *Rat Control.*

No. 1397F. *Mouse Control in Field and Orchard.*

No. 1716F. *Mole Control.*

[1] Note: There is a small charge for some government publications.

No. 1570F.   *Mosquito.*
No. 182L.   *Housefly Control.*
No. 145L.   *Clothes Moths.*
No. 147L.   *House Ants.*
No. 186L.   *Domestic Mosquito.*
No. 1638F.   *Rat Proofing Buildings and Premises.*
No. 423C.   *The House Rat.*
No. 1588F.   *Frost and Prevention of Frost Damage.*   (10¢)
No. 77F.   *Liming of Soils.*
No. 146L.   *Bedbugs.*
No. 144L.   *Cockroaches and Their Control.*
No. 101L.   *Injury to Buildings by Termites.*
No. 926F.   *Some Common Disinfectants.*

November Observations

Stars.   Find Orion on a star map, and then try to locate it in the sky.   Read about Orion and about the two great stars Betelgeuse and Rigel.   How do they compare with the sun in distance from the earth, in size, temperature, and brightness?

Again locate the "Milky Way" and the constellation The Swan (Northern Cross) with its great star Deneb.

Late in November is a good time to watch for meteors.   Why is the name "shooting stars" misleading?

Planets.   What's new in planets this month?   Check the location of Mars and Venus.   Is there a "morning" or "evening" star?   What is it?

Do you know why the planets and moon appear to travel across the sky in about the same paths?   Are the planets or the stars farther from the earth?

Try to locate someone who has a telescope and arrange to observe the planets and moon.

Weather.   Are the November clouds different in general from September clouds?   Describe.   Learn the symbols for the common clouds.

Do clouds at different heights travel in the same or different directions?   What does this indicate about air currents?   Which kinds of clouds are low, middle, and high clouds?   Use "L" for low, "M" for middle, and "H" for high.

Here is a good symbol to use in recording wind direction and

velocity: _o   Winds are named from the direction the air comes
from. A wind vane points into the wind; and the circled end of
the above symbol, when used on a weather map, is made to point
in the direction from which the wind is blowing. The "feather" on
the symbol represents 8 to 12 miles per hour. A short "feather"
stands for a wind force of 1 which equals 1 to 3 miles per hour. A
longer "feather" stands for a wind force of 2 which equals a wind
of 4 to 7 miles per hour. How would you represent a wind moving
with a force of 9? What wind velocity would that correspond to?
You will need to refer to the wind chart on page 57.

Keep up your wind direction reports on your weather chart.

In November early frosts are due in some parts of the country.
Watch out for your plants.

If you have learned to read a barometer, you will want to
record air pressures also on your weather charts.

What indications of weather changes, if any, can you observe
from the activities of animals? Record them.

Check to discover if any local industry is affected by the weather
changes.

Plants. If you live in the north, and started seedlings in
September, they probably need to be transplanted now.

September cuttings also should be transplanted now.

Which of the following trees grow abundantly where you live?
White pine, yellow pine, long-leaf pine, cherry, apple, pear,
orange, lemon, grapefruit, banana (should this really be called a
tree?), cabbage palmetto, cucumber tree, live oak, evergreen
magnolia, tulip tree, cypress, maple (any variety), hemlock, spruce,
arborvitae, cedar? Select one tree which you can study at first
hand and examine it for buds and branching arrangement.

Make a list of shrubs and vines that provide berries to feed the
birds in winter. Compare vegetables and fruits grown where you
live with those grown in other parts of the country. Try to
discover reasons for any differences.

This is a good time to plan for your Christmas tree and decorations. There is danger of fire and you may wish to fireproof
them. Leaflet 183 from the Department of Agriculture, *Fireproofing the Christmas Tree*, and 1786F, *Fireproofing Fabrics*, will
tell you how.

Animals. Continue your observations of bird arrivals and
departures.

Remember to put out food for winter birds when the snow may cover the natural feeding places.

Protect young fruit trees against damage by mice, rabbits, and other animals.

Special Item. Prepare now to avoid that cold. Get plenty of rest, exercise, and proper food. Do not neglect the vitamins. Do not over-eat. Neither should you eat too little as some do who want to keep thin. Avoid unnecessary crowds and keep away from people with colds.

December Observations

Stars. Read about the Star of Bethlehem. Was it a comet, a nova (new star), a meteor, or three planets close together?

This month our closest star — the sun — starts "traveling north" again after the shortest day about December 21 or 22. From where you live, make a note where on the southwestern horizon the sun sets on that day and compare it with its position when it sets next March 21 or 22. Explain what happens. If you lived on the equator or at the North Pole, where would the sun be on those two days?

Determine the direction of "true" north and the magnetic north. For which of these will you need a magnetic compass? How can you determine the other?

Observe the Pleiades, called also the Seven Sisters. Look again for Deneb and then for Vega. Which is larger? Farther away?

Planets. What planets are visible this month? Learn about at least one planet you do not already know about.

Weather. The First Cold Spell; The First Snow Storm; That Big Blow; will make good topics from which to choose for a scientific article for your English paper, and for your science class, too. Whichever topic you select consider the weather factors involved. Discuss the weather in terms of *cause* and *effect;* that is the scientific way.

Compare your weather on December 25 with the weather in other places in the United States. Compare it also with the weather in Manila, Honolulu, and Fairbanks.

Identify three or four different kinds of clouds and try to photograph them. Label the photographs and put them in your Science Discovery Book.

Plants. From the newspaper learn the wholesale market prices of some farm products.

What fruits and vegetables are being shipped into your town from other parts of the country? Why is this possible? Is it necessary?

If you have not completed your plans for winter flowers, refer back to November for suggestions.

Make a trip to a commercial greenhouse. However, do this before the Christmas rush.

Make a study of evergreens — trees, shrubs, and vines — used for Christmas decorations to determine if the needs for conservation are being observed. Consider especially American holly.

Do you know the story of mistletoe? If not, look it up and tell it as a Christmas story to your class.

During Christmas vacation, take a hike through the woods, open fields, or along a country road to study the trees and shrubs in winter. Note also grasses and weeds. Do any of these contain seeds? Do any of the plants furnish food for the winter birds?

Animals. Make a bird census on Christmas day.

If you have snow during December, go out into the woods and fields and find wild animal tracks. Photograph them or make sketches to illustrate. Tracks are better photographed with slanting rays of light which cause shadows. Be careful to make the correct exposure.

The following Farmer's Bulletins may help you.

844F.   *How to Attract Birds, Middle Atlantic States.* (5 ¢)

912F.   *How to Attract Birds in the East Central States.*

755F.   *Common Birds of the South Eastern States in Relation to Agriculture.*

506F.   *Food of Some Well-Known Birds of Forest, Farm, and Garden.*

1783F. *Feeding Wild Life in Winter*

Special Item. Investigate the heating and ventilating plant in your home, and at school. How does the heat get from the burning fuel to the air in the rooms? Have in mind the three ways by which heat is transferred — conduction, convection, and radiation. Conservation of fuel involves proper combustion, and insulation of the roof and walls of buildings. Is fuel being conserved? Look for fire hazards. If you find any, do something to prevent fires. Make diagrams to illustrate your discoveries. Observe the fire escape nearest to your classroom.

January Observations

Stars. Continue your study of prominent stars and constellations. Learn some interesting facts about them.

Planets. Are any of the planets visible last month now visible? If so, has their location among the stars changed? Draw their position on your star map.

Do you want to make a telescope? If you do, write to the magazine *Sky and Telescope* for help or read about it in *Starcraft* by Barton and Joseph, published by Whittlesey House, McGraw-Hill Book Co.

Weather. Morning and evening cloud forms and colors are most interesting to photograph, especially if you can use Kodachrome or Kodacolor. Do you believe that a "red sunset is followed usually by a fair day"? Check such observations with the prediction on the weather map or in the paper, and write what actually happens.

January and February are good months to keep weather records, using the chart found in your Science Discovery Book. Use the new symbols (see page 57) for recording weather facts.

Form a Weather Forecaster's Department of your science club.

The following Educational Series of the U. S. Weather Bureau is free to teachers and principals, others must pay a small fee:

The Educational Series contains:

> Cloud Forms
> Weather Forecasting No. 42
> Explanation of the Weather Map
> The Weather Bureau

Plants. How do trees differ in their branching arrangement? Why do they differ? Winter is a good time to observe and make drawings of the way trees branch.

Bring in bulbs — narcissi, daffodils, jonquils.

Send for your seed catalog and begin now to plan your garden. Make a diagram of your garden.

Fruit trees and vines may be pruned now.

Animals. Have you any winter birds about your house? What do they eat? Do you need to replenish the food counter? If you have hemlocks near by, look there for chickadees.

Continue your study of animal tracks in the snow. Compare tracks of wild animals and birds, with cats, dogs, horses, cows, chickens, and turkeys if you can.

Special Item. Do you know how sound travels and how fast it travels through air? This is a good month to experiment with sound. Get some boy or girl from the physics class to help you.

Here are some things you can do:

1. Note how much longer it takes for the sound of a steam whistle to reach you than for the light from the steam; or the sound of an ax after you *see* the blow.
2. Find out how tightening a violin string affects the pitch, or what effect a big string has as compared with a small (slender) string on the violin or banjo.
3. Use two empty tin cans and a long string or wire to make a telephone.
4. Find a place where you can call and hear an echo. Try to explain what causes the echo.

February Observations

Stars. Make a chart and keep a record of the times of sunrise and sunset for the month. Then on a piece of cross section or ruled paper plot the times from left to right. Are the days growing long faster in the morning or evening?

Planets. What is the "evening star"? "Morning star"?

What planet is visible now that you saw last month? Again mark its position on a star map.

Weather. Every day post a weather map from the newspaper on the bulletin board.

The Chief Weather Observer will have an interesting job this month tracing the paths of "highs" and "lows" across the country on a map of the United States.

Add another set of weather observations to your weather chart. Note especially the relationship between wind direction and cold spells.

Using the weather map, compare weather conditions in Southern California, Florida, Washington (state), Maine, and your home.

How about that cold? Have your Health Observer find out how many colds each member of your class has had so far this winter. Then try to discover why some have had more than others. What can be done to prevent colds?

Determine the temperature and relative humidity in your class-room each day for several days. If the humidity is too low, try to have it increased.

Plants. Now is the time to start seeds indoors for outdoor transplanting. Such seeds as verbena, phlox, larkspur, calendulas, stock, and snapdragons are suitable. Seeds of bedding plants — petunias, and salvias — may be started now. Consult your seed catalog for others.

Try some of your garden seeds for per cent of germination before planting.

Bring in your daffodil and jonquil bulbs, and if you bring in tulip, hyacinth, or crocus bulbs, keep them cool until they show green shoots.

Complete your garden plans.

Again visit the commercial greenhouse to see preparations for Easter flowers.

Animals. Remember the birds. Be sure there is food for them, especially if you live where winters are cold and the land covered with snow.

Make a record of your winter residents.

A bayberry bush supplies food for birds. Can you find one where you live?

Plan now to build nest boxes for birds. Have someone write to the Department of Agriculture for No. 1456F, *Houses for Birds*.

Make plans to build bird baths as soon as the weather permits.

Make a census of all the pets owned by members of your class. Then each pupil should make a special study of his own pet, or someone else's pet if he hasn't one of his own. Study what foods the pet needs, how much it requires, how often it should be fed, how much water it needs, its vitamin requirement, and about its bed. Be sure your pet receives scientific care.

Special Item. Make a study of the principal power used in your community or near-by city. Is it water, steam, or electric power? How is it produced, distributed, used?

March Observations

Stars. Are the days getting longer? Note the position of the sunset on the horizon on March 21 or 22 and compare this with its position on December 21 or 22. Try to measure the angle between the two positions. What has really happened since December 21–22?

How have the positions of some of the constellations changed since December when observed at the same time of night? Try to explain the changes. Remember stars rise about four minutes earlier each night.

How many stars can you recognize in the sky and name?

Planets. Continue your observation of the planets. Learn all about the ones that are visible. If you can do so, you will be interested to look at a planet through a telescope.

If you started to make a telescope, how is it coming along? Keep at it.

Weather. "If March comes in like a lamb, it will go out like a lion." Do you believe this statement? Check to find out if it is true.

Keep a record of March weather, especially wind direction and velocity. Is it true that March is an especially windy month? Compare with data for other months and get official data from the Weather Bureau.

Make a collection of "weather sayings" that apply to March and try to determine to what extent each one has a scientific reason back of it.

Plants. If you live in the northern part of the United States, you may wish to start more seeds in boxes indoors. Boys and girls in the south, of course, can safely plant seeds out of doors.

Pussy willows are beginning to blossom at latitudes about 40° N.

Bring in branches of forsythia to force the yellow blossoms to come out early.

On your garden plans, have you indicated second and third plantings of peas, beans, sweet corn, etc.? Why do you do this?

Remember to run the rows across the slopes and around the hills, not up and down the hillsides. This will help to conserve both soil and water.

In the north the pruning of fruit trees should be completed very soon before the sap begins to run.

Many states observe Arbor Day in April. When does your state observe it? Plan for it now.

Write for Farmer's Bulletin F1492, *Arbor Day, Its Purpose and Observance.*

Animals. Are your bird houses ready? They should be put out now at the latest in most states, except those farthest north. See Bulletin 621F.

Robins and bluebirds are finding their way north again. Watch for their migrations.

Keep a bird list all this month and during April and May, listing the birds that pass through your country and those that stay with you for the summer.

Prepare to observe Bird Day. This will be a good project for your Bird Club to plan and direct. The following bulletins from the U. S. Department of Agriculture will help:

363C.   *The Migration of North American Birds.*

1719F.   *Improving Farm Environment for Wild Life.*

Write to Biological Survey, Department of Agriculture, for copy of laws relating to bird migration.

Begin again your war on harmful insects. *Swat the fly.* Why? Write for the following bulletins:

182L.   *Housefly Control.*

145L.   *Clothes Moths.*

186L.   *Domestic Mosquito.*

1570F.   *Mosquito Remedies and Prevention.*

Oil on the surface of stagnant water pools will reduce the number of mosquitoes.

Remember cats are natural enemies of birds. Prevent your pets from killing birds, and take stray cats to the Animal Rescue League or Humane Society.

If you live on a farm, look for woodchuck holes. If in a field, they may cause a horse to break a leg. Kill the woodchuck and fill the hole. Bulletin:

21F.   *Woodchuck Control in Eastern States.*

Another animal to keep account of is the common meadow mole. Farmer's Bulletin 1716F, *Mole Control,* will tell you what to do.

Special Item. Science and Engineering Fair. Have your club members completed their exhibits for the Science and Engineering Fair? Be sure your exhibit is neatly arranged and labeled, and as perfect mechanically as you can make it. No exhibit is too simple to be worth entering in the Fair.

Water Storage. Spring is the time of floods, so now will be a good time for your class to make a special investigation of floods in your locality, the damage that usually results, and what steps are being taken to prevent flood damage.

In connection with your study, look up about one of the great flood control projects and find out what was done and how worthwhile it is.

Now is a good time to plan your soil conservation projects.   The following charts may be obtained free by libraries, schools, and teachers from the Soil Conservation Service, Washington, D. C.

No. 1.   Soil Erosion, Cause and Effect.
No. 2.   Contour Farming for Soil and Water Conservation.
No. 3.   Strip Cropping and Erosion Control Practice.
No. 5.   Cover Crops Protect Soil.
No. 6.   Gully Control.
No. 8.   Trees and Shrubs for Erosion Control.

The following bulletins are also helpful:

No. 1737F.   *Stop Gullies — Save Your Farm.*
No. 1758F.   *Cover Crops for Soil Conservation.*
No. 1795F.   *Conserving Corn Belt Soil.*
No. 33C.   *Soil Erosion — A National Menace.*
No. 286MP.   *What Is Soil Erosion?*

April Observations

Stars.   Keep a record this month of time of sunrise and sunset. Compare with previous records.

Determine the differences in the sunlight and in the shadow, other things being the same.   Explain any differences you discover. How does War Time save daylight?

Planets.   What planet is brightest now?   Where is it located among the stars?   Is it a "morning" or an "evening" star?

Weather.   "April showers bring May flowers."   How accurate is this statement?   Why?

Observe and record wind directions and velocity, temperatures, kind of precipitation, and kinds of clouds.   Keep trying your hand at weather forecasting.   Watch out for the "cold bug."

What weather factors are related to spring foods?   What can be done about it?   Write for Miscellaneous Publication 286, U. S. Department of Agriculture, and your State Conservation Commission.   All out for conservation.

Plants.   Observe the buds of trees and shrubs.   Are they showing signs of opening?   Are they located at the ends of twigs or along the sides?   What difference does their location make in pruning?

In the latitude of New York, red maples and shad bush are in bloom.   What are the early spring blossoms where you live?

Remember to do all that you can to protect the wild flowers.

Outdoor planting can begin for some seeds even in the north.

Harden up seedlings by exposing them to cool air for gradually increasing periods before transplanting them out of doors.

Clean up around the stems of trees and shrubs. Even in the north such seeds as asters, calendulas, cosmos, snapdragons, verbenas, and zinnias can be started safely out of doors.

As soon as you can get at your spring garden work, pull or dig up all weeds. That will save work later on.

Look for early wild flowers, but do not pick them. Many localities where wild flowers grew are no longer suitable for wild things because of storage dams, draining swamps, and clearing woods for crops and buildings; therefore wild flowers are precious. Learn how to protect those you have. If there are laws to protect wild flowers in your state, learn them and do what you can to have them obeyed.

Organize a Wild Flower Protective Club. If there is an adult nature club or garden club where you live, ask it to help you. If there is none, perhaps your teacher and parents will want to organize for conservation of the wild plants.

Do something to observe Arbor Day. Plant a tree, plant a shrub, or take steps to protect plants you have against damage.

Make a record of the dates when different kinds of trees and shrubs blossom. Do the leaves or blossoms appear first? If you have cold frames or hot beds, remember to ventilate and water them.

Send for No. 161L, *Eastern Tent Caterpillars*, if your trees are likely to be troubled with this insect.

Animals. Spring migration of birds has started, so start your bird lists.

When migration is under way, nesting time for some birds is near. Do they need nesting material and nest boxes where you live? If so, your Chief Bird Observer should be on the alert. Be prepared for your bird guests.

Are your trees likely to be harmed by white marked tussock moths? You can help protect your trees by tying cotton gunny sacks or sticky flypaper around the stem.

Your trees may need to be sprayed to protect them against insects and disease. Be sure to get the advice of experts, not quack tree doctors.

Remember to kill every fly you can, and so help to prevent the spread of certain diseases. What diseases do scientists tell us are spread by flies? Mosquitoes?

Plan to control mosquito breeding places.

This month has Be Kind to Animals Week. Why not be kind to animals all the time? If you observe cases of cruelty to animals, report them or try to prevent it.

Special Items. Make a study of some local industry. Are its processes mainly physical, chemical, or biological? In how many ways is the industry important to you? How does it affect the wild life in your community?

May Observations

Stars. What constellations are visible these nights that were not visible during the winter? Can you account for the changes?

Planets. Do the planets or the moon have anything to do with the time for planting? What evidence can you give to help prove your ideas?

Weather. Have the planets or the moon any effect on the weather? What evidence can you give to help prove your ideas?

What weather factors do you need to observe to forecast the weather? What instruments are needed?

Continue your weather records and your forecasting. Compare the weather with your forecasts and with official forecasts to test their accuracy.

Plants. Care for your garden. It will be interesting for you to keep an account of the cost of seeds, and the value of your garden products. Is a garden worth-while? Consider not only the value of the vegetables and flowers, but also the value of the exercise to your health and the satisfaction you get from the accomplishment.

If you have a camera in which you can use color film, try your skill at photographing flowers. Be sure to make a note of the name of each flower and the date. Try to show leaves as well as flowers.

Make a collection of different kinds of woods. If possible, cut out a piece that will include the bark. If you start with green wood, it must be dried out very slowly. When the piece is dry, sandpaper and polish the surface so the grain will show. If you have a magnifier, examine a cross section, and make a drawing to show what it is like.

Animals. Baby-bird time is here in many localities. Watch the cats.

Plan early bird hikes. Learn to know the birds by their "calls" and songs as well as by their looks.

If you have patience and proper camera equipment, try to photograph the birds.

Have you insect enemies in your garden? If so, write to the U. S. Department of Agriculture for help. The following bulletins are useful:

2L.   *Cutworms in the Garden.*
1102F.   *The Crow in Relation to Agriculture.*
1495F.   *Insect Enemies of the Flower Garden.*
370C.   *Food Habits of Common Hawks.*

Earthworms are garden helpers. Observe the earthworm to learn its habits and how it is helpful.

Special Item. What kind of transportation is most important to your community? Make a study of it and its importance. What scientific principles are especially related to it? Try to make a model of some kind to illustrate important things about the industry.

June Observations

Are you busy at this time reviewing the year's school work, taking examinations, going to school picnics, and generally rounding out another successful school year? As you look back over the year's work in science, what important things stand out? How has science helped you? It's great to be alive and live in a country where everyone is free to do as he pleases so long as he does not trespass upon the rights of others. It's a grand country.

Let us now plan our science adventures for the summer so that everyone may have interesting experiences and tales to tell and interesting treasures of science to exhibit when school opens again in September.

What to Do in the Summer

Many of you will have jobs of one kind or another to earn money or to get experience. Your work may be caring for city lawns and gardens, or helping a farmer with his work. Perhaps you will take an auto trip to our parks or spend time in a summer camp. Whatever you do or wherever you are, you will have the great outdoors with all its treasures on land, in the water and soil, and in the air. Use every opportunity to know something better than before through your own effort.

Summer adventures will be much more valuable and interesting if you carry a pocket notebook with you for immediate records of what you observe or experience. Whenever you collect a specimen, no matter what it is, always make a note telling exactly when and where you found it and any interesting things about it that you can discover at the time. All specimens collected should be accurately identified and labeled.

Some of you will continue stargazing and renew your acquaintance with the most prominent stars and constellations, perhaps discovering new ones. Some constellations to be seen in summer are Boötes, with the bright star Arcturus, and the Swan (more often called the Northern Cross), with the very brilliant star, Deneb at the northern end of the cross. Another interesting star to watch through the summer is Vega, in the constellation Lyra, the Harp, and, of course, you will follow the planets as they move among the stars.

Summer clubs might be formed, such as the "Fruit Tree Club," the "Broad Leaf Club," or the "Evergreen Club." Each club would study the particular trees or shrubs represented by its name. The members would learn the shape of the leaf, the bark, the way the tree branches, and other facts about each tree or shrub. All leaves collected should be mounted and labeled. With an ink pad and a roller you can make ink prints of leaves in your books.

Other clubs might be the "Garden Club," the "Vegetable Club," the "Flower Club," or the "Weed Collectors' Club." In these clubs samples of plants, flowers, and even seeds might be collected and visits made to different gardens.

Garden insects, butterflies, and moths also present interesting opportunities for adventure in the summer.

The "Mineral Collectors' Club" represents a hobby that a great many people enjoy. The *Boy Scout Book on Minerals* or books from the public library will help you to identify minerals. Be sure to label each one as you find it, telling where you found it, and all about it. Many minerals occur as little crystals in rocks such as limestone. Watch for such crystals as well as for larger samples.

A "Bird Club," like all science clubs, is most successful if its work continues all through the year. Summer records, of course, should continue to give the name of the bird, the date and place seen, what the bird was doing, its song, and any special information.

Finally, a "Science Readers' Club" is suggested. Perhaps we should think of this as a "Rainy Day Club," because it is on rainy days that you may feel inclined to go to the library to read about science things you have seen or collected. Rainy days are good days for putting your records and collections in order.

APPENDIX

Table of Relative Humidity in Per Cent

Locate the dry-bulb temperature in the column at the left marked t, and opposite this, in the column headed by the number of degrees difference in temperature between your wet- and dry-bulb readings, you will find the number of per cent of humidity.

t	DIFFERENCE BETWEEN THE DRY- AND WET-BULB THERMOMETERS																
	1°	2°	3°	4°	5°	6°	7°	8°	9°	10°	11°	12°	13°	14°	15°	16°	
55	94	88	82	76	70	65	59	54	49	43	39	34	29	24	19	15	55
56	94	88	82	77	71	65	60	55	50	44	40	35	30	25	21	16	56
57	94	88	83	77	71	66	61	55	50	45	40	36	32	27	22	18	57
58	94	89	83	78	72	67	61	56	51	46	42	37	33	28	24	19	58
59	94	89	83	78	72	67	62	57	52	47	43	38	34	29	25	21	59
60	94	89	84	78	73	68	63	58	53	48	44	39	34	30	26	22	60
61	94	89	84	78	73	68	63	58	54	49	44	40	35	32	27	23	61
62	95	89	84	79	74	69	64	59	54	50	45	41	37	32	28	24	62
63	95	89	84	79	74	69	64	60	55	51	46	42	38	33	29	26	63
64	95	90	85	79	74	70	65	60	56	51	47	43	38	34	30	27	64
65	95	90	85	80	75	70	65	61	56	52	48	44	39	35	31	28	65
66	95	90	85	80	75	71	66	61	57	53	49	45	40	36	32	29	66
67	95	90	85	80	76	71	66	62	58	53	49	45	41	37	33	30	67
68	95	90	85	81	76	71	67	63	58	54	50	46	42	38	34	31	68
69	95	90	86	81	76	72	67	63	59	55	51	47	43	39	35	32	69
70	95	90	86	81	77	72	68	64	60	55	52	48	44	40	36	33	70
71	95	91	86	81	77	72	68	64	60	56	52	48	45	41	37	34	71
72	95	91	86	82	77	73	69	65	61	57	53	49	45	42	38	35	72
73	95	91	86	82	78	73	69	65	61	57	53	50	46	42	39	35	73
74	95	91	86	82	78	74	70	66	62	58	54	50	47	43	40	36	74
75	95	91	87	82	78	74	70	66	62	58	55	51	47	44	40	37	75
76	95	91	87	82	78	74	70	66	63	59	55	52	48	45	41	38	76
77	95	91	87	83	78	74	71	67	63	59	56	52	49	45	42	39	77
78	96	91	87	83	79	75	71	67	63	60	56	53	49	46	42	39	78
79	96	91	87	83	79	75	71	68	64	60	57	53	50	47	43	40	79

Nutrient Solution for Plant Growth

The following solution contains the necessary minerals for plant growth. For testing, make three solutions as follows:

1. Containing all minerals
2. Containing all minerals except potassium nitrate
3. Containing all minerals except calcium sulfate. Compare growth of seedlings in each of the three solutions and in distilled water.

Water (distilled)	2 quarts
Sodium chloride (table salt)	$\frac{1}{32}$ oz.
Calcium sulfate	$\frac{1}{32}$ oz.
Magnesium sulfate	$\frac{1}{32}$ oz.
Calcium phosphate	$\frac{1}{32}$ oz.
Potassium nitrate (saltpeter)	$\frac{1}{16}$ oz.

Add one drop of a dilute solution of iron chloride.
See also references for "Soilless gardening" and use of hormones and vitamins for stimulating plant growth.

Comparison of Boiling Points of Water, Atmospheric Pressure, and Altitude

(Taylor Instrument Co. calculations)

BOILING POINTS OF WATER	BAROMETER READINGS INCHES OF MERCURY	APPROXIMATE ALTITUDES IN FEET
200° F.	23.45	6650
201° F.	23.94	6070
202° F.	24.44	5510
203° F.	24.95	4950
204° F.	25.46	4390
205° F.	25.99	3830
206° F.	26.52	3280
207° F.	27.06	2730
208° F.	27.62	2170
209° F.	28.18	1620
210° F.	28.75	1080
211° F.	29.33	530
212° F.	29.92	Sea Level 0
213° F.	30.52	−550

Millibars and Inches of Air Pressure

(U. S. Department of Agriculture, Weather Bureau calculations)

MB.	INCHES	MB.	INCHES	MB.	INCHES	MB.	INCHES	MB.	INCHES	MB.	INCHES
940	27.76	960	28.35	980	28.94	1000	29.53	1020	30.12	1040	30.71
941	27.79	961	28.38	981	28.97	1001	29.56	1021	30.15	1041	30.74
942	27.82	962	28.41	982	29.00	1002	29.59	1022	30.18	1042	30.77
943	27.85	963	28.44	983	29.03	1003	29.62	1023	30.21	1043	30.80
944	27.88	964	28.47	984	29.06	1004	29.65	1024	30.24	1044	30.83
945	27.91	965	28.50	985	29.09	1005	29.68	1025	30.27	1045	30.86
946	27.94	966	28.53	986	29.12	1006	29.71	1026	30.30	1046	30.89
947	27.96	967	28.56	987	29.15	1007	29.74	1027	30.33	1047	30.92
948	27.99	968	28.58	988	29.18	1008	29.77	1028	30.36	1048	30.95
949	28.02	969	28.61	989	29.21	1009	29.80	1029	30.39	1049	30.98
950	28.05	970	28.64	990	29.23	1010	29.83	1030	30.42	1050	31.01
951	28.08	971	28.67	991	29.26	1011	29.85	1031	30.45	1051	31.04
952	28.11	972	28.70	992	29.29	1012	29.88	1032	30.47	1052	31.07
953	28.14	973	28.73	993	29.32	1013	29.91	1033	30.50	1053	31.10
954	28.17	974	28.76	994	29.35	1014	29.94	1034	30.53	1054	31.12
955	28.20	975	28.79	995	29.38	1015	29.97	1035	30.56	1055	31.15
956	28.23	976	28.82	996	29.41	1016	30.00	1036	30.59	1056	31.18
957	28.26	977	28.85	997	29.44	1017	30.03	1037	30.62	1057	31.21
958	28.29	978	28.88	998	29.47	1018	30.06	1038	30.65	1058	31.24
959	28.32	979	28.91	999	29.50	1019	30.09	1039	30.68	1059	31.27

Table of Melting and Boiling Points of Common Substances

(Approximate)

SUBSTANCE	MELTING POINT	BOILING POINT
Alcohol (ethyl)	− 179° F.	172° F.
Butter fat	100°–107° F.	
Carbon tetrachloride	− 10° F.	214° F.
Crisco	71°–87° F.	
Lard	104°–116° F.	
Paraffin	122°–131° F.	
Tallow	109°–114° F.	
Gold	1945° F.	4698° F.
Iron	2786° F.	4442° F.
Lead	620° F.	2777° F.
Mercury	− 37° F.	675° F.
Phosphorus (Yellow)	111° F.	554° F.
Sulfur	235° F.	833° F.
Water	32° F.	212° F.

GLOSSARY

acid — A substance which has a sour taste and turns blue litmus red.

adaptation — Fitness to live in a particular place or to do a certain thing.

aeration — The process of putting air into water or soil.

air mass — A volume of air extending many miles over the earth's surface and up to several thousand feet in height. It is made up of air of approximately the same temperature and pressure, moving as a unit.

air pressure (atmospheric) — The pressure exerted by air against objects due to its weight.

alcohol (grain) — A liquid having narcotic properties; used in some thermometers, and as a solvent.

algae — Simple forms of plant life sometimes found in water.

alkali — A substance which has a slippery feeling and a bitter taste, and turns red litmus blue.

altitude — Distance above sea level; in astronomy, the angular distance of a star above the horizon.

ammonia (household) — A solution of ammonium hydroxide in water.

anemometer — An instrument used to measure the speed of the wind (velocity of air currents).

annuals — Plants that complete their life cycle of growth, reproduction, and death within a single year or season.

anther — Small knob at end of stamen of flower. Inside anther are the pollen grains.

anticyclone — As seen from above in the northern hemisphere, a clockwise-whirling mass of air having a high air pressure area.

area of high pressure — An anticyclone area.

area of low pressure — The center portion of a cyclonic storm.

atmosphere — The gases surrounding the earth.

atmospheric pressure — Air pressure: 14.7 lbs. to the square inch at sea level.

axis — A line about which a body turns.

bacteria — One-celled, non-green plants invisible to naked eye.

balance — An instrument for accurate weighing.

barometer — An instrument which measures changes in atmospheric pressure.

    aneroid — A barometer without liquid.

    mercurial — A barometer in which mercury is used.

beetles — Insects having armor-like wing covers.

Big Dipper — A portion of the constellation Ursa Major, in the form of a dipper, in the northern sky. It is called Big to distinguish it from a similar but smaller constellation.

blue vitriol — Copper sulfate; a solution sometimes used to kill algae in water, and as an ingredient of spray materials for the control of insects.

boiling point — The temperature to which a liquid must be heated to cause it to change rapidly to a gas (this temperature is constant for each pure liquid).

borax — A white alkaline powder often used for softening water.

budding — Propagating plants by inserting a bud into the growing part of the stem of another plant.

bulb — A special stem structure in which food is stored by a plant to start the growth the next season.

burdock — A weed.

capillarity — The lifting of certain liquids by means of small, tube-like spaces.

carbohydrates — Sugar, starch, and cellulose compounds made of carbon, hydrogen, and oxygen.

carbon tetrachloride — A non-combustible liquid commonly used for cleaning cloth and putting out fire. It is sold under various trade names.

Cassiopeia — A constellation forming a "W" in the northern sky. In certain positions it appears inverted.

cause and effect — A cause is a happening that always precedes another happening (the effect) and without which the second happening could not occur.

caustic soda — Sodium hydroxide; an alkaline substance used in making soap.

celestial — Referring to the heavens, the apparent sky sphere.

centigrade — A thermometric scale divided into one hundred divisions between the freezing temperature and the boiling temperature of water.

centripetal force — A force drawing a body toward the center about which it revolves.

cesspool — An underground tank with drain, for the disposal of sewage.

characteristics — The features which distinguish one substance from another and by which we recognize it.

chemically pure — The condition of a substance when it contains no foreign material.

chloride of lime — A white powder containing chlorine and used both to kill germs and as a deodorizer.

chlorination — Putting chlorine into a water supply for the purpose of killing bacteria.

chlorine — A greenish-yellow gas or liquid, sometimes used to destroy germs.

chlorophyll — Green coloring matter of leaves and bark.

chronometer — A ship's clock.

circle — Line all points of which are equal distances from center.

clinical thermometer — A fever thermometer.

cloud — Visible fog mass some distance above earth's surface.

cirrus — A feathery cloud, high above the earth.

cumulus — A cloud having a rounded or dome-shaped top.

nimbostratus — Usual rain clouds. Low-lying stratus clouds heavy with moisture which gives them dark color.

nimbus — A storm cloud.

storm — Rain- or snow-bringing clouds of dark gray aspect.

stratocumulus — Combination cloud, part stratus, part cumulus. Usually formed when cumulus clouds begin to spread out.

thunder — Dark cumulus clouds which give rise to thunder storms.

cocoon — Nest-like case in which larva rests while changing form.

codling moth — An insect whose larva is best known as the "worm" in the apple.

cold front — The advancing boundary of a large mass of cold air.

cold wave — A period of continued cold weather.

compass — A magnetic needle free to swing above a dial with the directions marked on it.

compost — A heap of decomposing (decaying) vegetable matter.

compound — A substance composed of two or more elements chemically combined.

condensation — The process by which a gas is changed to the liquid form.

condenser — A piece of apparatus used to cool a gas and so change it to a liquid.

conduction — The transfer of heat through solids from particle to particle.

conductor (electrical) — A metal rod or wire that transmits electricity efficiently.

conduit — A pipe used to conduct water from its source to a reservoir.

conservation — The careful and scientific method of using and, where possible, replacing natural resources.

constellation — A group (configuration) of prominent stars.

contamination — Making food or water unfit to be taken into the body.

contour planting — A scientific method of tilling the soil whereby rows are planted horizontally around hills rather than up and down.

contract — To draw together; to occupy less space because of cooling.

convection — The transfer of heat by the movement of gases and liquids.

corona — A ring of colored light appearing close around the sun or moon.

cotyledon — The part of a seed which contains the food needed to start the new plant.

cross-pollination — The transfer of pollen from one flower to the pistil of another.

cutting — A part of the stem of a plant which can be made to develop roots.

cutworm — An insect larva which eats stems of young plants.

cyclone — As seen from above in the northern hemisphere, a counter-clockwise-whirling mass of air having a low air pressure at the center.

DDT — A chemical which kills insects on touching their bodies.

decompose — To break up by decay or chemical action.

degree — One three-hundred-sixtieth of a circle; also intensity of heat.

density — The closeness or compactness of the particles composing a substance.

dentine — Bone-like substance of a tooth just inside the enamel.

deposit — Sediment.

dew — Moisture which collects on the surface of cool bodies.

diameter — The distance through the center of a circle or sphere.

dilution — The addition of large quantities of a liquid such as water to a solution to make it more dilute.

diphtheria — A contagious bacterial disease attacking the throat, appendix.

disinfectant — A chemical substance used to kill germs or to render them harmless.

disposal — Getting rid of material such as wastes of various kinds, *e.g.*, sewage, garbage.

dissolve — To cause a substance to be equally distributed throughout a liquid, so that it will not settle out and cannot be separated by filtering; *e.g.*, oxygen, sugar, or salt dissolved in water.

drainage area — All land drained by a river system.

earth — The third planet in the solar system.

eclipse — The cutting off of the light from a lighted body.

effluent — The liquid products of treated sewage.

electric charge — A quantity of electricity on a body.

electricity — A form of energy.

element — A substance which cannot be separated into simpler substances by ordinary chemical means.

ellipse — An oval figure with both ends alike.

elliptical — Shaped like an ellipse.

emulsion — A liquid mixture containing small fat particles equally distributed throughout.

enamel — The hard outer covering of the teeth.

energy — The ability to do work; manifest as heat, light, electricity, and mechanical and chemical energy.

epidermis — The outer layer of the skin.

equator — An imaginary great circle about the earth, midway between the poles.

equinox — Time of equal day and night all over the earth.

evaporation — To change from liquid to gas; the process by which a liquid is changed to a gas.

expand — To grow larger in volume or size; to take up more space.

Fahrenheit — A thermometer scale divided into 180 divisions between the freezing temperature and boiling temperature of water.

fat — A greasy, easily melted or liquid compound, found in animal and vegetable tissues.

faucet — The part of the plumbing that controls the flow of water from pipes.

fertilization — The second step in plant reproduction, consisting of the union of the nucleus of a pollen grain with the nucleus of an ovule (egg cell).

fertilizer — A substance used to enrich the soil to improve plant growth.

filter — Device for straining out undissolved materials from liquids.

flats — Shallow boxes filled with soil for starting seeds indoors.

fluoride — Poisonous chemical. Combined with certain other chemicals, it forms a compound which seems to help prevent tooth decay.

flushing — Washing out waste by means of a flow of water.

fog — Fine drops of water visible in the atmosphere near the earth.

freeze — To change from a liquid to a solid state.

freezing point — The temperature at which a liquid changes to the solid state.

frost — Frozen water vapor; minute crystals on grass, window panes, and other objects, formed by the freezing of moisture as it is deposited from the air.

fungus — A kind of plant which gets its food from other organic material. Because it contains no chlorophyll, it cannot make its own food as do the green plants.

galaxy — An astronomical system made up of vast numbers of suns.

garbage — Food waste from the kitchen.

gas — A form of matter which has no definite shape and no definite volume; *e.g.*, air, hydrogen.

sewer — Gas arising from the decaying matter in a sewer.

gasoline — An inflammable, volatile liquid used as fuel and as a solvent.

germ — A one-celled plant or animal.

germinate — To start to grow.

gills — Organs needed to enable fish, tadpoles, and similar animals to get oxygen from water.

glands, sweat — Glands in the skin which secrete sweat (perspiration).

glycerine — A by-product of soap making.

grafting — To propagate plants by inserting a piece of the stem of one plant into the growing layer of another plant.

gravitation — The attraction that every body has for every other body in the universe.

gravity, force of — The attraction or pull between the earth and other objects.

gravity pressure — The pressure exerted by any substance due to its weight (or to the force of gravity).

gravity system — A method of obtaining a water supply from a higher source by means of the force of gravity.

grease — Fats and oils.

Greenwich — A borough of London, England; the prime meridian passes through it.

grubs — Larvae of some insects.

hail — Ice globules built up of ice layers deposited on a frozen raindrop.

halo — A ring of light similar to a corona but appearing farther away from the sun or moon.

hardness, permanent — Hardness of water due to the presence of dissolved minerals that cannot be removed by boiling.

hardness, temporary — Hardness of water due to the presence of dissolved minerals that may be removed by boiling.

hard water — Contains minerals in solution which combine with soap and retard the formation of suds.

heat capacity — The quantity of heat which a definite quantity of a given substance can absorb before it changes its temperature one degree.

hemisphere — Half a sphere.

hibernate — To pass the winter season in a state of sleep or near sleep.

horizon — The line where the sky and earth seem to meet.

hot wave — A period of continuing hot weather.

house fly — The fly most common in and about houses.

humidity — The invisible gaseous moisture in the air.

relative — The ratio of the amount of moisture in the air to the amount needed to saturate the air at a given temperature.

hydrogen — The lightest known gas; a combustible gas.

hygrometer — An instrument for measuring the relative humidity of the air.

ichneumon fly — A useful insect.

illuminate — To light up or make visible by reflected light.

impurities — Substances not belonging in (foreign to) the substance where they occur, *e.g.*, minerals dissolved in water.

insoluble — Impurities which are not dissolved.

soluble — Impurities found in a dissolved state.

incinerator — A special firebox or oven in which to burn garbage and rubbish.

inclination — The tipping of the earth's axis toward the plane of its orbit.

insect — A small animal that lives in various stages and has six legs at the final stage.

insect pests — Insects of such habits and occurring in such abundance that they are harmful to man.

insoluble — Not capable of being dissolved in a particular liquid. (No substance is absolutely insoluble. The terms *soluble* and *insoluble* are relative.)

insulate — To prevent the transfer of heat (or electricity).

iron, galvanized — Iron (sheet or wire) coated with zinc.

irrigation — Artificial watering of land by means of ditches, sprinkling pipes, etc.

isobar — A line drawn on a weather map through places having the same barometric reading (air pressure) at a given time.

isotherm — A line drawn on a weather map through places having the same thermometer reading (temperature) at a given time.

Jupiter — The fifth and largest planet.

lady-bird beetle (sometimes called lady-bug) — A useful insect which helps to control the cottony-cushion scale of California.

land breeze — A breeze moving from the land toward the water.

larva — The second stage of development in many insects; *e.g.*, caterpillar, grub, maggot.

latitude — Distance in degrees north or south of the equator.

life history — The history of any organism (living thing) from the beginning to the end of its life.

lightning — A discharge of electricity between two or more clouds or between clouds and objects on the earth.

lightning rod — A metal rod that attracts and conducts to the ground any lightning charges which may strike in the near vicinity of the building to which it is attached.

light year — The distance that light travels in a year (about six trillion miles).

lime — A common name for substances (calcium bicarbonate or calcium sulfate) that cause hardness in water.

liquid — A substance which takes the form of the containing vessel and fills a definite part of it. One of the three states of matter, *e.g.*, water, mercury.

litmus — A chemical substance used for detecting acids and alkalies; it turns red in acid and blue in alkali.

longitude — Distance in degrees east or west of the prime meridian.

magnet — A piece of iron that can attract other iron.

magnitude — In the astronomical sense magnitude means relative brightness of the stars.

Mars — The fourth planet; earth's second nearest planet neighbor.

matter, inorganic — That which has never had life.

matter, organic — That which forms a part of, or has come from, living things.

melting point — The temperature at which a solid changes to the liquid state.

mercury (quicksilver) — A heavy, silver-white, liquid metal.

Mercury — The smallest planet and nearest the sun.

meridian — Any great circle about the earth which passes through both poles.

migrate — To move from one locality or place of living to another.

mildew — A variety of fungus.

Milky Way — A luminous band encircling the heavens, composed of many stars so distant that they are separately invisible to the naked eye.

mineral — Inorganic matter of which rocks and soil are composed, usually occurring as crystals.

molar — A tooth adapted for grinding, located at the back of the jaw.

mold (bread) — A variety of fungus.

molecule — A very tiny particle of matter.

moon — A satellite of the earth.

mulching — Covering surface soil with a layer of dust, humus, dead leaves, straw or paper, in order to break up capillary spaces or to protect plant roots.

negative — In the electrical sense, having relatively low potential.

Neptune — The planet second farthest from the sun; not visible to the naked eye.

nitrify — To produce nitrogen compounds as in the case of certain bacteria on plants.

node — The part of a stem from which a bud grows.

non-conductor — A substance that prevents to a considerable extent the transfer of heat (or electricity).

noon — The exact time at which the sun passes across the zenith meridian of a given place.

North Star (pole star) — The star toward which the north end of the axis of the earth points.

nucleus — The center of development of a cell.

oil — A liquid fat usually of vegetable origin.

oil, kerosene — An inflammable liquid sometimes used as fuel, obtained from petroleum by distillation.

orbit — The path of a planet or other body around the sun or other heavenly body.

organism — Any living thing.

Orion — A constellation.

osmosis — The process by which liquids or gases pass through a membrane and become mixed.

ovary — The seed case of a flower.

oxidize — To combine with oxygen as in burning, rusting, decaying.

oxygen — The active gas which makes up about 21% by volume of the air.

parallels — Circles about the earth running east and west, parallel with the earth's equator.

parasite — An organism which gets its food from other living things, living within or upon it.

pasteurize — To heat a food (milk) to 145° F. for thirty minutes to destroy bacteria.

perennials — Plants that form flowers and seeds year after year.

perspiration (sweat) — Water, containing other substances, given out by sweat glands.

phases of the moon — The different forms that the lighted half of the moon appears to have during each month.

pistil — The part of a flower which receives the pollen.

plane — A level surface.

planet — A heavenly body shining by reflected light and revolving about the sun.

plumbing — The pipes, traps, etc., which carry fresh water into a house and waste water out.

Pluto — Farthest known planet from the sun.

Pointers — Two stars of the Big Dipper that are in line with the North Star.

Polar Front Theory — A theory which explains how cyclones are formed where masses of cold air and warm air meet.

polar regions — Regions near the north pole and the south pole.

pollen — Cells formed in the anthers of flowers and necessary for fertilization.

polluted — Made impure; capable of producing sickness.

positive — In the electrical sense, having relatively high potential.

potential — Stored-up electrical energy, similar to water pressure.

precipitation — Moisture falling from the clouds or separating from the air; *e.g.*, rain, snow, sleet, hail, fog, frost, dew; or solids separating from solution.

predict — To foretell; to tell what is likely to happen.

preservative — A substance added in small quantities to food to keep it from spoiling for a time.

pressure (air). See *atmospheric pressure.*

prime meridian — The meridian which passes through Greenwich.

propagation — Producing new plants or animals.

property — A characteristic of a substance which helps one to recognize it.

pumping system — The method of obtaining a water supply from a source by means of force pumps.

pupa — The resting stage of an insect before it becomes an adult.

pure — Containing no foreign or other material.

radiant — Energy as heat or light, given off in all directions from a highly heated body.

radiation — Sending out energy (heat or light) in all directions from a body.

rain — Drops of water falling from clouds.

rainbow — An arch of light, showing the colors of the spectrum.

rain gauge — An instrument to measure the amount of rainfall or snowfall.

rays — Imaginary lines representing the direction or motion of energy (heat or light).

reduce — To separate certain parts of a compound in order to obtain some desired product; *e.g.*, fertilizer from garbage by removal of fats. — (In chemistry) To remove oxygen from a compound.

reflect — To turn something back, as a body turns back, reflects, light or heat directed against it.

reproduction — The process by which plants and animals produce offspring.

reservoir — A large tank or basin where water or other material is stored.

retort — Ovens in which coal or wood or other substances can be heated without burning, to drive off gases.

revolution — The movement of a body in its orbit traveling around another body.

rotation — The turning of the earth or some other body on its axis.

sanitation — The scientific control of conditions required to produce healthful surroundings.

saturated — The condition of a substance when it can hold or absorb no more of another substance; *e.g.*, a sponge filled with water; air filled with moisture.

Saturn — The sixth planet; the planet with rings.

sea breeze — A breeze moving from the sea towards the land.

season — A division of the year, as determined by the earth's position with respect to the sun.

seed — A ripened ovule which will produce a new plant if placed under suitable conditions.

septic tank — A tank containing sewage in which bacteria are allowed to decompose the organic matter.

sequence — Events or happenings following one another in a regular order, as cause and effect.

sewage — Water containing wastes from the body.

sextant — An instrument used to determine when the sun crosses the zenith meridian of a place.

sidereal day — A twenty-four-hour day as measured by reference to a star.

sleet — Very small, frozen raindrops.

sludge — Sediment from sewage.

snow — Ice crystals formed from frozen water vapor.

soap — A chemical compound made from an alkali and a fat.

sodium hydroxide. See *caustic soda*.

solar system — The sun and the planets as well as about one thousand smaller, invisible bodies.

solar time — Time measured by reference to the sun.

solid — A form of matter that holds its shape under ordinary conditions.

soluble — Capable of being dissolved in water or other liquids.

solute — A dissolved substance.

solution — A clear even mixture of a soluble substance and its solvent. (See *dissolve*.)

solvent — A liquid or gas which is able to dissolve another substance; *e.g.*, alcohol is a solvent.

sperm cell — Male reproduction cell.

sphere — A solid object on whose surface all points are at equal distance from the center.

spring — The season between winter and summer; underground water appearing in a stream at the surface.

stars — Other suns like ours generating (producing) their own light.

storm — An atmospheric disturbance, usually accompanied by rain, or snow, or hail, and wind.

storm area — Cyclone area — a "low."

storm paths — The route followed by a storm area, cyclone.

strip planting — A scientific method of tilling the soil whereby strips of soil-binding crops are planted alongside crops which have little ability to hold soil.

sucking insects — A class of insects whose mouth parts are adapted for sucking liquids from plants or animals.

suns — Stars.

superstition — Belief in happenings having supernatural explanations, or coincident relations instead of scientific cause and effect.

telescope — An instrument for magnifying distant objects such as ships at sea, or stars.

temperature — The degree of heat of a substance.

thermometer — An instrument to measure the temperature.

thunder — The report following a lightning discharge.

tide — The raising and lowering of ocean water due to the attraction between the earth and the sun and moon.

time, standard — The clock time for a time zone.

time zone — A belt (region) of the earth, running north and south, using the same clock time throughout.

toad — A small animal having a warty skin and living on insects found in gardens and fields.

tornado — A storm with very high wind.

torrid (tropical) zone — The part of the earth between the tropics of Cancer and Capricorn.

transplanting — Transfer of a plant from one position to another.

trap — A U or S bend in a waste pipe of a plumbing system, provided to prevent entrance of sewer gases into the room from which the pipe serves as a waste outlet.

twilight — Diffused light between sundown and darkness.

typhoid fever — A contagious disease attacking the digestive system (intestines), and commonly spread through water or milk, or by the housefly.

aniverse — The great system of galaxies.

unsanitary — Not healthful.

Uranus — The seventh planet; not visible to the naked eye.

velocity — Speed.

Venus — The second planet in distance from the sun; the earth's sister planet.

vernal — Belonging to springtime.

volatile — Easily changing to a gas when exposed to the atmosphere.

volume — The size of anything, the space (room) it occupies.

warm front — The advancing boundary of a large mass of warm air.

warts — Small growths formed on and rooted in the skin.

washing soda — Sodium carbonate — used to soften water for household and industrial uses.

water — A compound of hydrogen and oxygen.

water cycle — The circulation of water in nature through the processes of evaporation, condensation, and precipitation.

water, distilled — Pure water obtained by the process of distillation (evaporation and condensation).

water, hard — Water containing a large amount of dissolved minerals such as sulfates and bicarbonates of calcium and magnesium.

water pressure — The force of water exerted against objects due to its weight, or pressure of water caused by mechanical means.

water, soft — Water containing little hardness-causing minerals.

water table — The level or surface of underground water.

weather — The condition of the atmosphere for any part of the country at a given time.

weather factors — Conditions which make up the weather; *i.e.,* precipitation, temperature, humidity, wind velocity and direction, condition of the sky, and atmospheric pressure.

weather map — A map upon which weather factors at United States Weather Stations are indicated for a given hour of the day.

weather vane — An instrument for indicating the direction from which the wind is blowing.

well — A hole dug deep enough to obtain water or oil.

wind — Air in motion.

zenith — The point in the sky directly overhead.

zinc — A bluish-white metal, used to coat iron to prevent rusting.

BIBLIOGRAPHY

ATHEY, LILLIAN COX, *Along Nature's Trails.* American Book Company.

BAER, MARIAN E., *Pandora's Box, The Story of Conservation.* Farrar and Rinehart.

BALL, *Astronomy in a Nutshell.* G. P. Putnam's Sons.

BALTHIS, FRANK K., *Plants in the Home.* American Museum of Natural History.

BAYNES, ERNEST H., *Wild Bird Guests.* E. P. Dutton and Co.

BEBBE, *Beneath Tropic Seas.* G. P. Putnam's Sons.

BENNETT, IDA D., *The Vegetable Garden.* Doubleday, Doran and Co.

BETTER VISION INSTITUTE, *Why We See Like Human Beings.*

BLANCHAN, NELTJE, *How to Attract the Birds.* Doubleday, Doran and Co.

BLOUNT, R. E., *Health, Public and Personal.* Allyn and Bacon.

BOGEN, EMIL, and L. W. S. HISEY, *What about Alcohol?* Angeles Press, Los Angeles.

BRAND, ALBERT R., *Songs of Wild Birds.* Thomas Nelson and Sons.

BROADHURST, JEAN, *Home and Community Hygiene.* J. B. Lippincott Company.

BROOKS, CHARLES F., *Why the Weather?* Harcourt, Brace and Co.

BURROUGHS, JOHN, *Squirrels and Other Fur Bearers.* Houghton Mifflin Company.

CHAMBERS, *The Story of Eclipses.* D. Appleton-Century Company.

COLLINS, ARCHIE F., *The Boy Astronomer.* Lothrop, Lee and Shepard Company.

COLLINS, *Inventing for Boys.* Thomas Nelson and Sons.

COLLINS, FREDERICK, *The Boys' Book of Model Airplanes.* D. Appleton-Century Company.

COMPTON and NETTLES, *Conquests of Science.* Harcourt, Brace and Co.

COMSTOCK, ANNA B., *Handbook of Nature Study.* Comstock Publishing Company.

CONANT and BRIDGES, *What Snake Is That?* American Museum of Natural History.

COWARD, *Migration of Birds.* G. P. Putnam's Sons.

DARROW, FLOYD L., *Thinkers and Doers.* Silver, Burdett and Co.

DARROW, FLOYD L., *Masters of Science and Invention.* Harcourt, Brace and Co.

DOWNING, E. R., *Our Living World.* Longmans, Green and Co.

DOWNING, E. R., *Science in the Service of Health.* Longmans, Green and Co.

DUGMORE, A. R., *Bird Homes* ("Nature Library," A14–1730). Doubleday, Doran and Co.

DUPUY, WILLIAM A., *Our Insect Friends and Foes.* John C. Winston Company.

EMERSON, HAVEN, *Alcohol: Its Effects on Man* (Student's Edition). D. Appleton-Century Company.

FISHBEIN, *Shattering Health Superstitions.* Horace Liveright.

FLOHERTY, JOHN J., *Youth at the Wheel.* J. B. Lippincott Company.

GAER, JOSEPH, *Fair and Warmer.* Harcourt, Brace and Co.

GEORGIA, ADA E., *Manual of Weeds.* The Macmillan Company.

GIBSON, *Blossom Hosts and Insect Visitors.* Newson and Co.

HEADSTROM, RICHARD, *Adventures with a Microscope.* Stokes.

HOLLAND, W. J., *The Moth Book* ("Nature Library," A14–1732). Doubleday, Doran and Co.

HOWARD, L. O., *Insect Book* ("Nature Library," A14–1741.) Doubleday, Doran and Co.

HOWARD, *The House Fly.* Henry Holt and Co.

HUMPHREYS and HOSEY, *Romance of the Air.* Ginn and Co.

HUMPHREYS, W. J., *Weather Proverbs and Paradoxes.* Williams and Wilkins, Waverly Press, Baltimore.

JEANS, SIR JAMES, *The Stars in Their Courses, the Universe around Us.* The Macmillan Company.

JOHNSON, *Sky Movies.* The Macmillan Company.

KENLY, JULIE C., *Voices from the Grass.* D. Appleton-Century Company.

KING, MRS. FRANCIS, *The Flower Garden Day by Day.* Stokes Co.

LAWRENCE and BJDOUD, *The Pond World.* American Museum of Natural History.

LESTER, R. M., *Weather Prediction.* Chemical.

LEWIS, ISABEL MARTIN, *Astronomy for Young Folks.* Duffield and Co.

LOOMIS, FREDERICK B., *What Rock Is That?* American Museum of Natural History.

LOUNSBERRY, ALICE, *Southern Wild Flowers and Trees.* Stokes Co.

LULL, RICHARD SWANN, *Fossils.* The University Society.

LYNDE, CARLETON J., *Science Experiments with Ten-Cent Store Equipment.* International.

MANN, P. B., and G. T. HASTINGS, *Out of Doors.* Henry Holt and Co.

MATHEWS, FERDINAND S., *Field Book of American Wild Flowers.* Doubleday, Doran and Co.

MATHEWS, FERDINAND S., *Field Book of Wild Birds and Their Music.* G. P. Putnam's Sons.

McKREADY, KELVIN, *What Star Is That?* American Museum of Natural History.

McPHERSON, *Romance of Modern Astronomy.* J. B. Lippincott Company.

MELBO, IRVING R., *Our Country's National Parks.* Vols. I and II. Bobbs-Merrill Company.

MENZEL, DONALD H., *Stars and Planets.* The University Society.

MORGAN, ALFRED, *Simple Chemical Experiments.* D. Appleton-Century Company.

MORGAN, ALFRED POWELL, *Boys' Home Book of Science and Construction.* Lothrop, Lee and Shepard Co.

MOSELY, E. L., *Trees, Stars, and Birds.* World Book Company.

PARSONS, MARY ELIZABETH, *The Wild Flowers of California.* Crocker Co.

PROCTOR, *Evenings with the Stars.* Harper and Brothers.

PROCTOR, *Romance of the Planets.* Harper and Brothers.

REEDS, CHESTER A., *The Earth.* The University Society.

ROCKWELL, *Around the Year in the Garden.* Doubleday, Doran and Co.

ROCKWELL, *Gardening under Glass.* Doubleday, Doran and 'Co.

SERVISS, *Starland.* Ginn and Co.

SIEPERT, *Bird Houses Boys Can Build.* Manual Arts Press.

STEVENS, BERTHA, *How Miracles Abound.* John Day.

Periodicals, Pamphlets, and Reference Texts

Bulletins. U. S. Department of Agriculture.

Bulletins. U. S. National Park Service.

Compton's Pictured Encyclopedia. F. E. Compton and Co.

Current Science. American Education Press.

Natural History. The American Museum of Natural History.

Nature Magazine.   American Nature Association.

The Book of Popular Science.   The Grolier Society.

Safeguarding America against Fire.   National Board of Fire Underwriters.

Science Newsletter.   Science Service, Inc., 1719 N St., N. W., Washington, D. C.

Sky and Telescope.   Sky Publication Corporation, 91 Huguenot St., New Rochelle, N. Y.

The World Book.   W. F. Quarrie and Company.

The Progress of Science (Published each year).   The Grolier Society.

INDEX

INDEX

References in parentheses refer to diagrams.
References in italics refer to half-tone illustrations.

Accidents, 526, 533–534; first aid for, 535–538, 541; kinds of, 534–535, *534;* prevention of, 5, 538–540, *539,* 541

Accuracy, test for, in thermometer, 36–39

Acid, 311, 357, 492, 493; carbonic, 322; properties of, 331; soil, 400, 407, 415

Adaptation of living things, 1, 228–233, 528–540, 541; to accidents, 533–540; to environment, 541; to food supply, 532–533, 541; to heat, 528–529; to laws of nature, 1; to sanitation, 531–532; to seasons, 228–233, 527–528, 541; to water supply, 530–531, 541; to weather and climate, 116–124, 528–529, *529,* 533

Adenoids, 355

Aeration, 311; of sewage, *381,* 382; of soil, 445

Agriculture (see *Farming*); aided by weather reports, 9; colleges, 429, industry of, 426–429

Air, 2, 16, 17, 18, 21, 24–28, 42–51, 399; about earth (atmosphere), 46, 164; as diffuser of light, 165; as heat conductor, 42, 44, 45, 500; bubbles, 269, 337; circulation of, 45, 89, 122, 502; composition of, 46–47, 190, 322, 399, 414, 421, 462; compression of, 69, 273–274, 302–303, 318; conditions for storage, 479–481; cooling of, 43, 45, 68–70, 79, 88, 89, 93; currents, 17, 18, 21, 45, 55, 70, 71, 73, 83, 93, 113, 114, 120, 467 (wind); dry, 502; effect of altitude on, 68–70, 71; expansion of, 69, 88, 89, 93, 114,

304; fronts, 53–55, 73, 89–91, 98; gases of, 46, 47, 59, 69, 163; heat capacity of, 42, 110, 113; humidity, 58–60, 507, (see *Moisture of air*); Kennelly-Heaviside layer of, 160; in soil, 397, 398; masses, 52, 73, 89, *90,* 92, 93, 98, (102); moisture, 17, 24, 25, 26, 28, 45, 46, 58–60, *59,* 63, (64), *65,* 67, 69, 74, 88, 89, 90, 91, 93, 95, 96, 99, 101, 165, 481, 502, 507; motion, 25, 26, 28, 51–58, 73, 98, 102, 119–120; need of, for plants, 413, 414, 421; pressure, 24, 25, 26, 46–51, 54, 55, 73, 77, 88–90, 95, 99, 101, 102, 103, 108, 109, 113, (114), 123, 273–274, *273,* 282, 486–487; properties of, 47; rarefying, 46, 47; sound waves, 85, 166; temperatures, 24, 25, 26, 42–45, 59, 64–65, 68–70, 71, 73, 78, 85, 88, 90–91, 95, 96, 100, 101, 111, 481; velocity, 51, 55–58, 74; vibration of, 85; water in (see *Moisture*); waves (see *Waves*); in refrigerators, 499

Airplane, 1, 2, 3, 95, *98,* 106, 129; pilots, 1, 98, *98;* planting, 512

Airway weather station, 98–99

Albany, *278*

Alcohol, 31, 61, 73; and weather, 121–122; as a narcotic, 122, 505, 508; denatured, 347; distillation of, 315–316; uses of, 31, 121–122, 275, 337–338, 347

Alfalfa, 414, 415, *415*

Algae, 281, 462

Alkalies, 280, 330, 331, 333, 334–335, 336, 337, 338, 393, 492

Alkaline, 331; soil, 400, 415

Alpha Centauri, 140, 141, 142, 207

1